PHYSICS OF DROP FORMATION IN THE ATMOSPHERE

Yu. S. Sedunov

PHYSICS OF DROP FORMATION IN THE ATMOSPHERE

Translated from Russian by D. Lederman
Translation edited by P. Greenberg

A HALSTED PRESS BOOK

JOHN WILEY & SONS
New York · Toronto

ISRAEL PROGRAM FOR SCIENTIFIC TRANSLATIONS
Jerusalem · London

PHYSICS

Sole distributors for the Western Hemisphere and Japan

HALSTED PRESS, a division of
JOHN WILEY & SONS, INC., NEW YORK

Library of Congress Cataloging in Publication Data

Sedunov, I͡U. S.
Physics of drop formation in the atmosphere.

Translation of *Fizika obrazovanii͡a zhidkokapel'noĭ fazy v atmosfere.*
"A Halsted Press book."
1. Cloud physics. 2. Condensation. 3. Drops.
I. Title.
QC921.5.S413 551.5'76 74-8198
ISBN 0-470-77111-9

Distributors for the U.K., Europe, Africa and the Middle East

JOHN WILEY & SONS LTD., CHICHESTER

Distributed in the rest of the world by

KETER PUBLISHING HOUSE JERUSALEM LTD.
ISBN 0 7065 1383 5
IPST 22094

This book is a translation from Russian of
FIZIKA OBRAZOVANIYA ZHIDKOKAPEL'NOI FAZY V ATMOSFERE
Gidrometeoizdat
Leningrad, 1972

Printed in Israel

FOREWORD

The problem of a quantitative description of heterogeneous condensation and of the subsequent behavior of the liquid droplet phase has great practical importance and transcends purely scientific interest. Condensation processes are employed extensively in the chemical industry, are an important part of the production technology of a number of materials, manifest themselves as a side effect in various engineering facilities, and finally, occur on a gigantic scale in the atmosphere during phase transitions of water.

Research on the growth by condensation and evaporation of droplets has been conducted over a long period of time and many aspects of the theory of these processes can be regarded as understood. Nevertheless, there still remain a number of problems which have not yet been solved, such as the growth and evaporation of droplets at intermediate Knudsen numbers, the value of the condensation coefficient, hydration of particles at low relative humidities, growth and evaporation of droplet populations, and the dynamics of phase transitions in turbulent flows.

Particular attention should be paid to the development of phase transition theory with allowance for the mutual effect of particles, and to the study of phase transition features in a turbulent medium or in a medium subject to pressure and temperature fluctuations. Recent studies have been concerned with these problems, and the theory of the growth and evaporation of a droplet population will probably be rapidly developed on the basis of an examination of the kinetic equation of condensation.

Not very many surveys have dealt with condensation processes. Research on the growth and evaporation of droplets is treated in the book by N. A. Fuchs, *Evaporation and Droplet Growth in Gaseous Media,* and in the book by V. I. Smirnov, *Rate of Coalescence and Growth by Condensation of Aerosol Particles*. These problems were touched upon in a number of books on cloud physics, but have not been thoroughly examined in detail as regards atmospheric processes.

This book is an attempt at such a survey of condensation processes, starting with hydration of solid particles in the atmosphere, followed by an examination of their transition into droplets, the kinetics of this transition in a droplet population, and then the evolution of droplet size distributions with allowance for various effects, including turbulence. Since the purpose of the book is not a survey of achievements in this field but rather an attempt at constructing a systematic model of growth by condensation of droplet populations with allowance for atmospheric features, the references were selected with this idea in mind. The author apologizes for the fact that the book is not exhaustive and that important and interesting studies may have been omitted.

The author was assisted in writing the book by staff of the Department of Cloud Physics and Modification at the Institute of Experimental Meteorology. He wishes to thank V. M. Voloshchuk who induced him to write the book, O. A. Volkovitskii who read the manuscript and made a number of useful comments and additions, E. L. Aleksandrov for assistance in the presentation of experimental data, and staff of the theoretical team, V. A. Borzilov, K. I. Vasil'eva, N. V. Klepikova, A. S. Kabanov and L. P. Semenov, for discussions pertaining to individual chapters.

CONTENTS

PRINCIPAL NOTATION

C – activity of condensation nucleus, quantity proportional to the mass of dissolving substance
c – concentration of solution
c_p – specific heat of air
c_2 – specific heat of water
D_v – coefficient of diffusion of vapor
e – vapor pressure
e_0 – saturated vapor pressure above a flat water surface
$f(r, t)$ – droplet size distribution function
g – acceleration of gravity
K – eddy diffusion coefficient
k_1 – thermal conductivity of air
k_2 – thermal conductivity of water
L – heat of condensation
L_1 – heat of solution
l – mean free path, scaling ratio
M – molecular weight of vapor
M_1 – molecular weight of air
p_1 – air pressure
R_v – gas constant of vapor
R_a – gas constant of air
R, r – droplet radii
T – temperature
t – time
$\mathbf{v}$ – velocity
$\mathbf{v}_1$ – velocity of air
$\mathbf{v}_2$ – velocity of water
v_s – sedimentation rate
α – condensation coefficient
β – reciprocal of time, characterizing the inertia of droplet motion
δ – supersaturation, delta function
δ_0 – supersaturation at infinity
ε – energy dissipation rate
$\varkappa_1$ – thermal diffusivity of air
$\varkappa_2$ – thermal diffusivity of water
$\bar{v}$ – mean absolute velocity of molecules
ν_1 – kinematic viscosity of air
ν_2 – kinematic viscosity of water
ν – exponent in Junge's distribution
ρ – density of vapor
ρ_0 – saturated vapor density
ρ_1 – density of air
ρ_2 – density of water

σ — coefficient of surface tension, distribution variance

τ — characteristic time

CHARACTERISTIC PARAMETERS

$A=\dfrac{K_3\alpha}{R_vTF_1}$, characteristic parameter of the kinetic equation of stochastic condensation

$B=\dfrac{2\sigma}{\rho_2R_vT}$, quantity defining the effect of surface tension forces

Parameters defining the growth by condensation of droplet populations:

$$K_1=\left(\frac{M}{M_1}\frac{L}{c_pT}-1\right)\frac{v_z}{p_1}$$

$$K_2=4\pi K_3\frac{\rho_2}{\rho_0}\left(1+\frac{L^2\rho_0}{R_vc_pT^2\rho_1}\right)$$

$$K_3=\frac{D_v\rho_0}{\left[1+\dfrac{D_v\rho_0L}{\varkappa_1T}\left(\dfrac{L}{R_vT}-1\right)\right]\rho_2}$$

$$K_4=PK_2(2K_3)^{1/2}$$

$$K_5=\frac{2B}{9K_3}$$

$\mathrm{Kn}=\dfrac{l}{R}$, Knudsen number

$$F_1=4\pi\frac{\rho_2}{\rho}K_3\int_0^\infty\frac{r^2}{r+\xi}f(r,t)\,dz$$

$$F_2=4\pi\frac{\rho_2}{\rho}K_3\int_0^\infty\frac{r^2}{r+\xi}\left[\Phi(c)-\frac{B}{r}\right]f(r,t)\,dz$$

$\mathrm{Re}=\dfrac{\rho vR}{\eta}$, Reynolds number

$\mathrm{Pe}=\dfrac{vR}{D}$, diffusion Peclet number

$\mathrm{Pe}_T=\dfrac{vR}{\varkappa}$, thermal Peclet number

$$\alpha=\frac{\left(1-\dfrac{LM}{c_pM_1}\right)}{\left(1+\dfrac{L^2}{c_pR_aT}\dfrac{\rho_0}{\rho_1}\right)}$$

Chapter 1

INTRODUCTION

1. FEATURES OF CONDENSATION IN THE ATMOSPHERE

Transport and phase transitions of water play an important role in many atmospheric phenomena. The effects associated with the release and absorption of heat during phase transitions and variations in the radiation balance due to the presence of cloud droplets have a marked effect on atmospheric energetics and are important for forecasting weather-forming processes. Dangerous weather phenomena, such as storms, hail, fogs and low clouds, are closely associated with phase transitions. Finally, the formation of precipitation and its fall are also governed by features associated with phase transitions of atmospheric water.

In many respects the formation and subsequent transformation of clouds is a reflection of processes occurring on quite a large scale. Nevertheless, one can detect in the dynamics of cloud development fundamental laws in accordance with which microscale phenomena, which determine the fate of an individual droplet, result in a certain behavior of the droplet population and of a cloud as a whole. The discrete structure of clouds is frequently disregarded. However, it is quite clear that the dynamics of moisture accumulation, formation of precipitation, hail and storm phenomena, and glaciation processes cannot be thoroughly investigated without a detailed study of the microphysical laws governing droplet populations and phase transitions in a disperse medium. The same problem has recently attracted the attention of scientists dealing with disperse media in various technological processes.

The formation and growth by condensation of droplets determine to a certain degree the subsequent features of cloud development and have been examined quite extensively. It has been shown that droplets form on cloud condensation nuclei, which are present in large quantities in the atmosphere. Droplet growth by condensation has been studied in detail. A great deal of attention has lately been paid to the evolution of droplet populations. A new theory has been presented of condensation in a random density and temperature field, which in many aspects is typical of atmospheric conditions. At the same time droplet growth by condensation in clouds is far from fully understood and the study of related microphysical processes continues to be of great interest.

In spite of the increasing number of publications, the problem of a quantitative description of processes associated with the formation of water droplets has not been solved, and as regards some problems there is no agreement even on the basic features (such as those concerning the theory of stochastic condensation and calculation of the collision efficiency).

Nevertheless, successful research in a number of directions has been based on specific features of condensation processes in the atmosphere. In virtually every case droplets are found under conditions of reasonably slow air mass cooling, when the supersaturation produced amounts to fractions of one percent. As a result individual droplets grow by condensation quite slowly and the equations of their growth can be substantially simplified. The medium within which the droplets are produced contains a sufficient quantity of impurities, some of which serve as condensation nuclei. For this reason, effects associated with homogeneous condensation on ions (for example, in the Wilson cloud chamber) should not occur in the atmosphere.

The size range of droplets whose growth should be considered lies within the region of several microns. Small droplets cannot exist stably due to the effect of surface tension. For larger droplets ($r > 30\mu$) a more important role is played by coalescence processes. For this reason it is important to consider surface tension and the content of dissolved salts and neglect effects such as those resulting from the convective transport of vapor.

Growth of droplets by condensation in the atmosphere occurs when the vapor temperature and density fields undergo fluctuations owing to atmospheric turbulence, which should have a marked effect on the formation of the droplet spectrum.

Finally, condensation processes in the atmosphere occur on scales of the order of hundreds of meters and kilometers, which sometimes makes it possible to introduce conditions of spatial homogeneity and disregard boundary effects. In other cases one must examine eddy transport and mixing processes while leaving space for a semiempirical approach.

The presentation of the material and the utilization of the main simplifying assumptions in this book are suited to the necessity of making allowance for these features of condensation processes. Large droplets with $r > 30\mu$ are not considered here, since for them condensation is not the principal factor, the main role being played by coalescence. For this reason the derived expressions refer directly to the initial development stage of a cloud which does not yet contain large droplets capable of capturing smaller ones.

2. PRINCIPAL FACTORS DETERMINING EQUILIBRIUM CONDITIONS AT A VAPOR-FLUID INTERFACE

Phase transitions of atmospheric water can be treated on the basis of known laws of thermodynamics. Since we shall subsequently be interested in systems close to a state of equilibrium, some basic relationships characterizing these states are cited without derivation. More details can be found in books on thermodynamics.

Conditions of phase equilibrium. Equilibrium between two phases requires equality of temperatures

$$T_1 = T_2, \tag{1.2.1}$$

equality of pressures

$$p_1 = p_2, \tag{1.2.2}$$

and equality of chemical potentials

$$\mu_1 = \mu_2. \tag{1.2.3}$$

For bodies consisting of one substance $\mu = \zeta - Ts + pv$, where ζ, s and v are the energy, entropy and volume referring to one molecule.

The Clausius-Clapeyron equation follows from equality (1.2.3) differentiated with respect to T. Since $\mu = \mu(p, T)$,

$$\frac{\partial \mu_1}{\partial T} + \frac{\partial \mu_1}{\partial p}\frac{dp}{dT} = \frac{\partial \mu_2}{\partial T} + \frac{\partial \mu_2}{\partial p}\frac{dp}{dT}, \tag{1.2.4}$$

and making use of the fact that $\left(\frac{\partial \mu}{\partial T}\right)_p = -s$, $\left(\frac{\partial \mu}{\partial p}\right)_T = v$, we obtain

$$\frac{dp}{dT} = \frac{s_1 - s_2}{v_1 - v_2}. \tag{1.2.5}$$

The heat of transition from one phase to another is $L = \frac{T(s_2 - s_1)N_a}{M}$, where N_a is Avogadro's number, and M is the molecular weight of water. Subscript 2 pertains to the gaseous state and $v_2 \gg v_1$. Hence equation (1.2.5), with consideration of the equation of state for an ideal gas, yields

$$\frac{d \ln p}{dT} = \frac{L}{R_v T^2}, \tag{1.2.6}$$

whence

$$p = p_0 \exp\left(-\frac{L}{R_v T}\right), \tag{1.2.7}$$

where L is the heat of condensation of 1 gram of water, and R_v is the gas constant of the vapor.

Conditions of phase transition above the droplet surface. Unlike a flat surface, in examining the conditions of equilibrium over the surface of a droplet one must take into account the effect of surface tension forces. For small droplets this effect can be substantial, since the relative contribution of these forces to the thermodynamic potential increases with decreasing radius. The effect of surface tension forces σ results in the fact that the pressure p_1 inside a droplet of radius R is not equal to the vapor pressure p. In fact

$$p_1 = p + \frac{2\sigma}{R}, \tag{1.2.8}$$

where σ is the coefficient of surface tension. It follows that equilibrium can set in only when the pressure p is higher than the saturation pressure p_s above the flat surface. Condition (1.2.3), with allowance for the pressure difference, now assumes the form

$$\mu_1\left(p + \frac{2\sigma}{R}, T\right) = \mu_2(p, T). \tag{1.2.9}$$

For small $p_1 - p$, the expansion $\mu_1(p, T) = \mu_1(p, T) + \frac{\partial \mu_1}{\partial p}(p_1 - p)$ and the relationship $\left(\frac{\partial \mu_1}{\partial p}\right)_T = v_1$ yield

$$\mu_1(p, T) - \mu_2(p, T) = -\frac{2\sigma v_1}{R}. \tag{1.2.10}$$

For small deviations from equilibrium $p \approx p_s$, expansion of μ_1 and μ_2 leads to the formula

$$p = p_s + \frac{2\sigma v_1}{(v_2 - v_1) R} \approx p_s + \frac{2\sigma v_1}{v_2 R}. \qquad (1.2.11)$$

Equilibrium vapor pressure above a solution. The theory has been developed quite well for weak solutions. The chemical potential of the solvent can be expressed as

$$\mu_1 = \mu_1^0 - kTc, \qquad (1.2.12)$$

where μ_1^0 is the chemical potential of the pure substance, c is the concentration of the solute, and k is the Boltzmann constant. The equilibrium conditions will be examined on the assumption that they pertain to the solvent:

$$\mu_1^0(p, T) - kTc = \mu_2^0(p, T). \qquad (1.2.13)$$

In the absence of a solute, equilibrium would have occurred at some other pressure:

$$\mu_1^0(p_0, T) = \mu_2^0(p_0, T). \qquad (1.2.14)$$

If the chemical potentials in (1.2.13) are expanded as a power series in $(p - p_0)$, where the latter is assumed to be small, and

$$\Delta p = p - p_0 = \frac{kTc}{v_1 - v_2} \approx -\frac{kTc}{v_2} \qquad (1.2.15)$$

and $\frac{kT}{v_2} = p_0$, we derive Raoult's law

$$\frac{\Delta p}{p_0} = -c, \qquad (1.2.16)$$

which shows that the relative lowering of the saturated vapor pressure is equal to the concentration of the solution. However, Raoult's law in the form of (1.2.16) is inapplicable for real solutions.

The dissolution of substances is in many cases accompanied by dissociation of molecules, which increases the effective number of particles. Dissolution in water is associated with hydration (the ions become bound with a number of water molecules), which reduces the free energy of molecules and is accompanied by effects due to the ion charge in the solution. Molecules of the solute start interacting with one another at sufficiently high concentrations. It thus becomes necessary to introduce, for dilute solutions, the van't Hoff coefficient i (the value of which should be determined separately for each substance) into the right-hand side of relationship (1.2.16). For nearly saturated solutions one must resort to empirical relationships.

Effect of electric charges on the equilibrium condition. In accordance with the Thomson formula the pressure in a charged droplet is

$$p_1 = p + \frac{2\sigma}{R} - \frac{e^2\left(1 - \frac{1}{\varepsilon}\right)}{8\pi R^4}, \qquad (1.2.17)$$

where ε is the dielectric permeability of the fluid, while e is the droplet charge.

Proceeding as in the case of surface tension forces, we arrive at the expression

$$p = p_s + \frac{2\sigma v_1}{v_2 R}\left[1 - \frac{e^2\left(1 - \frac{1}{\varepsilon}\right)}{16\pi\sigma R^3}\right]. \qquad (1.2.18)$$

Estimates show that charges make themselves felt only for small droplets.

Condensation and thermal accommodation coefficients. Below, we shall make allowance for features peculiar to the interaction between gas molecules and the surface of a liquid. If this problem is approached from the phenomenological point of view, allowance for this interaction will consist in the following. We shall treat the phase interface as some partition. Then the flux of vapor molecules being converted into a liquid is equal to αN_2, where N_2 is the number of molecules impacting on unit surface per unit time, and α is the fraction of molecules which then become liquid. On the other hand, the molecular flux N_1 is equal to the flux of molecules approaching the surface, multiplied by coefficient β, characterizing the fraction of molecules which became gas. The resultant flux is then given by

$$I = \beta N_1 - \alpha N_2. \qquad (1.2.19)$$

Under equilibrium conditions $I=0$, in which case

$$\beta N_1^0=\alpha N_2^0. \tag{1.2.20}$$

Upon varying the pressure (or temperature) one can equate to βN_1 the equilibrium flux αN_2, corresponding to some value of p_s. In near-equilibrium conditions equations (1.2.19) and (1.2.20) yield

$$I=(p_s-p)\frac{\partial}{\partial p}(\alpha N_2). \tag{1.2.21}$$

Thus if equilibrium conditions are employed to eliminate coefficient β, there still remains another unknown coefficient affecting the total flux and is termed the condensation coefficient α. Unfortunately, reliable experimental values of this quantity are presently unavailable. Experiments have led to two, very different results: $\alpha\approx 0.03$ /9, 12, 14–16/ and $\alpha\approx 1$ /13/.

For a similar treatment of the heat flux it becomes necessary to take into account the thermal accommodation coefficient ω, which represents the mean fraction of the difference between the thermal energy of air and liquid molecules absorbed or released on collision with a surface. This fraction depends on the nature of gas molecule reflection from the water surface. The thermal accommodation coefficient is generally close to unity ($\omega\approx 1$).

3. CLOUD DROPLET DISTRIBUTION FUNCTIONS

Subsequently we shall make extensive use of the distribution function with respect to some variable, generally the droplet radius r. The differential distribution function $f(r)$ multiplied by dr characterizes the number of particles lying in the size range from r to $r+dr$:

$$dn=f(r)\,dr. \tag{1.3.1}$$

The curve described by function $f(r)$ is called the distribution density curve, or the differential distribution curve. Subsequently the term differential is dropped and $f(r)$ will be termed simply the distribution function. Usually the distribution function is normalized such that

$$\int_0^\infty f(r)\,dr=1. \tag{1.3.2}$$

However, since the particle concentration plays an important role in phase transitions, we shall use in our discussions function $f(r)$ normalized to the concentration:

$$\int_0^\infty f(r)\,dr = n, \tag{1.3.3}$$

where n is the particle concentration, while $f(r)$ has dimension cm^{-4}. Much research on the microstructure of clouds has shown that the droplet distribution function is quite stable, unimodal, and can be approximated quite satisfactorily by an analytical equation containing three variables.

The most successful approximation of a real distribution is the gamma distribution /1, 2/

$$f(r) = \frac{n}{\Gamma(\mu+1)} \frac{r^\mu}{\beta^{\mu+1}} \exp\left(-\frac{r}{\beta}\right), \tag{1.3.4}$$

where μ and β are some parameters, while $\Gamma(\mu+1)$ is the gamma function.

Such a distribution is valid over the droplet size range $2\mu < r < 15$–20μ. In the region $r < 2\mu$ there are virtually no measurements, although (as can be judged on the basis of a study by Deloncle /11/) $f(r)$ attains a minimum at $r \approx 0.5\mu$ and starts increasing with a decrease in r. When $r > 20\mu$, due to a strong reduction in droplet concentration the data are unreliable owing to their insufficient volume. Other approximating formulas include the lognormal distribution /2/

$$f(r) = \frac{n}{\sqrt{2\pi}\,\sigma r} \exp\left[-\frac{1}{2\sigma^2}\left(\ln\frac{r}{r_0}\right)^2\right], \tag{1.3.5}$$

where σ is the variance of the logarithm of the particle radius, while r_0 is the most probable radius; the Khrgian-Mazin formula /7, 8/

$$f(r) = \frac{n}{2} \frac{r^2}{\beta^3} \exp\left(-\frac{r}{\beta}\right), \tag{1.3.6}$$

which is a particular case of the gamma distribution ($\mu = 2$); and Best's distribution /10/

$$f(r) = A r^{m-4} \exp\left[-\left(\frac{r}{\beta}\right)^m\right]. \tag{1.3.7}$$

The applicability of these expressions was checked on the basis of a large amount of experimental data by many investigators. It was found that these equations describe with reasonable accuracy the microstructure in clouds of different types. (Formula (1.3.6), containing one less adjustment parameter, has more limited utility.) If we consider the stability of the distribution parameters, the most variable is the droplet concentration which can vary quite widely, from tens to several hundreds of particles per 1 cm^3. In the gamma distribution quantities β and μ are more stable; however, analysis shows that μ varies between 0.33 and 10, and β between 3 and 10 microns. As regards the variation of the average radius, one must also consider its dependence on the height above the cloud base /6/.

As a rule, in purely dropwise clouds the mean droplet radius r_{av} increases with altitude and attains a maximum somewhat below the upper boundary. In mixed clouds the variation of r_{av} with altitude is more complicated.

It should be noted that real distributions, particularly in cumulus, fluctuate highly and can differ strongly from the suggested approximating curves /17, 18/. Thus, bimodal distributions are frequently observed in cumulus.

The distribution of large droplets ($r > 20\mu$) obeys other laws. According to measurements /5/ the distribution of droplets with $r > 75\mu$ usually obeys a power law. Finally, in rains one encounters droplet size distributions obeying the exponential law /3/.

Chapter 2

THE THEORY OF GROWTH OF A SINGLE DROPLET BY CONDENSATION

1. EQUATIONS DESCRIBING DROPLET GROWTH BY CONDENSATION

Condensation processes in droplets involve a large range of droplet sizes, from fractions to hundreds of microns. As a result, the relative role of various corrections and effects affecting the condensation rate changes markedly, depending on the range of droplet sizes under study. Thus, for very small particles the growth regime is near-kinetic and hence diffusion equations cannot be employed directly. During the condensation of large droplets, convective transport of vapor and heat assumes importance and the effects of asphericity begin to be felt.

Since the simultaneous consideration of every factor would unjustifiably complicate the problem, it appears expedient to analyze equations with respect to the most typical size range of droplets determining phase transitions in clouds. From this standpoint it is less important to consider condensation of large droplets, since in a cloud their growth proceeds primarily by coalescence; in addition, one need not examine in detail the growth of very small particles, since droplets form on condensation nuclei of the order of 1 μ in size already at 100% humidity.

In the subsequent analysis we shall therefore deal mainly with droplets from several to tens of microns in size. For such droplets an attempt can be made at constructing sufficiently universal equations, defining the growth by condensation (or evaporation) of droplets in a vapor-air medium, and to then simplify them. Here it can be assumed that the transport of vapor and heat in the droplet–vapor-air medium can be described by diffusion equations, introducing for small particles corrections which make allowance for conversion to kinetic conditions when the Knudsen number $\left(\mathrm{Kn}=\frac{l}{R}\right.$, where l is the mean free path and R the droplet radius) is not too small compared with unity, and for large particles corrections making allowance for convection.

The system of equations describing vapor and heat transport and droplet growth can be expressed in the form

$$\frac{\partial\rho}{\partial t}+\mathbf{v}_1\nabla\rho=D_{\text{v}}\,\Delta\rho,$$

$$\frac{\partial T_i}{\partial t}+\mathbf{v}_i\nabla T_i=\varkappa_i\,\Delta T_i\quad(i=1,\ 2),$$

$$\frac{dm}{dt}=D_{\text{v}}\iint\limits_S\frac{d\rho}{dr}\bigg|_{r=R}dS, \tag{2.1.1}$$

where ρ and D_{v} are the density and coefficient of diffusion of the vapor, respectively; T_i, $\mathbf{v}_i$ and $\varkappa_i$ are the temperature, velocity and thermal diffusivity of air ($i = 1$) and liquid ($i = 2$); m and S are the mass and surface area of the droplet. In their general form the right-hand sides of the first and third equations can be supplemented by functions characterizing the operation of external sources.

The equations should be solved under the following conditions:

$$\rho=\rho_\infty,\ T_1=T_\infty\ \text{for}\ r\to\infty,$$

$$\rho=\rho_0,\ T_1=T_2=T\ \text{for}\ r=R,$$

$$\left(LD_{\text{v}}\frac{\partial\rho}{\partial r}+k_1\frac{\partial T_1}{\partial r}+k_2\frac{\partial T_2}{\partial r}\right)\bigg|_{r=R}=0, \tag{2.1.2}$$

where L is the heat of condensation; k_1 and k_2 are the thermal conductivities of air and water, respectively. We recall that the thermal diffusivity and thermal conductivity are related by the expression

$$\varkappa=\frac{k}{\rho c_p},$$

where c_p is the specific heat and ρ the density of the substance.

The above system of equations is not closed, since the velocity field inside and outside the droplet is not defined. If it is assumed that the droplet motion is due to the gravity field and reference is made to the size range of these droplets, then for such small dimensions this motion can be regarded as viscous.

The velocity field due to viscous motion of the droplet in a spherical coordinate system moving together with the droplet is cited by Levich /21/ in the form

$$v_{1,r}=\left(\frac{b_1}{r^3}+\frac{b_2}{r}+b_3\right)\cos\theta,$$
$$v_{2,r}=v_0\left(1-\frac{r^2}{R^2}\right)\cos\theta,$$
$$v_{1,\theta}=\left(\frac{b_1}{2r^3}-\frac{b_2}{2r}-b_3\right)\sin\theta,$$
$$v_{2,\theta}=-v_0\left(1-\frac{2r^2}{R^2}\right)\sin\theta. \quad (2.1.3)$$

Here

$$v_0=\frac{\eta_1}{2(\eta_1+\eta_2)}v_\infty,$$

$$v_\infty=\frac{2(\rho_2-\rho_1)gR^2(\eta_1+\eta_2)}{3\eta_1(2\eta_1+3\eta_2)},$$

$$b_1=-\frac{\eta_2}{2(\eta_1+\eta_2)}R^3v_\infty,$$

$$b_2=\frac{2\eta_1+3\eta_2}{2(\eta_1+\eta_2)}Rv_\infty,\quad b_3=-v_\infty,$$

where $\eta_{1,2}$ and $\rho_{1,2}$ are the dynamic viscosity and density, respectively, of air and water; v_∞ is the droplet velocity relative to the medium; g is the acceleration of gravity.

The relative role of convection and diffusion can be easily estimated by converting to dimensionless variables. Then the motion, vapor and heat transport will be defined by the following characteristic parameters: Reynolds numbers $\mathrm{Re}_1=\frac{\rho_1 v_\infty R}{\eta_1}$, $\mathrm{Re}_2=\frac{\rho_2 v_0 R}{\eta_2}$, which characterize the motion of air and circulation of liquid in the droplet; Peclet numbers $\mathrm{Pe}=\frac{v_\infty R}{D_v}$, $\mathrm{Pe}_{1,T}=\frac{v_\infty R}{\varkappa_1}$ and $\mathrm{Pe}_{2,T}=\frac{v_0 R}{\varkappa_2}$, which characterize the relationship between the convective and diffusive transfer of vapor, and also of heat, to the droplet and within it.

For low Reynolds numbers, the droplet velocity relative to that medium is /31, 33/

$$v_\infty=\frac{2}{3}\frac{R^2g}{\eta_1}\frac{(\rho_2-\rho_1)(\eta_1+\eta_2)}{2\eta_1+3\eta_2}\left[1+a_1\frac{l}{R}+a_2\frac{l}{R}\exp\left(-\frac{a_3R}{l}\right)\right], \quad (2.1.4)$$

where l is the mean free path, while a_1, a_2 and a_3 are experimentally determined constants. At atmospheric pressure and room temperature it is usually assumed that /33/ $a_1 = 1.246$, $a_2 = 0.42$, and $a_3 = 0.87$.

The motion of liquid within the droplet is defined by the characteristic velocity v_0. For water and air

$$v_0 = 0.9 \cdot 10^{-2} v_\infty. \tag{2.1.5}$$

Neglecting corrections for the mean free path and making use of the fact that $\eta_2 \gg \eta_1$ and $\rho_2 \gg \rho_1$, the Reynolds and Peclet numbers assume the form

$$\begin{aligned}
\mathrm{Re}_1 &= \frac{2}{9} \frac{\rho_1 \rho_2 g}{\eta_1^2} R^3; \\
\mathrm{Re}_2 &= \frac{1}{9} \frac{\rho_2^2 g}{\eta_2^2} R^3; \\
\mathrm{Pe} &= \frac{2}{9} \frac{\rho_2 g}{\eta_1 D_v} R^3; \\
\mathrm{Pe}_{1,T} &= \frac{2}{9} \frac{\rho_2 g}{\eta_1 \varkappa_1} R^3; \\
\mathrm{Pe}_{2,T} &= \frac{1}{9} \frac{\rho_2 g}{\eta_2 \varkappa_2} R^3.
\end{aligned} \tag{2.1.6}$$

All the dimensionless quantities are functions of droplet radius. This dependence is quite strong and has the same form for all the dimensionless numbers. The coefficients of R^3 are quite small (if we deal with particles of the order of 10^{-3} cm), and assume the values: $0.81 \cdot 10^7$ cm^{-3}, $0.88 \cdot 10^6$ cm^{-3}, $0.71 \cdot 10^7$ cm^{-3}, $0.75 \cdot 10^7$ cm^{-3} and $0.55 \cdot 10^7$ cm^{-3}. Hence convective transport is felt only for sufficiently large particles with radii of several tens of microns (e.g., $\mathrm{Pe} = 1$ when $R \sim 5.6 \cdot 10^{-3}$ cm, $\mathrm{Pe}_{1,T} = 1$ when $R \sim 4.1 \cdot 10^{-3}$ cm, and $\mathrm{Pe}_{2,T} = 1$ when $R = 5.2 \cdot 10^{-3}$ cm).

It was hence demonstrated that in considering the growth or evaporation of droplets with $r < 30\mu$ it is possible to neglect circulation within the droplet and air motion outside it. This implies that in subsequent calculations one may consider the following simpler system of equations:

$$\frac{\partial \rho}{\partial t} = D_v \, \Delta \rho,$$

$$\frac{\partial T_l}{\partial t} = \varkappa_l \, \Delta T_l,$$

$$\frac{dm}{dt} = 4\pi r^2 D_v \left. \frac{d\rho}{dr} \right|_{r=R} . \qquad (2.1.7)$$

Direct application of system (2.1.7) to practical calculations results in quite complex mathematical manipulations. Further simplifications are thus desirable. This can be done by employing the fact that atmospheric processes occur slowly. In other words, if the external conditions (temperature, pressure) vary reasonably slowly and if the rate of droplet growth is sufficiently slow, the fields of vapor density and temperature have sufficient time to adjust to the changed conditions and to depend on time alone in parametric form. The process can then be treated as quasi-steady and simpler equations can be used. The applicability of quasi-steadiness to cloud processes and of the corresponding approximations is examined in the next section.

2. RELAXATION PROCESSES AND APPLICABILITY OF THE QUASI-STEADY APPROXIMATION

The question of the applicability of the quasi-steady approximation is very important from the viewpoint of the feasibility of simplifying the principal equations describing droplet growth. These simplifications imply that when the droplet radius and external conditions vary more slowly than the establishment of vapor concentration and temperature fields, calculations can be conducted with characteristics of these fields obtained by solving steady-state diffusion equations.

An assumption of this kind can be justified for processes occurring in clouds, so the droplet growth is usually calculated in the quasi-steady approximation. Nevertheless, although the physical probability of the quasi-steady approximation of growth by condensation of cloud droplets is not particularly objectionable, estimates must still be made.

This is necessitated primarily by the fact that in examining droplet growth in a turbulent flow when the temperature field changes with time (as in the case of the acoustic field) lag effects may arise which, in turn, will make it possible to introduce corrections for the growth rate. The effect of droplet size variation on its rate of growth in reference to meteorological problems was first examined by Timofeev and Shvets /29/. Subsequently, conversion to quasi-steady conditions was considered /6, 8–10/, but it was shown /12/ that the latter treatment involved a mathematical error.

Some information on the applicability of the quasi-steady approximation can be obtained from a qualitative analysis of the starting equations. First we shall solve two auxiliary problems.

Consider the diffusion process inside a sphere of radius R with the following initial and boundary conditions:

$$t=0, \qquad X=X_0;$$
$$r=R, \qquad X=X_0+\Delta X. \tag{2.2.1}$$

For spherical symmetry, the equation

$$\frac{\partial X}{\partial t}=h\left(\frac{\partial^2 X}{\partial r^2}+\frac{2}{r}\frac{\partial X}{\partial r}\right) \tag{2.2.2}$$

has the following solution, depending on the two dimensionless variables $\frac{r}{R}$ and $\frac{ht}{R^2}$:

$$X=X_0+\Delta X\left\{1+\frac{2R}{\pi r}\sum_{n=1}^{\infty}\frac{(-1)^n}{n}\sin\frac{\pi n r}{R}\exp\left(-\frac{\pi^2 n^2 ht}{R^2}\right)\right\}. \tag{2.2.3}$$

At the center of the sphere

$$X=X_0+\Delta X\left\{1+2\sum_{n=1}^{\infty}(-1)^n\exp\left(-\frac{\pi^2 n^2 ht}{R^2}\right)\right\}. \tag{2.2.4}$$

It is evident that the characteristic time for smoothing X is $\frac{R^2}{\pi^2 h}$. Figure 1 illustrates the variation of X as a function of time $\frac{ht}{R^2}$ /18/. The difference between the values of X at the center and on the surface decreases approximately by a factor of two during time

$$\tau\approx\frac{R^2}{7h}. \tag{2.2.5}$$

Consider the external diffusion time for a sphere of radius R under the following initial and boundary conditions:

$$t=0, \qquad X=X_0;$$
$$r=R, \qquad X=X_0+\Delta X. \tag{2.2.6}$$

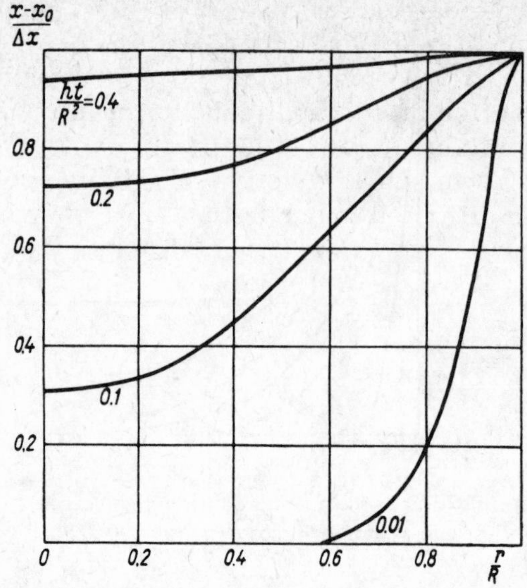

FIGURE 1. Heating of a sphere. Temperature distribution within the sphere at various times

This problem has been solved in the case of condensation processes for a droplet /30/. The solution to equation (2.2.2) in this case is

$$X = X_0 + \frac{R}{r}\,\Delta X\left[1 - \operatorname{erf}\left(\frac{r-R}{2\sqrt{ht}}\right)\right], \qquad (2.2.7)$$

where

$$\operatorname{erf} y = \frac{2}{\sqrt{\pi}} \int_0^y e^{-z^2}\,dz.$$

Here, X is a function of the same two dimensionless variables, $\frac{r}{R}$ and $\frac{h^2 t}{R}$. This function is plotted in Figure 2.

In the external problem it is more expedient to estimate the characteristic time by examining the variation in the flux to the sphere rather than the value of X itself, since X does not vary on the surface of the sphere while the flux to the sphere does vary and is given by

$$I = -4\pi r^2 h \left.\frac{\partial X}{\partial r}\right|_{r=R} = 4\pi R h\,\Delta X\left(1 + \frac{R}{\sqrt{\pi h t}}\right). \qquad (2.2.8)$$

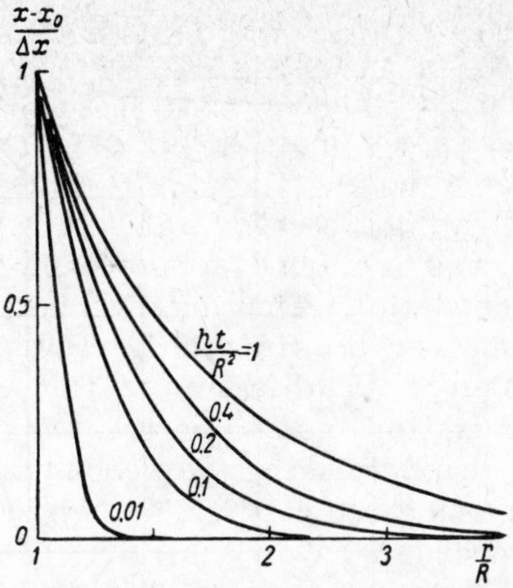

FIGURE 2. Temperature distribution outside the sphere at various times

Under equilibrium conditions $I_0 = 4\pi Rh\Delta X$. If the characteristic time is taken as the value of τ at which I exceeds I_0 only twofold, then

$$\tau = \frac{R^2}{\pi h}. \qquad (2.2.9)$$

In spite of some nonequivalence of the dimensionless ratios used in considering the external and internal problems, the introduction of characteristic times provides a sensible basis for the study of more complex relaxation processes, one of which was encountered in investigating droplet growth by condensation. In this case there occurs interrelated diffusion reconstruction of the vapor density and temperature fields outside the droplet and of the temperature field inside the droplet, since condensation leads to changes in the temperature of the surface layer of the droplet and, conversely, a change in the surface temperature alters the condensation rate. In addition, it is necessary to take into account the shift of the droplet boundary in the course of its growth or evaporation and the variation in external conditions, which express themselves by altering the vapor concentration and ambient temperature.

In considering such a complicated problem one can attempt either to solve it as a whole (if possible), or to estimate the time characteristics of the separate processes, introduce sensible approximations and obtain an approximate solution. The latter approach appears preferable and more rational. The idea to be utilized here consists in investigating the characteristic times of each individual process. If the times are found to be commensurable, then we are dealing with an interaction which must be taken into account rigorously. If, however, the times differ by orders of magnitude, then a simplification is possible subject to which the process with the small characteristic time can be treated as proceeding under steady conditions characterizing the second process, while the process with the large characteristic time can be treated as proceeding during a steady process first.

On the basis of such an approach, and employing the solutions to the auxiliary problems, the three characteristic process times are

$$\tau_1=\frac{R^2}{\pi D_v}, \quad \tau_2=\frac{R^2}{\pi \varkappa_1}, \quad \tau_3=\frac{R^2}{7\varkappa_2}, \tag{2.2.10}$$

where τ_1, τ_2 and τ_3 represent, respectively, the reconstruction times of the vapor density field, the temperature field outside the droplet, and the temperature field inside the droplet. Since $D_v \approx 0.22$ cm^2/sec $\varkappa_1 \approx 0.17$ cm^2/sec and $\varkappa_2 \approx 0.144 \cdot 10^{-2}$ cm^2/sec,

$$\frac{\tau_2}{\tau_1} \approx 1.3, \quad \frac{\tau_3}{\tau_1} \approx 65. \tag{2.2.11}$$

These relationships show that the vapor density field is established first, and almost simultaneously with it the temperature field outside the droplet, after which the temperature within the droplet equalizes much more slowly. Due to the fact that condensation is accompanied by droplet size variation and release of heat (which results from heating), it is necessary to further estimate the characteristic times of a number of processes. The characteristic time of droplet heating (thermal inertia) is determined by the heat flux or by heat generation during condensation.

The characteristic heating time due to the heat flux can be derived from the expression

$$I_1=4\pi k_1 R(T_\infty - T), \tag{2.2.12}$$

where I_1 is the diffusion heat flux. (It is clearly assumed that the characteristic time of this process is much greater than τ_3.)

Then the variation in droplet temperature satisfies

$$\frac{4}{3}\pi c_2\rho_2 R^3 \frac{dT}{dt} = 4\pi R k_1 (T_\infty - T), \qquad (2.2.13)$$

where c_2 is the specific heat of water, Hence

$$T = T_\infty - \Delta T \exp\left(-\frac{3k_1 t}{c_2\rho_2 R^2}\right). \qquad (2.2.14)$$

The characteristic time τ_4 of initial heating can be represented in the form

$$\tau_4 = \frac{c_2\rho_2 R^2}{3k_1} = \frac{\pi c_2\rho_2}{3c_p\rho_1}\tau_2 \approx 5 \cdot 10^3 \tau_2. \qquad (2.2.15)$$

We shall consider the initial heating of a droplet due to the heat of condensation. The heat flux I_2 can be estimated from the equation

$$I_2 = 4\pi r^2 D_v L \left.\frac{\partial\rho}{\partial r}\right|_{r=R} \approx 4\pi R D_v L \rho_0 (T_\infty) \times$$

$$\times \left[\delta_0 + \left(\frac{L}{R_v T} - 1\right)\frac{T_\infty - T}{T_\infty}\right], \qquad (2.2.16)$$

where ρ_0 is the saturated vapor pressure, R_v is the gas constant of the the vapor, and $\delta_0 = \left(1 - \frac{\rho_0}{\rho}\right)$ is the supersaturation. It can be seen from the latter equation that the release of heat results, first, from condensation due to supersaturation δ_0, and second, from the temperature difference between the droplet surface and the surroundings. Heating due to the temperature difference has the characteristic time

$$\tau_5 = \frac{c_2\rho_2 R^2 T_\infty}{3D_v L\left(\frac{L}{R_v T} - 1\right)\rho_0(T_\infty)} = \frac{k_1 T_\infty}{D_v L\left(\frac{L}{R_v T} - 1\right)\rho_0(T_\infty)}\tau_4 \approx 0.8\tau_4. \qquad (2.2.17)$$

The time needed for heating the droplet by condensation of supersaturated vapor is

$$\tau_6 = \frac{c_2\rho_2 R^2 \Delta T}{3D_v L\rho_0\delta_0}. \qquad (2.2.18)$$

Calculations show that for atmospheric processes the supersaturation is very small ($\delta_0 \approx 10^{-5}$). For this reason

$$\tau_6 \gg \max(\tau_1;\ \tau_2;\ \tau_3). \qquad (2.2.19)$$

Under atmospheric conditions the heat fluxes are balanced (condensation heating is compensated by heat release) and it is necessary to consider only small-amplitude deviations from equilibrium. In this case elementary estimates yield

$$\tau_6 \approx \tau_5. \tag{2.2.20}$$

The characteristic time τ, making allowance for a combination of three effects – effect of the heat flux, heat release during condensation as a result of temperature difference, and heat release due to condensation in the presence of general supersaturation in the system – was obtained by Fuchs /30/ on the basis of the heat balance equation. For small ΔT,

$$\tau = \frac{c_2 \rho_2 R^2}{3k_1 \left(1 + \frac{\rho_0 D_v L^2}{k_1 R_v T^2}\right)}. \tag{2.2.21}$$

It should, however, be noted that (2.2.19) and (2.2.20) may not apply in considering processes when the droplet – medium temperature difference or the saturation is large (such a situation may occur in certain facilities).

Consider now the characteristic time of movement of the droplet boundaries. It follows from the equation of droplet growth that

$$\tau_7 = \frac{\rho_2 R^2}{D_v \rho_0 \left[\delta_0 + \left(\frac{L}{R_v T} - 1\right) \frac{T_\infty - T}{T_\infty}\right]}. \tag{2.2.22}$$

Finally, having reference to the fact that droplet growth by condensation occurs when the external conditions vary with time according to some law, we shall introduce the characteristic time τ_8 pertaining to the variation of external parameters.

Thus, for droplet growth by condensation it is possible to introduce eight characteristic times. If all of them are of the same order, then we are dealing with the interaction of various phenomena and the process must be examined in an integrated manner. If, however, these times differ highly from one another and can be subdivided into groups, the examination can be simplified. Note that all these characteristic times with the exception of τ_8 depend on the radius in the same manner. Their interaction is universal for droplets of all sizes (within the limits of applicability of the starting equations). For atmospheric processes the characteristic times can be grouped as follows:

$$\tau_1 \approx \tau_2 < \tau_3 \ll \tau_4 \approx \tau_5 \approx \tau_6 \ll \tau_7.$$

Since droplet condensation is determined by the variation in external conditions, this group of times should be compared with τ_8. In considering regular condensation processes τ_8 is commensurable with τ_7.

This means that the vapor temperature and density fields are described by the equation of steady diffusion and that the droplet can be treated as being heated throughout and possessing the psychrometric temperature. For more rapid processes (such as the behavior of droplets in an acoustic field, turbulent flow) τ_8 can be commensurable with $\tau_{4,5,6}$, in which case the heating effect must be taken into account while the vapor density and temperature fields can be defined by the quasi-steady approximation. Finally, for very rapid processes, the existence of which for small droplets is quite problematical (when $R \approx 10\mu$, $\tau_1 \approx 10^{-6}$ sec), it is necessary to consider effects associated with the reconstruction of fields.

Although the above analysis shows that processes of growth by condensation of droplets in clouds can be described quite satisfactory in the quasi-steady approximation, it is of interest in a number of cases to examine the transition itself to this regime. Such an approach has been examined in extensive detail /12/. Consider first equations (2.1.7) on the assumption that τ_7 is sufficiently large and the movement of the boundary can be neglected. In this case

$$\frac{\partial \rho}{\partial t} = D_v \Delta \rho$$

and

$$\frac{\partial T_i}{\partial t} = \varkappa_i \Delta T_i. \tag{2.2.23}$$

The initial and boundary conditions are taken in the form

$$\begin{gathered} T_1 = T_\infty, \quad T_2 = T_0, \quad \rho = \rho_\infty \text{ for } t = 0, \ r \neq R; \\ T_2 \neq \infty \text{ for } r = 0; \quad T_1 \to T_\infty, \ \rho \to \rho_\infty \text{ for } r \to \infty; \\ T = T_1 = T_2, \ \rho = \rho_0 \text{ for } r = R, \ t \neq 0; \\ \left(L D_v \frac{\partial \rho}{\partial r} + k_1 \frac{\partial T_1}{\partial r} + k_2 \frac{\partial T_2}{\partial r} \right) \bigg|_{r=R} = 0, \\ \rho_0(T) = \rho_0(T_\infty) \left(1 + \beta \frac{T - T_\infty}{T_\infty} \right) \text{where } \beta = \left(\frac{L}{R_v T_\infty} - 1 \right). \end{gathered} \tag{2.2.24}$$

Application of the Laplace transforms

$$F_i=\frac{r}{R}\int_0^\infty \frac{T_i-T_\infty}{T_\infty}\exp(-st)\,dt,$$

$$G=\frac{r}{R}\int_0^\infty \frac{\rho-\rho_\infty}{\rho_\infty}\exp(-st)\,dt \tag{2.2.25}$$

reduces the starting equations to the form

$$sG=D_v\frac{d^2G}{dr^2},$$

$$sF_1=\varkappa_1\frac{d^2F_1}{dr^2},$$

$$sF_2=\varkappa_2\frac{d^2F_2}{dr^2}+\frac{T_0-T_\infty}{T_\infty}\frac{r}{R}; \tag{2.2.26}$$

the boundary conditions become:

$$F_1\to 0,\ G\to 0 \text{ for } r\to\infty;$$

$$F_2=0 \quad \text{for } r=0;$$

$$F_1=F_2=F \text{ for } r=R;$$

$$G=G_R=\frac{\rho_0(T_\infty)-\rho_\infty}{s\rho_\infty}+\beta\frac{\rho_0(T_\infty)}{\rho_\infty}T \text{ for } r=R;$$

$$\left[\frac{LD_v\rho_\infty}{T_\infty}\left(\frac{dG}{dr}-\frac{G}{R}\right)+k_1\left(\frac{dF_1}{dr}-\frac{F_1}{R}\right)+k_2\left(\frac{dF_2}{dr}-\frac{F_2}{R}\right)\right]\Bigg|_{r=R}=0. \tag{2.2.27}$$

The solutions to these equations, subject to the boundary conditions, are:

$$G=G_R\exp\left[-\sqrt{\frac{s}{D_v}}(r-R)\right],$$

$$F_1=F\exp\left[-\sqrt{\frac{s}{\varkappa_1}}(r-R)\right],$$

$$F_2=F\frac{\operatorname{sh} r\sqrt{\frac{s}{\varkappa_2}}}{\operatorname{sh} R\sqrt{\frac{s}{\varkappa_2}}}+\frac{1}{s}\frac{T_0-T_\infty}{T_\infty}\left(\frac{r}{R}-\frac{\operatorname{sh} r\sqrt{\frac{s}{\varkappa_2}}}{\operatorname{sh} R\sqrt{\frac{s}{\varkappa_2}}}\right), \tag{2.2.28}$$

where F, derived from the thermal balance conditions on the droplet surface, is given by

$$F = \frac{R^2}{q\varkappa_2} \frac{M + N\sqrt{q} + \frac{T_0 - T_\infty}{T_\infty}(1 - \sqrt{q}\coth\sqrt{q})}{M_* - N_*\sqrt{q} - \sqrt{q}\coth\sqrt{q}},$$

where

$$q = \frac{R^2 s}{\varkappa_2}; \quad M = \frac{LD_\text{п}}{T_\infty k_2}[\rho_0(T_\infty) - \rho_\infty];$$

$$M_* = 1 - \frac{k_1 T_\infty + \rho_0(T_\infty)\beta L}{k_2 T_\infty};$$

$$N = \frac{\rho_\infty}{T_\infty} L\sqrt{D_\text{v}\varkappa_2} \frac{\rho_0(T_\infty) - \rho_\infty}{k_2};$$

$$N_* = \frac{\rho_0(T_\infty)}{T_\infty} \frac{\beta L}{k_2} \sqrt{D_\text{v}\varkappa_2} + \frac{k_1}{k_2}\sqrt{\frac{\varkappa_2}{\varkappa_1}}. \quad (2.2.29)$$

The vapor density and temperature fields can be found by determining the inverse transform for function F. A detailed analysis /12/ showed that the roots of the denominator of the fraction in expression (2.2.29) lie outside the main branch of arg q and that this expression does not have poles in the domain $|\arg q| < \pi$. For this reason the evaluation of the integral while deriving the inverse transform reduces to evaluating its value at the lower and upper edges of the section taken along the negative part of the real axis, and to an integral over a circle of infinitesimal radius, enclosing the point $q = 0$. The integration in the first approximation leads to

$$\frac{T - T_\infty}{T_\infty} = -\frac{M}{1 - M_*} + \left(\frac{T_0 - T_\infty}{T_\infty} + \frac{M}{1 - M_*}\right)\exp\left(-\frac{t}{\tau}\right), \quad (2.2.30)$$

where

$$\tau = \frac{R^2}{3\varkappa_2(1 - M_*)}$$

and

$$\frac{4R^2}{9\pi^2\varkappa_2} \ll t \leqslant \frac{R^2}{3\varkappa_2(1 - M_*)},$$

and to the expression

$$\frac{T - T_\infty}{T_\infty} = -\frac{M}{1 - M_*}\left[1 + \left(\frac{N}{M} - \frac{N_*}{1 - M_*}\right)\frac{R}{\sqrt{\pi\varkappa_2 t}}\right] \quad (2.2.31)$$

for

$$t \gg \frac{R^2}{3\varkappa_2} \frac{N_*^2}{(1-M_*)^2}, \quad t \gg \frac{R^2}{3\varkappa_2 (1-M_*)}.$$

Similarly for the diffusion regime, density j of the vapor flux is given by

$$j(t) = \frac{D_v}{R}\left\{(\rho_0(T_0) - \rho_\infty)\left(1 + \sqrt{\frac{R^2}{\pi D_v t}}\right) + \beta\rho_0(T_\infty)\frac{T(t) - T_\infty}{T_\infty} - \right.$$
$$\left. - 3N\sqrt{\frac{\varkappa_2}{D_v}}\beta\rho_0(T_\infty)\exp\left[-\frac{3\varkappa_2(1-M_*)}{R^2}t\right]\right\}, \qquad (2.2.32)$$

where

$$\frac{4R^2}{9\pi^2\varkappa_2} \ll t \leqslant \frac{R^2}{3\varkappa_2(1-M_*)}.$$

It can be shown that quasi-steady conditions exist if

$$\left|\frac{T - T_\infty}{T_\infty}\right| \gg \left|3N\sqrt{\frac{\varkappa_2}{D_v}}\right|,$$

or

$$\rho_2 c_2 |T_0 - T_\infty| \gg 3L|\rho_0(T_\infty) - \rho_\infty|.$$

When

$$t \gg \frac{R^2}{3\varkappa_2}\frac{N_*^2}{(1-M_*)^2},$$
$$t \gg \frac{R^2}{3\varkappa_2(1-M_*)}$$

we obtain

$$j(t) = \frac{D_v}{R}\left[\left(1 + \sqrt{\frac{R^2}{\pi D_v t}}\right)(\rho_0(T_\infty) - \rho_\infty) + \beta\rho_0(T_\infty)\frac{T - T_\infty}{T_\infty} - \right.$$
$$\left. - \frac{\beta\rho_0(T_\infty)M}{1 - M_*}\sqrt{\frac{R^2}{\pi D_v t}}\right]. \qquad (2.2.33)$$

3. DIFFUSION APPROXIMATION AND ITS APPLICABILITY

It is known that the diffusion equation is applicable for scales greater than the mean free molecular path. In atmospheric conditions the mean free path is of the order of 10^{-5} cm. This means that already for particles of about 1μ the question of the applicability of the diffusion approximation is of paramount importance. Although the Knudsen number ($\mathrm{Kn} = \frac{l}{R}$) for cloud droplets is small, the diffusion approximation cannot be regarded as sufficiently rigorous and when using this approximation it is necessary to make a correction for the rate of the growth by condensation.

The question of condensation at not too small Kn has recently attracted a great deal of attention. Nevertheless, at present one can refer only to some, more or less satisfactory models, since the problem has not been yet solved rigorously.

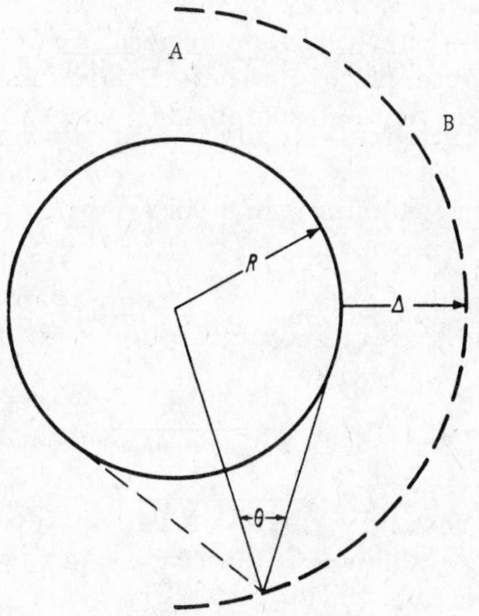

FIGURE 3. Model pertaining to the boundary sphere method:

A) region of kinetic approach; B) region of diffusion approach.

The most extensively used method is that of the boundary sphere, developed by Fuchs /32/. The underlying idea is as follows. The space outside the droplet is subdivided into two parts (Figure 3). It is assumed that in a spherical layer, adjoining the droplet and having thickness of the order of the mean free path, the molecules move without collisions. The vapor flow in this layer is calculated in an elementary manner, on the basis of the velocity distribution of molecules. As a rule, the latter is specified in the form of a Maxwellian distribution. For the region outside a sphere of radius $R+\Delta$ the diffusion equation is regarded as valid and the flux is determined by solving this equation. The fluxes are matched at the surface of the boundary sphere. The diffusion flux to the boundary sphere is

$$I=4\pi D_v(R+\Delta)\left[\rho_\infty-\rho(R+\Delta)\right]. \qquad (2.3.1)$$

On the other hand, the vapor flux to the droplet, calculated from the number of molecules impinging on its surface per unit time with allowance for their capture, can be determined as follows. The flux is proportional to the surface area from which the particles arrive ($S=4\pi(R+\Delta)^2$), the particle concentration $\rho(R+\Delta)$ on this surface, and the integral characterizing the flux of particles through unit area within a solid angle beneath which the droplet is seen:

$$\int_0^\infty\int_0^{2\pi}\int_0^\theta v^3 f(v)\sin\theta\cos\theta\,d\theta\,d\varphi\,dv=\pi\sin^2\theta\int_0^\infty v^3 f(v)\,dv=\bar{\nu}\sin^2\theta. \qquad (2.3.2)$$

Quantity $\bar{\nu}$ is one-quarter of the mean absolute velocity of vapor molecules. From purely geometric considerations (see Figure 3)

$$\sin^2\theta=\frac{R^2}{(R+\Delta)^2}.$$

The average absolute velocity is easily determined by assuming that the distribution of molecules traveling toward the sphere satisfies a Maxwellian distribution,

$$\bar{\nu}=\left(\frac{kT}{2m}\right)^{1/2}, \qquad (2.3.3)$$

where k is the Boltzmann constant while m is the mass of the molecule.

This assumption is the roughest in the suggested model. However, foregoing it would have involved solving the kinetic equation. Hence finally

$$I_+=4\pi R^2\alpha\bar{\nu}\rho(R+\Delta), \qquad (2.3.4)$$

where α is the condensation coefficient.

In the overall balance one must include the flux of vapor molecules leaving the surface. This can be expressed in the form

$$I_- = 4\pi R^2 N, \tag{2.3.5}$$

where N is the number of molecules emitted per unit sphere area per unit time. The value of N is determined by the properties of the surface and is a function of temperature. Under equilibrium conditions, when $I_+ = I_-$, N can be expressed in terms of the vapor density under saturation conditions:

$$N = \alpha \bar{v} \rho_0 (R + \Delta). \tag{2.3.6}$$

In terms of this notation, the vapor flux to the droplet is given by

$$I = I_+ - I_- = 4\pi R^2 \alpha \bar{v} (\rho - \rho_0) \big|_{r=R+\Delta}. \tag{2.3.7}$$

As regards matching at the boundary sphere, it is easy to determine the vapor concentration:

$$\rho(R + \Delta) = \frac{D_v (R + \Delta) \rho_\infty + R^2 \alpha \bar{v} \rho_0}{D_v (R + \Delta) + R^2 \alpha \bar{v}}, \tag{2.3.8}$$

which, upon substitution into equation (2.3.1), yields the flux

$$I = 4\pi D_v R (\rho_\infty - \rho_0) \frac{1 + \dfrac{\Delta}{R}}{1 + \dfrac{D_v (R + \Delta)}{\alpha \bar{v} R^2}}. \tag{2.3.9}$$

Formally, quantity I can be obtained by solving the diffusion equation on the assumption that the vapor concentration at the droplet surface is equal to some quantity $\rho\big|_{r=R} = \rho_0 + \rho'$. The fictitious correction ρ' can be easily determined using the solution to the diffusion equation and requiring that the flux correspond to (2.3.9):

$$\rho' = \frac{\dfrac{D_v (R + \Delta)}{\alpha \bar{v} R^2} - \dfrac{\Delta}{R}}{1 + \dfrac{D_v (R + \Delta)}{\alpha \bar{v} R^2}}. \tag{2.3.10}$$

This quantity is frequently termed the vapor concentration jump, formal allowance for which enables one to employ the diffusion approximation also at not too small Kn.

We introduce the notation

$$\frac{4}{3} l_{tr} = \frac{D_v}{\bar{v}}, \tag{2.3.11}$$

where quantity l_{tr} ("transport") has the dimensions and meaning of the mean free path. However, here the diffusion coefficient takes into account the persistence of velocities in the course of collisions between vapor and air molecules and is greater than the mean free path l.

The difference between l_{tr} and l is determined by the relationships between the masses of the vapor and air molecules. Quantity Δ also has a value close to l_{tr}, since in selecting the radius of the concentric sphere quantity Δ should be defined as that distance at which the direction of particle motion changes substantially, i. e., the velocity persistence should also be taken into account. It should, however, be noted that one cannot expect complete equality between l_{tr} and Δ, and that Δ depends on the particle radius and on the degree of deviation of the velocity distribution from the Maxwellian distribution near the surface. Different versions of computing Δ have been examined, for example, by Smirnov /25/.

By virtue of the approximate nature of the method itself the above expressions represent interpolation equations, and without an exact solution to the problem it is impossible to guarantee that corrections of Δ, which make allowance for some effects, will produce a more exact result. Only a careful experiment or complete solution of the problem can resolve this question.

In this sense it is reasonable to resign oneself to the presence of an error in determining Δ, as to the error of the method itself, and to set $\Delta \approx l_{tr}$. Then

$$I = 4\pi D_v R (\rho_\infty - \rho_0) \frac{1 + \frac{l_{tr}}{R}}{1 + \frac{4 l_{tr}}{3\alpha R} + \frac{4 l_{tr}^2}{3\alpha R^2}}. \tag{2.3.12}$$

Consider the case of small Kn. Here

$$I \approx 4\pi D_v R (\rho_\infty - \rho_0) \frac{1}{1 + \left(\frac{4}{3\alpha} - 1\right) \frac{l_{tr}}{R}}, \tag{2.3.13}$$

which is used extensively in practical calculations.

It should be emphasized again that the method of the boundary sphere is a nonrigorous attempt at representing the transport of vapor in the form of diffusion flux far from the droplet and in the form of a kinetic flux near it. The method can be reduced only to some interpolation equations. The nature, sign, and magnitude of the corresponding error cannot be established within the limits of this idealized model.

Results with a similar meaning can be obtained using the method of effective boundary conditions. The prerequisite conditions of this method are that it is possible to so adjust the boundary conditions for the diffusion equation that, upon distorting the distribution of vapor molecule concentrations near the droplet, one obtains an adjusted expression for the flux, making allowance for the nature of vapor transport through a layer of the order of the mean free path.

The boundary conditions can be written by representing the boundary in the form of some surface, in a manner similar to that in the theory of neutron transport /16, 23/, making allowance for transport due to external forces /24/ and the reflux of vapor molecules. The scheme for constructing the solution will be similar to that in the method of the boundary sphere. The difference consists in that the kinetic flux is matched with the diffusion flux at the boundary and there is no necessity to divide the external space into two parts. In this case fluxes (2.3.1) and (2.3.7) are written directly for the boundary surface. Equating them, we arrive at the expression

$$4\pi D_v R\left[\rho_\infty-\rho(R)\right]=4\pi R^2\alpha\bar{v}\left[\rho(R)-\rho_0\right],$$

whence

$$\rho(R)=\frac{D_v\rho_\infty+\alpha\bar{v}R\rho_0}{D_v+\alpha\bar{v}R}, \qquad (2.3.14)$$

$$\rho'=\frac{D_v}{\alpha\bar{v}R}\,\frac{1}{1+\dfrac{D_v}{\alpha\bar{v}R}}, \qquad (2.3.15)$$

$$I=4\pi D_v R\left(\rho_\infty-\rho_0\right)\frac{1}{1+\dfrac{D_v}{\alpha\bar{v}R}}. \qquad (2.3.16)$$

This approach yields similar results (possibly less exact), making it possible to immediately obtain expressions for fluxes without additional introduction of the boundary sphere. By virtue of the fact that the above relationships are interpolation equations, they should yield a reasonable accuracy for near-limiting condensation regimes, i. e., kinetic and diffusion.

For an exact solution to the problem one must turn to the kinetic equation describing the transport of vapor molecules on the droplet to the vapor-air medium. Unfortunately, this problem has not been solved exactly and there is no basis for assuming that an exact solution will be obtained in the near future. In recent literature on atmospheric physics use was made of a solution to a somewhat different problem, associated with the problem of neutron transport /25, 26/.

In essence, the problem is considered of isotropic scattering, in a binary mixture, of light particles against heavy particles (which are regarded as stationary and having a random distribution if the concentration of the light particles is so small that their mutual collisions can be neglected) when the absolute speed of light particles is equal to some constant quantity and absorption occurs at some spherical surface. The problem of determining the intensity of the flux of light diffusing particles to a spherical absorber was examined in detail in the transport theory of neutrons and has been termed the spherical Milne problem. The kinetic equation which, in this formulation, is linear was solved by a number of investigators /14, 38, 40, 45, 46/ and analyzed by Smirnov /25/.

It is noteworthy that the flux intensity can be expressed in the form

$$I = \frac{4\pi D_v r \rho_\infty}{1 + \lambda_0 \frac{l}{r}}, \qquad (2.3.17)$$

where λ_0 is a function of ratio $\frac{l}{R}$ and ranges from $^4/_3$ (when $\frac{r}{l} \to 0$) to 0.7104 (when $\frac{r}{l} \to \infty$). Different calculations have resulted in different expressions for function λ_0. However, Smirnov /25/ has shown that the differences in the fluxes are small (fractions of a percent).

Since the above model is far removed from the real problem of vapor transport to a growing droplet, Smirnov attempted to extend the above results to the case when not all the vapor molecules impinging on the surface are absorbed. He did not try to solve the kinetic equation, but based his construction on balance considerations and considered the probability of absorption after the nth collision of given molecules with the surface. Here he showed that the flux is expressed similarly to (2.3.17), the only difference being that λ_0 should be replaced by λ, where

$$\lambda = \lambda_0 + \frac{4}{3}\frac{(1-\alpha)}{\alpha}, \qquad (2.3.18)$$

α being the probability of absorption of a molecule during its collision with the surface. It is easy to guess that the appearance of the factor $^4/_3$ in (2.3.18) is related to the fact that the scheme for incorporating the correction hardly differed from the method of the boundary sphere and made no allowance in the kinetic regime for the transport of rebounding molecules.

In effect, Smirnov assumed incorrectly that the fraction of particles returning again to the sphere after being repulsed is determined by quantity A, which is not a function of $\frac{l}{r}$. Elementary considerations show that this is incorrect. Subsequently, he found A from the condition when the flux to the droplet is determined by the limiting kinetic regime; he did not obtain the value of A, but its asymptotic value ($\frac{r}{l} \ll 1$) which, similar to λ_0, yields at $\frac{r}{l} \to 0$ the same value of the factor, i.e., $^4/_3$. The exact solution to the problem should apparently result in A as some function of $\frac{r}{l}$, having a somewhat different form than λ_0 by virtue of differences in the boundary conditions, but the same asymptotic behavior as when $\frac{r}{l} \to 0$.

In conclusion, it should be noted that also in the model representation the spherical Milne problem for a sphere was not solved, since the correction for rebounding was obtained roughly, and not on the basis of exact calculations. In addition, the model itself is hardly suitable for investigating vapor diffusion to a droplet in air, for the following reasons. The vapor molecules have some velocity distribution, different from the Maxwellian distribution near the particle surface. These are scattered on air molecules of commensurable mass; here the scattering is not isentropic, the droplet emits vapor molecules with some specific distribution; at high temperature during saturation, intermolecular collisions of the vapor start assuming a substantial value.

Since consideration of the above factors results in a quite complex, and as yet unsolved problem, there is no point in considering the accuracy of the above equations. Most likely these should be treated as interpolation equations. These expressions should be approached in such a manner that, for the most successful selection of the equation from the standpoint of making allowance for the more important of the above factors, it is necessary to use an expression such as (2.3.9) with a correction expressed in terms of diffusion coefficient D_v and velocity $\overline{v}$.

This is associated with the fact that in air, containing about 78% nitrogen (molecular weight 28.016) and about 21% oxygen (molecular weight 32), the nature of the collision of vapor molecules (molecular weight 18) is taken into account experimentally by quantity D_v, which results in some characteristic scale, different from the mean free path l. On the other hand, it is necessary to introduce quantity l_{tr}, making allowance for the persistence of velocities during the collision of molecules of commensurable masses. This, apparently principal factor is precisely what is ignored in the transport theory of neutrons applied by Smirnov to the growth by condensation of droplets.

4. HEAT TRANSFER BETWEEN A DROPLET AND ITS SURROUNDINGS. PSYCHROMETRIC CORRECTION

The growth or evaporation of droplets is accompanied by the corresponding release or absorption of heat. In the first case the droplet is always warmer than the ambient medium, while in the second it is cooler. The temperature difference is governed by heat transfer, during the examination of which it is also necessary to consider deviations from the diffusion regime, provided Kn is not too small.

Since heat transfer is described similarly to mass transfer, it is possible to utilize the results obtained in the preceding section when considering droplet growth by condensation. If the thermal accommodation coefficient is denoted by ω, then heat flux in accordance with (2.3.13) assumes the form

$$I = 4\pi k_1 R \, \Delta T \frac{1}{1 + \left(\frac{4}{3\omega} - 1\right) \frac{l_{tr}}{R}}. \tag{2.4.1}$$

Quantity ω is determined by the nature of the reflection of air molecules from the droplet surface. According to present ideas this quantity cannot differ substantially from unity.

To estimate the temperature difference between the surroundings and the droplet during its growth or evaporation, we shall use results obtained in section 2 of this chapter. We start from the fact that the time of growth or evaporation of droplets (small supersaturation) is much greater than the heating time ($t \gg \tau_{4,5}$), which is of the order of $10^{-4}R^2$ sec (droplet radius in microns). Then, equating the amount of heat released during condensation to the heat flux yields ΔT:

$$4\pi D_v LR(\rho_\infty - \rho_0)\frac{1}{1+\left(\frac{4}{3\alpha}-1\right)\frac{l_{tr}}{R}} = 4\pi k_1 R\,\Delta T\frac{1}{1+\left(\frac{4}{3\omega}-1\right)\frac{l_{tr}}{R}}. \quad (2.4.2)$$

Since the concentration of saturated vapor depends on the temperature, we shall make allowance for the difference between the droplet surface temperature and the temperature of the medium. For small ΔT, the Clausius-Clapeyron relation allows us to write

$$\rho_0(T+\Delta T,\ R) \approx \rho_0(T,\ R)\left[1+\left(\frac{L}{R_v T}-1\right)\frac{\Delta T}{T}\right]. \quad (2.4.3)$$

Using equations (2.4.2) and (2.4.3), we have

$$\Delta T = \frac{D_v L\left[\rho_\infty - \rho_0(T,\ R)\right]}{\frac{D_v L\rho_0}{T}\left(\frac{L}{R_v T}-1\right)+k_1\frac{1+\left(\frac{4}{3\alpha}-1\right)\frac{l_{tr}}{R}}{1+\left(\frac{4}{3\omega}-1\right)\frac{l_{tr}}{R}}}. \quad (2.4.4)$$

Quantity ΔT is termed the psychrometric correction. It is positive during condensation ($\rho_\infty > \rho_0$) and negative during evaporation If no allowance is made for the effect of surface tension forces on ρ_0, then ΔT virtually does not depend on radius R. This means that sufficiently large droplets are at the same temperature. This does not apply to small droplets owing to the strong dependence of ρ_0 on the surface temperature. In the simplest case

$$\Delta T = \frac{D_v L}{k_1}(\rho_\infty - \rho_0).$$

This equation was derived by Maxwell /41/. It should, however, be stipulated that allowance for air flow past the droplet with large R results in the appearance of a dependence of ΔT on droplet size. For this reason it is sometimes more convenient to employ the expression

$$\Delta T = \frac{\rho_2 L}{k_1}\left[1+\left(\frac{4}{3\omega}-1\right)\frac{l_{tr}}{R}\right]R\frac{dR}{dt}. \quad (2.4.5)$$

The weak dependence of the psychrometric correction on droplet size leads to the following conclusion. The variation in droplet size during its growth or evaporation, by virtue of the above feature, is virtually independent of temperature field reconstruction. This means that the process of temperature equalization within the droplet is not disturbed by the release of heat on its surface and almost the entire heat during condensation (with the exception of some fraction which is expended on heating the newly condensed liquid) is removed to the surroundings. On the other hand, the temperature field within the droplet can be treated as constant.

5. EFFECT OF CONVECTIVE TRANSPORT ON THE RATE OF GROWTH BY CONDENSATION

In considering the growth and evaporation of droplets allowance should be made for the fact that they generally move relative to air and this can affect the magnitude of the vapor flux. The air motion relative to the droplets is determined by two factors: falling of droplets under gravity and turbulent motion of the medium. The second factor has a limited effect, since the cloud particles are quite satisfactorily carried by turbulent fluctuations and for droplets in clouds the air motion relative to them (induced by turbulence at typical rates of eddy energy dissipation) is small compared with their movement due to gravity.

The parameter determining the relationship between diffusion and convective transport of vapor is the Peclet number $\mathrm{Pe} = \frac{v_\infty L}{D_v}$. For fall under gravity (on the assumption that the drag is determined by the Stokes law) Pe can be expressed in the form

$$\mathrm{Pe} = \frac{2}{9}\,\frac{\rho_2 g R^3}{\rho_1 \nu_1 D_v}, \tag{2.5.1}$$

where g is the acceleration of gravity while ν_1 is the kinematic viscosity of air.

For droplets with radii of several microns Pe is small, so it can be assumed that the air flow past the droplet has no substantial effect on the rate of cloud droplet growth. Nevertheless, corresponding calculations should be made, although purely mathematical difficulties have prevented the problem of the correct consideration of convective transport from being solved with sufficient completeness.

A similar problem of heat transfer from a moving sphere was investigated elsewhere /36, 47/. The heat conduction equation was solved by Taylor /47/ using inner and outer expansions, used extensively in hydrodynamics /11/. Taylor's solution /47/ can also be used in considering the transport of vapor. Moreover, having reference to the fact that the air flow past the particle is due to its fall under gravity, by virtue of which it starts being felt for dimensions much greater than the mean free path, it is possible to neglect effects associated with the concentration jump and surface slip of molecules.

For this case the dimensionless transport equation is

$$\Delta x = \mathrm{Pe}\,\mathbf{u}\,\nabla x, \tag{2.5.2}$$

where

$$x = \frac{\rho_\infty - \rho}{\rho_\infty - \rho_0}, \quad \mathbf{u} = \frac{\mathbf{v}}{|\mathbf{v}_\infty|},$$

$$\Delta = \frac{1}{r^2}\frac{\partial}{\partial r}\left(r^2\frac{\partial}{\partial r}\right) + \frac{1}{r^2}\frac{\partial}{\partial \zeta}\left[(1-\zeta^2)\frac{\partial}{\partial \zeta}\right], \quad \zeta \equiv \cos\theta,$$

$$\mathbf{u}\nabla = u_r\frac{\partial}{\partial r} + \frac{u_\theta}{r}\frac{\partial}{\partial \theta},$$

$$u_r = \left[1 - \frac{3}{2r} + \frac{1}{2r^3}\right]\zeta,$$

$$u_\theta = \left[-1 + \frac{3}{4r} + \frac{1}{4r^3}\right](1-\zeta^2)^{1/2}.$$

The inner expansion is sought in the form

$$x = \sum_{n=0}^{\infty} x_n(r, \theta)\, f_n(\mathrm{Pe}) \tag{2.5.3}$$

subject to the condition that

$$\lim_{\mathrm{Pe}\to 0} \frac{f_{n+1}}{f_n} \to 0.$$

The outer expansion is sought in the form

$$h(z, \theta) = \sum_{n=0}^{\infty} h_n(z, \theta)\, F_n(\mathrm{Pe}), \tag{2.5.4}$$

where

$$\lim_{\mathrm{Pe}\to 0} \frac{F_{n+1}}{F_n} \to 0 ,$$

and should satisfy the equation

$$\Delta h = u_z \frac{\partial h}{\partial z} + \frac{u_\theta}{z} \frac{\partial h}{\partial \theta} , \tag{2.5.5}$$

where $z = \mathrm{Pe} \cdot r$. In addition, x and h should satisfy the following conditions:

$$\begin{gathered} x = 1, \quad r = 1; \\ x \to 0, \quad r \to \infty; \\ h \to 0, \quad z \to \infty; \\ x(z, \theta) \to h(z, \theta) \text{ for } z \to 0. \end{gathered} \tag{2.5.6}$$

To a first approximation x_0 and h_0 satisfy

$$\begin{gathered} \Delta x_0 = 0, \\ \Delta h_0 = u_z \frac{\partial h}{\partial z} + \frac{u_\theta}{z} \frac{\partial h}{\partial \theta} . \end{gathered} \tag{2.5.7}$$

The solution to these equations, satisfying the boundary conditions, have the form

$$\begin{gathered} x_0 = \frac{1}{r} , \\ h_0 = \frac{1}{z} \exp\left[\frac{z(\zeta - 1)}{2} \right] . \end{gathered} \tag{2.5.8}$$

Here f_0 should be set equal to unity, and it follows from the matching conditions that $F_0 = \mathrm{Pe}$. To find the subsequent terms of the expansion we assume that $f_1(\mathrm{Pe}) = \mathrm{Pe}$ and, substituting the expansions for x and h into equations (2.5.2) and (2.5.5) and retaining first-order infinitesimals, we obtain

$$\begin{gathered} \Delta x_1 = -\left(1 + \frac{3}{2r} + \frac{1}{2r^3}\right) \frac{\zeta}{r^3} , \\ \Delta h_1 = \zeta \frac{\partial h_1}{\partial z} + \frac{(1 - \zeta^2)}{z} \frac{\partial h_1}{\partial \zeta} - \frac{3\zeta}{2z} \frac{\partial h_0}{\partial z} - \frac{3(1 - \zeta^2)}{4z^2} \frac{\partial h_0}{\partial \zeta} . \end{gathered} \tag{2.5.9}$$

The general solution to these equations can also be obtained in the form of an expansion in Bessel functions K_i and Legendre polynomials P_i :

$$x_1 = \frac{1}{2}\left(-1+\frac{1}{r}\right)+\frac{1}{4}\frac{P_1(\zeta)}{r^2}+\left(\frac{1}{2}+\frac{3}{4r}-\frac{1}{8r^3}\right)P_1(\zeta),$$

$$h_1 = \left[\left(\frac{\pi}{z}\right)^{1/2}\sum_{i=0}^{\infty} d_i K_{i+\frac{1}{2}}\left(\frac{z}{2}\right)P_i(\zeta)+\sum_{i=0}^{2} g_i(z)P_i(\zeta)\right]\exp\left(\frac{z\zeta}{2}\right); \quad (2.5.10)$$

here

$$d_0 = \frac{1}{2\pi}(1+\ln\gamma),$$

$$d_1 = \frac{3}{4\pi}(1-\ln\gamma),$$

$$d_2 = \frac{1}{4\pi}(\ln\gamma-3),$$

$$d_i = 0 \text{ for } i\geqslant 3,$$

$$g_0 = -\frac{1}{2z}\left[\mathrm{Ei}(-z)\exp\left(\frac{z}{2}\right)-\ln z\exp\left(-\frac{z}{2}\right)\right],$$

$$g_1 = -\frac{3}{4z}\left[\left(1-\frac{2}{z}\right)\mathrm{Ei}(-z)\exp\left(\frac{z}{2}\right)+\left(1-\frac{2}{z}\right)\ln z\exp\left(-\frac{z}{2}\right)+ +\frac{2}{\rho}\exp\left(-\frac{z}{2}\right)\right],$$

$$g_2 = -\frac{1}{4z}\left[\left(1-\frac{6}{z}+\frac{12}{z^2}\right)\mathrm{Ei}(-z)\exp\left(\frac{z}{2}\right)- -\left(1+\frac{6}{z}+\frac{12}{z^2}\right)\ln z\exp\left(-\frac{z}{2}\right)-2\left(1+\frac{6}{z}\right)\exp\left(-\frac{z}{2}\right)\right],$$

where

$$\mathrm{Ei}(-x) = -\int_x^{\infty}\frac{e^{-t}}{t}\,dt;$$

$\gamma = 0.577215$ is the Euler constant. It follows from the matching conditions that $F_1(\mathrm{Pe}) = \mathrm{Pe}^2$.

It was found that the matching conditions can be satisfied only when

$$x_2 f_2 = \mathrm{Pe}^2 x_2^1 + \mathrm{Pe}^2\ln\mathrm{Pe}\, x_2^2, \quad (2.5.11)$$

where

$$\Delta x_2^1 = \sum_{k=0}^{2} H_i(r)P_i(\zeta),$$

$$\Delta x_2^2 = 0,$$

$H_i(r)$ is some function of r, while $P_i(\zeta)$ is a Legendre polynomial.
The equation for h_2 then assumes the form

$$\Delta h_2 = \zeta \frac{\partial h_2}{\partial z} + \frac{(1-\zeta^2)}{z} \frac{\partial h_2}{\partial \zeta}, \qquad (2.5.12)$$

and its solution is

$$h_2 = \frac{1}{2z} \exp\left[\frac{z}{2}(\zeta - 1)\right];$$

$$F_2(\mathrm{Pe}) = \mathrm{Pe}^3 \ln \mathrm{Pe}.$$

The total flux at the sphere is defined as

$$\mathrm{Nu} = -\int_{-1}^{1} \left(\frac{\partial x}{\partial r}\right)\Big|_{r=1} d\zeta. \qquad (2.5.13)$$

Now $\int_{-1}^{1} P_i(\zeta)\, d\zeta = 0$ when $i \neq 0$. Therefore using the above expression for x_i we can derive the series

$$I = 4\pi D_v R(\rho_\infty - \rho_0)\left[1 + \frac{\mathrm{Pe}}{2} + \frac{1}{2}\mathrm{Pe}^2 \ln \mathrm{Pe} + 0.415\,\mathrm{Pe}^2 + \right.$$
$$\left. + \frac{1}{4}\mathrm{Pe}^3 \ln \mathrm{Pe} + \ldots\right]. \qquad (2.5.14)$$

The above expression for the flux is valid only for $\mathrm{Pe} < 1$. Although the Peclet number is small for the entire range of cloud droplets ($\mathrm{Pe} = 1$ for $R \approx 55\mu$) at which condensation of vapor in the cloud primarily occurs, it is of some interest to examine the process of vapor transport at larger particles. It should, however, be remembered that in this case too the problem of growth by condensation or evaporation has not been solved rigorously enough.

Although the methods developed for taking the boundary layer into account make it apparently possible to solve the problem with reasonable accuracy, the situation is highly complicated by the fact that it is necessary to allow for two (diffusion and hydrodynamic) boundary layers. The principal complicating factor is that due to the closeness of the Prandtl number ($\mathrm{Pr} = \frac{D_v}{\nu_1}$) to unity, the diffusion and hydrodynamic layers virtually coincide.

This means that inside and outside the diffusion layer it is necessary to use with great care different simplifications for the velocity field, usually used in similar solution techniques. For the same reason there is no sense in retaining many terms of the expansion in Pe in equation (2.5.14), where allowance is made for the fine structure of the diffusion region while disregarding the deviation from the Stokes velocity field.

It should, however, be noted that for small Pe (Re) the relationship between Re and Pe is not as important, since the region determining the vapor flow at the droplet has a characteristic size of the order of its radius, and the boundary layer thicknesses substantially exceed R, and their mutual effect no longer has any significance. On the other hand, in the case of large Pe, when the region of vapor flow is commensurable with the thickness of the layers, their mutual effect plays a certain role.

For this reason there is no sense in matching the outer and inner solutions and one should restrict oneself to the zero approximation, corresponding to the solution in the diffusion boundary layer, for which the velocity field is written in the boundary layer approximation. This solution is satisfactory when the boundary layer thickness exceeds the diffusion layer thickness, i. e., when $\Pr < 1$. Hence for $\Pr = 1.3$ ($D_v = 0.22$, $\nu_1 = 0.17$) it can be treated as quite approximate.

In the boundary layer approximation the equation for x is reduced to the form

$$u_\zeta \frac{\partial x}{\partial \zeta} + u_y \frac{\partial x}{\partial y} = \mathrm{Pe}^{-1} \frac{\partial^2 x}{\partial y^2}, \tag{2.5.15}$$

where

$$u_\zeta = \frac{3}{2} y (1 - \zeta^2), \quad u_y = \frac{3}{2} \zeta y^2.$$

The problem is solved for the boundary conditions

$$\begin{aligned} x &= 0, \quad y \to \infty, \\ x &= 1, \quad y = 0. \end{aligned} \tag{2.5.16}$$

Following Levich /21/, who examined in detail a large number of problems of this type, and using the technique developed in /20/, we transform equation (2.5.15) to variables ζ and ψ, where $\psi = (1 - \zeta^2)^{1/2} y$ is the first integral of the equations of motion in the boundary layer. Thus

$$\frac{1}{(1-\zeta^2)^{1/2}} \frac{\partial x}{\partial \zeta} = \frac{2}{3\,\mathrm{Pe}} \frac{1}{\psi} \frac{\partial^2 x}{\partial \psi^2}. \tag{2.5.17}$$

By introducing the variable $\varphi=\frac{2}{3\,\mathrm{Pe}}\int(1-\zeta^2)^{1/2}d\zeta$ this equation is reduced to the form

$$\frac{\partial x}{\partial\varphi}=\frac{1}{\psi}\frac{\partial^2 x}{\partial\psi^2}. \tag{2.5.18}$$

The fact that the boundary conditions are homogeneous makes it possible to seek the self-similar solution in the form $x=x(\eta)$, where $\eta=\frac{\psi^3}{\varphi}$.

The resulting second-order ordinary differential equation is easily solved:

$$x=B_1\int_0^\eta x^{-2/3}\exp\left(-\frac{x}{9}\right)dx+B_2, \tag{2.5.19}$$

where

$$\eta=\frac{y^3(1-\zeta^2)^{3/2}}{\frac{2}{3\,\mathrm{Pe}}\int_0^\zeta(1-\zeta^2)^{1/2}d\zeta+B_3}.$$

The constants of integration are found from the boundary conditions. It follows that since $x=1$ at $y=0$, $B_2=1$, and that since $x=0$ at $y\to\infty$, $B_1=-\frac{1}{\int_0^\infty x^{-2/3}\exp\left(-\frac{x}{9}\right)dx}$. Since x is nonzero at $\zeta=0$, it follows that $B_3=0$.

Therefore

$$x=1-\frac{\int_0^\eta x^{-2/3}\exp\left(-\frac{x}{9}\right)dx}{\int_0^\infty x^{-2/3}\exp\left(-\frac{x}{9}\right)dx}. \tag{2.5.20}$$

The expression for the flux density has the form

$$j=-\left(\frac{\partial x}{\partial y}\right)\Big|_{y=0}=\frac{6^{2/3}(1-\zeta^2)}{2\Gamma\left(\frac{1}{3}\right)\mathrm{Pe}^{2/3}}\frac{1}{\left[\int_0^\zeta(1-\zeta^2)^{1/2}d\zeta\right]^{1/3}}, \tag{2.5.21}$$

while the total dimensionless flux is given by

$$\mathrm{Nu}=\int_{-1}^{1}\left(\frac{\partial x}{\partial y}\right)_{y=0}d\zeta=\frac{6^{2/3}}{2\Gamma\,(1/3)\,\mathrm{Pe}^{2/3}}\int_{-1}^{1}\frac{(1-\zeta^2)^{1/2}\,d\zeta}{\left[\int_0^{\zeta}(1-\zeta^2)^{1/2}\,d\zeta\right]^{1/3}}. \quad (2.5.22)$$

Integration and conversion to dimensional quantities yields

$$I=4\pi D_v R\,(\rho_\infty-\rho_0)\,\frac{6^{1/3}\pi^{2/3}}{4\Gamma\,(1/3)}\,\mathrm{Pe}^{-2/3}\approx 4\pi D_v R\,(\rho_\infty-\rho_0)\cdot 0.625\,\mathrm{Pe}^{-2/3}. \quad (2.5.23)$$

The above expression should satisfactorily describe the transport when the diffusion layer thickness is much smaller than the velocity boundary layer thickness. In the given case the thicknesses of these layers are commensurable, so one must approach equation (2.5.23) with caution and treat it as approximate. It appears to this author that the determination of the vapor flux at a moving droplet is of great importance for the physics of precipitation genesis and of processes of precipitation evaporation beneath a cloud, but is not so important when examining the growth of cloud particles.

6. EQUATION OF DROPLET GROWTH BY CONDENSATION

The growth of a cloud droplet over a wide range of conditions can be treated in the quasi-steady approximation without making allowance for internal or external convection and considering (in the form of a correction) the jump in concentration and the temperature jump. In this case the equation of droplet growth assumes the form

$$\frac{dR}{dt}=\frac{D_v}{\rho_2 R}\,f_1(R,\ l)\,[\rho_\infty-\rho_0(R,\ T,\ c)], \quad (2.6.1)$$

where c is the concentration of the solution, while f_1 is a correction for the kinetic regime:

$$f_1(R,\ l)=\frac{1}{1+\dfrac{D_v}{\alpha\bar{v}R}}. \quad (2.6.2)$$

This simplified form is valid, because for cloud droplets the kinetic regime should be taken into account in the form of a correction only when $\alpha \ll 1$. The saturated vapor pressure above the droplet surface is determined basically by the temperature of the droplet surface, but a substantial role can be played by the surface curvature and the content of dissolved hygroscopic substances in the surface layer. Allowance for these corrections in one form or another was made by a number of investigators /3, 22, 26, 38, 42, 43/ Following them, we shall consider the dependence of ρ_0 on the above quantities. The temperature dependence of the saturated vapor pressure above a flat surface of pure water is defined by the Clausius-Clapeyron equation

$$e_0(T) = A \exp\left(-\frac{L}{R_v T}\right), \tag{2.6.3}$$

where A is some constant.

The effect of the droplet surface curvature on the saturated vapo pressure can be taken into account by means of the expression

$$e_0(R, T) = e_0(T) \exp \frac{2\sigma}{\rho_2 R_v T R}, \tag{2.6.4}$$

where e_0 is the saturated vapor pressure above a flat surface of pure water, and σ is the coefficient of surface tension. If it is assumed that in the course of the growth or evaporation of the droplet the temperature of its surface differs from the ambient temperature, and if it is remembered that this difference is small, then the expression for $e_0(T)$ can be expressed in the form

$$e_0(T) = e_0(T_\infty) \exp\left[-\frac{L}{R_v} \frac{(T_\infty - T)}{T T_\infty}\right] = e_0(T_\infty) \exp\left[\frac{L}{R_v T_\infty} \frac{\Delta T}{T}\right] \approx$$

$$\approx e_0(T_\infty)\left[1 + \frac{L}{R_v T_\infty} \frac{\Delta T}{T_\infty}\right], \tag{2.6.5}$$

where $\Delta T = T - T_\infty$.

Finally, it is also necessary to consider the reduction in vapor pressure due to the presence of the dissolved substance in the droplet. The saturated vapor pressure above the solution droplet has the form

$$e_0(R,\ T,\ c)=e_0(R,\ T)[1-\Phi(c)]=e_0(T_\infty)[1-\Phi(c)]\times$$
$$\times\exp\left[\frac{L}{R_v T_\infty}\frac{\Delta T}{T_\infty}+\frac{2\sigma}{\rho_2 R_v T R}\right], \qquad (2.6.6)$$

where c is the concentration of the solute while $\Phi(c)$ is a function characterizing the pressure drop. In general, for such an approach it must be remembered that the solute affects the condition of phase equilibrium also via the coefficient of surface tension σ, which usually increases with concentration.

In many solutions σ is quite satisfactorily described by the following empirical formula:

$$\sigma=\sigma_0\left(1+\frac{a}{R^3}\right), \qquad (2.6.7)$$

where σ_0 is the surface tension of pure water and a is some coefficient. If this factor is not regarded as very essential, which is apparently true for atmospheric condensation nuclei not containing [dissolved] substances specifically affecting the surface properties of the droplets, then one may limit oneself to making allowance only for quantity $\Phi(c)$.

The effect of the solvent is usually taken into account by Raoult's law which, however, is of limited utility for practical purposes. It is valid only for ideal solutions, when the solution concentration is low and the molecules of the dissolved substance do not interact with the solvent molecules. With allowance for electrolytic dissociation an expression for $\Phi(c)$ in accordance with Raoult's law has the form /1.4/*

$$\Phi(c)=\frac{i m_c M}{\left(\frac{4}{3}\pi\rho_s R^3-m_c\right)M_c}=\frac{iMc}{(\rho_s-c)M_c}, \qquad (2.6.8)$$

where m_c and M_c are the mass and molecular weight of the solute, M is the molecular weight of the vapor, c is the solute concentration in g/cm^3, ρ_s is the density of the solution, and i is the van't Hoff coefficient, characterizing the degree of dissociation of the solute.

The value of i depends on the concentration of the solution and temperature. However, for dilute solutions the solute is treated as being fully dissociated and i is assumed constant, which in this case is determined by the number of ions forming upon dissociation of a

* When referring to the bibliography of another chapter the first numeral denotes the number of the chapter.

single molecule. Thus, for sodium chloride $i=2$ and for calcium chloride $i=3$. It should nevertheless be remembered that cloud condensation nuclei on which cloud droplets form contain a mixture of solutes, and hence the value of i must be determined specially.

It is assumed by Mason /1.4/ that for all condensation nuclei one can set $i=2.22$. Since an equation in the form of (2.6.8) has a very limited range of applicability, the more so since it makes no allowance for electrostatic interaction as well as hydration of ions, in practical calculations one uses extensively various empirical equations based on experimental data /19, 27, 28, 39, 44/.

These relationships were compared with experimental data for NaCl and CaCl and the following empirical expression suggested, which approximates with reasonable accuracy experimental results for $R > b^{1/3}R_0$ /2/:

$$\Phi(c) = \frac{a}{\dfrac{R^3}{R_0^3} - b} - \frac{ac}{\rho_c - bc}, \tag{2.6.9}$$

where ρ_c is the density of the salt, R_0 is the radius of the saturated solution, a and b are constants. For sodium chloride /2/ $a = 1.215$, $b = 1.815$, while for calcium chloride $a = 0.910$, $b = 3.16$. The difficulty in using this formula consists in the fact that the composition of atmospheric condensation nuclei is not known sufficiently well and hence it is impossible to determine a and b with sufficient reliability. Nevertheless, there is some basis for assuming that the cloud nuclei can be roughly subdivided into two groups, nuclei of marine and continental origin, and for assuming that in the first case they consist wholly of a dissolved substance, such as NaCl, and that in the second they contain about 30% of the solute /35/.

If it is assumed that the effect of the solute can be taken into account by means of some generalized relationship which is a function of the total solute concentration c, then the equation of droplet growth assumes the form

$$\frac{dR}{dt} = \frac{D_v}{\rho_2 R}\frac{f_1(R, l)}{R_v T_\infty}\left\{e_\infty - e_0(T_\infty)\left[1 - \Phi(c)\right]\left(1 - \frac{\Delta T}{T_\infty}\right)\times\right.$$
$$\left.\times\exp\left[\frac{L}{R_v T_\infty}\frac{\Delta T}{T_\infty} + \frac{2\sigma}{\rho_2 R_v T R}\right]\right\}. \tag{2.6.10}$$

If the exponent is sufficiently small (which is almost always the case) then

$$\frac{dR}{dt}=\frac{\rho_\infty D_v}{\rho_2 R} f_1(R, l)\left\{1-\frac{e_0(T_\infty)}{e_\infty}[1-\Phi(c)]\left[1+\left(\frac{L}{R_v T}-1\right)\frac{\Delta T}{T_\infty}+\right.\right.$$
$$\left.\left.+\frac{2\sigma}{\rho_2 R_v T_\infty R}\right]\right\}. \qquad (2.6.11)$$

The supersaturation δ_0 above the flat surface is given by the expression

$$\delta_0=1-\frac{e_0(T_\infty)}{e_\infty}. \qquad (2.6.12)$$

Making use of the fact that $\delta_0 \ll 1$, the equation of droplet growth becomes

$$\frac{dR}{dt}=\frac{\rho_\infty}{\rho_2}\frac{D_v}{R} f_1(R, l)\left\{1+\delta_0-[1-\Phi(c)]\left[1+\right.\right.$$
$$\left.\left.+\left(\frac{L}{R_v T_\infty}-1\right)\frac{\Delta T}{T_\infty}+\frac{2\sigma}{\rho_2 R_v T_\infty R}\right]\right\}. \qquad (2.6.13)$$

Further simplification of the equation involves writing $\Phi(c)$ and ΔT in explicit form. Since this form of the equation for the growth of a droplet on an, as yet undissolved nucleus differs from that for a droplet of a solution, the corresponding transformations will be dealt with below separately.

7. DROPLET GROWTH ON A PARTIALLY DISSOLVED HYGROSCOPIC NUCLEUS

In considering the formation of droplets on hygroscopic particles one must consider two growth stages. During the first stage the droplet grows in the presence of a nondissolved salt nucleus, which makes it possible to maintain the solute concentration on the droplet surface at near-saturation. During the second stage droplet growth is attended by a reduction in solution concentration. We shall investigate the first stage on the assumption that the salt particle lies at the droplet center and is spherical. Although this assumption is somewhat difficult to validate from the physical point of view, it enables one to substantially simplify the solution to the problem by virtue of spherical symmetry. From the standpoint of the nature of the principal regularities it does not result in any substantial distortion of results.

Consequently, the system of equations governing the course of droplet growth, dissolution of the nucleus and distribution of the solute concentration c is

$$\frac{dR}{dt}=\frac{D_v f_1(R,\ l)}{\rho_s R}\left[\rho_\infty-\rho_0(R,\ T,\ c)\right],$$

$$\frac{dr_T}{dt}=\frac{D_c}{c_T}\left(\frac{\partial c}{\partial r}\right)\bigg|_{r=r_T},$$

$$\frac{\partial c}{\partial t}=\frac{D_c}{r^2}\frac{\partial}{\partial r}\left(r^2\frac{\partial c}{\partial r}\right), \tag{2.7.1}$$

where c_T is the density of the hygroscopic substance in the solid state, r_T is the radius of the partially dissolved hygroscopic nucleus, ρ_s is the density of the solution, and D_c is the diffusion coefficient of the solute in the droplet. It will be assumed that the rate of substance dissolution is sufficiently high and is limited by the rate of its removal from the surface of the solid particle /1/. In this case concentration $c(r_T)$ at the solid surface should be taken equal to c_{sat}:

$$c(r_T)=c_{sat} \tag{2.7.2}$$

where c_{sat} is the concentration of the saturated solution.

The second boundary condition is derived from the balance equation of the solute:

$$\int_{r_T}^{R} r^2 c(r)\,dr=\frac{c_T}{3}\left(r_0^3-r_T^3\right), \tag{2.7.3}$$

where r_0 is the initial radius of the hygroscopic nucleus. For the inner problem (according to section 2 of the present chapter) the characteristic time of establishing equilibrium distribution is $\tau\approx\frac{R^2}{7D_c}$. Therefore, since when $R\approx 1\,\mu$ at $D_c\approx 10^{-5}$ cm^2/sec, $\tau\approx 1.4\cdot10^{-4}$ sec, the distribution can be regarded as being near-steady and can be written in the form

$$c=\frac{c_{-1}}{r}+c_0.$$

In accordance with the above, following /3/, we shall seek the solution to the third of equations (2.7.1) in the series form

$$c(r, t) = \frac{c_{-1}(t)}{r} + c_0(t) + rc_1(t) + r^2 c_2(t) + \ldots \qquad (2.7.4)$$

Substituting this expansion into equation (2.7.1) and collecting terms with the same power of r yields

$$\frac{dc_{-1}}{dt} = 1.2 D_c c_1;$$

$$\frac{dc_0}{dt} = 2.3 D_c c_2;$$

$$\frac{dc_1}{dt} = 3.4 D_c c_3 \ldots \qquad (2.7.5)$$

By expressing c_2, c_3 etc., in terms of c_0 and c_{-1}, one can define $c(r, t)$ in terms of only two time-dependent functions and their derivatives:

$$c(r, t) = \sum_{k=0}^{\infty} \left(\frac{r^2}{D_c}\right)^k \left[\frac{1}{r(2k)!} \frac{d^k c_{-1}}{dt^k} + \frac{1}{(2k+1)!} \frac{d^k c_0}{dt^k}\right]. \qquad (2.7.6)$$

The time dependence of c_0 and c_{-1} can be found from boundary conditions (2.7.2)–(2.7.3), which yield the differential equations

$$\sum_{k=0}^{\infty} \tau_1^k \left[\frac{1}{r_T (2k)!} \frac{d^k c_{-1}}{dt^k} + \frac{1}{(2k+1)!} \frac{d^k c_0}{dt^k}\right] = c_{\text{sat}},$$

$$\sum_{k=0}^{\infty} \tau_2^k \left\{\frac{1}{2(k+1)(2k)!} \left[1 - \left(\frac{r_T}{R}\right)^{2(k+1)}\right] \frac{d^k c_{-1}}{dt^k} + \right.$$

$$\left. + \frac{1}{(2k+3)(2k+1)!} \left[1 - \left(\frac{r_T}{R}\right)^{2k+3}\right] \frac{d^k c_0}{dt^k}\right\} = \frac{c_T}{3}(r_0^3 - r_T^3), \qquad (2.7.7)$$

where

$$\tau_1 = \frac{r_T^2}{D_c}, \quad \tau_2 = \frac{R^2}{D_c}.$$

We seek an asymptotic solution to the above system of equations which would not depend on the initial conditions. The special feature of this system of equations is that the coefficients of the series contain the small parameters τ_1 and τ_2 and that quantities r_T and R are functions of time. If the characteristic time of variation in r and R is much greater than τ_1 and τ_2, then the series in equations (2.7.7) can be truncated in line with the required accuracy by omitting higher-order infinitesimals.

Hence, in the zero approximation,

$$\frac{c_{-1}}{r_T}+c_0=c_{sat},$$

$$\frac{R^2-r_T^2}{2}c_{-1}+\frac{R^3-r_T^3}{3}c_0=\frac{c_T}{3}(r_0^3-r_T^3). \tag{2.7.8}$$

Then

$$c(r,\ t)=c_{sat}-\left[1-\frac{r_T(t)}{r}\right]\psi(t), \tag{2.7.9}$$

where

$$\psi(t)=\frac{\left[r_0^3-r_T^3(t)\right]c_T-\left[R^3(t)-r_T^3(t)\right]c_{sat}}{\frac{3}{2}r_T(t)\left[R^2(t)-r_T^2(t)\right]-\left[R^3(t)-r_T^3(t)\right]}.$$

Equation (2.7.9) is the quasi-steady concentration distribution with time-dependent coefficients. Since $\psi(t)$ is a function of r_T and R, both the rate of droplet growth and the rate of nucleus dissolution can be found by solving simultaneously the first and second of equations (2.7.1). The equation describing the variation in r_T has the form

$$\frac{dr_T}{dt}=-\frac{D_c}{c_T}\frac{R(c_{sat}-c_R)}{r_T(R-r_T)}, \tag{2.7.10}$$

where c_R is the concentration at the droplet surface:

$$c_R=c(R(t))=c_{sat}-\frac{(R-r_T)\left[(r_0^3-r_T^3)c_T-(R^3-r_T^3)c_{sat}\right]}{R\left[\frac{3}{2}(R^2-r_T^2)r_T-(R^3-r_T^3)\right]}. \tag{2.7.11}$$

The equation for the rate of droplet growth will be treated on the basis of equation (2.6.13). Since the process of dissolution can result in absorption or release of heat, we determine the temperature correction using the heat balance equation

$$\frac{k_1R}{1+\frac{D_v}{\omega\bar{v}R}}\Delta T=L\rho_2R^2\frac{dR}{dt}-L_1c_Tr_T^2\frac{dr_T}{dt}, \tag{2.7.12}$$

where L_1 is the heat of solution.

Making use of equation (2.7.10) we obtain

$$\Delta T=\left(1+\frac{D_v}{\omega\bar{v}R}\right)\left[\frac{\rho_2 RL}{k_1}\frac{dR}{dt}-\frac{L_1 D_c}{k_1}\frac{(c_{sat}-c_R)r_T}{R-r_T}\right]. \tag{2.7.13}$$

The equation for the droplet growth then has the form

$$\frac{dR}{dt}=\frac{\rho_\infty D_v f_1(R,l)}{\rho_2 R}\times$$

$$\times\frac{\left\{1+\delta_0-[1-\Phi(c_R)]\left[1+\left(\frac{L}{R_vT}-1\right)\frac{L_1D_c(c_{sat}-c_R)r_T}{k_1Tf_2(r,t)(R-r_T)}+\frac{2\sigma}{\rho_2R_vTR}\right]\right\}}{1+\frac{f_1(r,l)}{f_2(r,l)}\frac{\rho_\infty D_vL}{k_1T}[1-\Phi(c_R)]\left(\frac{L}{R_vT}-1\right)}, \tag{2.7.14}$$

where

$$f_2(r,l)=\frac{1}{\left(1+\frac{D_v}{\omega\bar{v}R}\right)};$$

the subscript ∞ of T has been dropped. Note that since for this stage the value of $\Phi(c_R)$ is not small, the effect of supersaturation on the rate of growth can be neglected in a number of cases.

To solve the problem of the time of dissolution of a nucleus it is necessary to solve system of equations (2.7.10), (2.7.11) and (2.7.14). This system has already been examined /15/. Analysis shows that at the point $R=r_0$, $r_T=r_0$ the system of equations has a singularity of hyperbolic type, and hence cannot be formally integrated. Numerical solution of the above system of equations showed that c_R is quite close to c_{sat} and decreases somewhat in the course of droplet growth. For this reason, at the moment of complete dissolution of the nucleus the average concentration c is smaller than c_{sat}; here the ratio of the droplet radius at the time of dissolution to r_0 has a tendency to increase with increasing r_0

Figures 4–6 illustrate computation results showing the time dependence of $\frac{R}{r_0}$, $\frac{r_T}{r_0}$ and $\frac{c_R}{c_{sat}}$, the relationship between $\frac{R}{r_0}$ and $\frac{r_T}{r_0}$, and the dependence of dissolution time τ on r_0. For NaCl the concentration undersaturation results in the following radii at the instant of complete dissolution: $R=1.96\,r_0$ when $r_0=1\mu$, $R=2\,r_0$ when $r_0=5\mu$, $R=2.3\,r_0$ when $r_0=10\mu$, while the radius for a saturated solution is given by $R_{sat}=\sqrt[3]{\frac{c_T}{c_{sat}}}\,r_0\approx$ 1.89 . This effect (on the dissolution time) was pointed out in experimental studies of droplet growth on hygroscopic nuclei /17/.

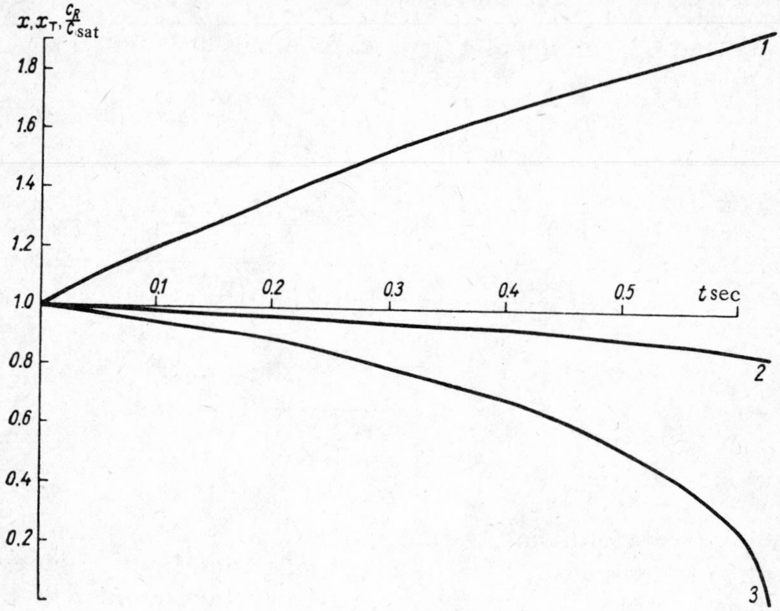

FIGURE 4. Time dependence of droplet radius $x = \frac{R}{r_0}$ (curve 1), radius of solid nucleus $x_T = \frac{r_T}{r_0}$ (curve 2), solution concentration at the droplet surface $\frac{c_R}{c_{sat}}$ (curve 3) during the dissolution of a NaCl nucleus when $r_0 = 5\,\mu$, $T = 0°$ C and $p_1 = 760$ mm Hg

An elementary computation will be conducted in order to examine the combination of parameters on which this small difference between c_R and c_{sat} depends. The flux of solvent to the solution in accordance with equation (2.7.10) is

$$I_1 = 4\pi D_c r_T^2 \left(\frac{\partial c}{\partial r}\right)\Big|_{r=r_T} = -4\pi G r_T^2 \frac{dr_T}{dt} = 4\pi D_c r_T \frac{(c_{sat} - c_R)}{\left(1 - \frac{r_T}{R}\right)}. \quad (2.7.15)$$

In the quasi-steady approximation this flux results in filling a layer of pure water with the solute to concentration c_R. The amount of such water supplied (according to equation (2.7.14)) per unit time (corrections for l, heat of condensation and curvature are neglected) is

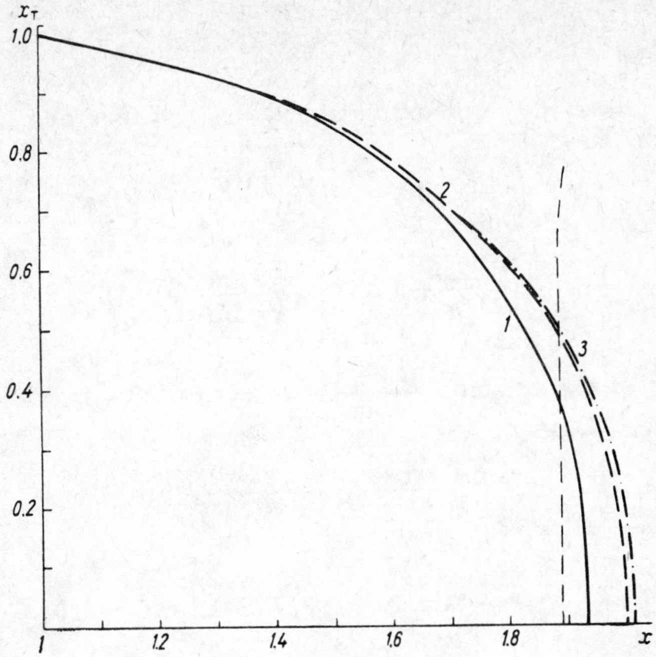

FIGURE 5. Size of solid nucleus $x_T = \frac{r_T}{r_0}$ as a function of droplet radius $x = \frac{R}{r_0}$:

1) $r_0 = 1\mu$; 2) $r_0 = 5\mu$; 3) $r_0 = 10\mu$.

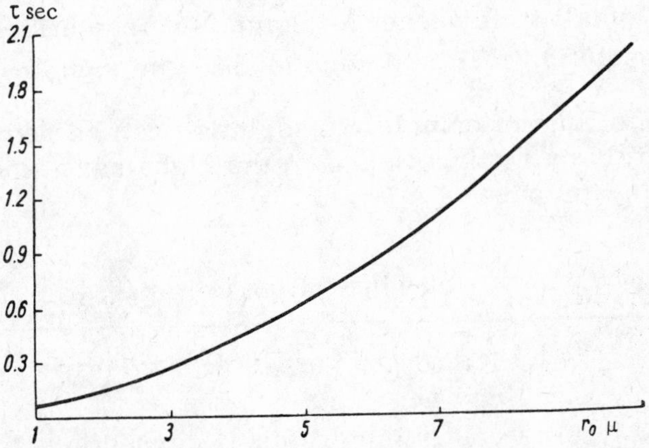

FIGURE 6. Time τ of complete dissolution as a function of initial radius r_0 ($T =$ 20°C, $p_1 =$ 760 mm Hg)

$$I_2 = 4\pi R \frac{\rho_\infty}{\rho_2} D_v \Phi(c_R). \qquad (2.7.16)$$

In the quasi-steady approximation $I_1 = c_R I_2$; therefore

$$\left(\frac{c_{sat}}{c_R} - 1\right) = \frac{\rho_\infty}{\rho_2} \frac{D_v}{D_c} \frac{(R - r_T)}{r_T} \Phi(c_R), \qquad (2.7.17)$$

whence

$$\frac{c_{sat}}{c_R} - 1 \leqslant \frac{\rho_\infty}{\rho_2} \frac{D_v}{D_c} \frac{R}{r_T} \Phi(c_{sat}).$$

In terms of the notation $\frac{c_{sat} - c_R}{c_{sat}} = \gamma$, it follows that

$$\gamma \leqslant \frac{\gamma}{1 - \gamma} \leqslant \frac{\rho_\infty}{\rho_2} \frac{D_v}{D_c} \frac{R}{r_T} \Phi(c_{sat}). \qquad (2.7.18)$$

Since

$$\frac{\rho_\infty}{\rho_2} \approx 10^{-5}; \quad \frac{D_v}{D_c} \approx 0.2 \cdot 10^5;$$
$$\frac{R}{r_T} \approx 2; \quad \Phi(c_{sat}) \approx 0.2,$$

we obtain $\gamma \approx 0.08$, which implies that until the nucleus dissolves entirely the inhomogeneity of the solute distribution is not great. Subsequently, when $0 < r_T \ll R$, the outer layer is enriched by the solute already in the solution, and this approach will be unsuitable for estimating γ. Nevertheless γ cannot increase substantially during the small time needed for complete dissolution of the nucleus, and the dissolution will be determined by the same quantity $\frac{\rho_\infty D_v}{\rho_2 D_c}$.

Hence the time of complete dissolution can be determined approximately by setting $c_R = c_{sat}$ in the right-hand side of equation (2.7.14). In this case

$$\frac{dR}{dt} = \frac{\rho_\infty D_v f_1(R, l)}{\rho_2 R} \frac{\left\{1 - [1 - \Phi(c_{sat})]\left[1 + \frac{2\sigma}{\rho_2 R_v T R}\right]\right\}}{1 + \frac{f_1(R, l)}{f_2(R, l)} \frac{\rho_\infty D_v L}{k_1 T} [1 - \Phi(c_{sat})]\left(\frac{L}{R_v T} - 1\right)}. \qquad (2.7.19)$$

Equation (2.7.19) is easily integrated, if corrections for surface tension and mean free path are neglected. This yields

$$t = \left\{1 + \frac{\rho_\infty D_v L}{k_1 T}\left(\frac{L}{R_v T} - 1\right)[1 - \Phi(c_{sat})]\right\} \frac{\left[\left(\frac{c_T}{c_{sat}}\right)^{2/3} - 1\right] r_0^2 \rho_2}{2\rho_\infty D_v \Phi(c_{sat})}. \qquad (2.7.20)$$

The actual time of dissolution will be somewhat greater, because the surface layer of the solution is undersaturated.

8. GROWTH OF SOLUTION DROPLETS BY CONDENSATION

Consider now the growth of a solution droplet. This process is of the greatest interest from the standpoint of investigating the liquid phase formation in clouds. As regards not too dilute solutions, the rate of droplet growth is mainly determined by concentration c_R; it is first necessary to consider the concentration distribution over the volume of the growing droplet.

The equation of solute diffusion has the form

$$\frac{\partial c}{\partial t}=\frac{D_c}{r^2}\frac{\partial}{\partial r}\left(r^2\frac{\partial c}{\partial r}\right) \tag{2.8.1}$$

and should be solved subject to the condition

$$\int_0^R r^2 c(r)\,dr=\frac{c_{\text{sat}}R_{\text{sat}}^3}{3}, \tag{2.8.2}$$

where R_{sat} is the radius of a droplet of the saturated solution.

We are interested in times much greater than $\frac{R^2}{D_c}$, so we shall seek the asymptotic (near-steady-state) solution. It is therefore unnecessary to specify initial conditions. The inhomogeneity is due to, and is maintained only by the influx of pure water to the droplet surface.

The concentration distribution is sought in series form similar to (2.7.4):

$$c(r,\ t)=c_0(t)+r^2c_2(t)+r^4c_4(t)+\ \dots \tag{2.8.3}$$

The odd terms of the expansion have been omitted, because since $c(r,\ t)$ remains bounded at the point $r=0$, $c_{-1}(t)$ should be identically equal to zero. Then $c(r,\ t)$ is derived from the series of equations for c in terms of c_0:

$$c(r,\ t)=\sum_{k=0}^{\infty}\left(\frac{r^2}{D_c}\right)^k\frac{1}{(2k+1)!}\frac{d^kc_0}{dt^k}. \tag{2.8.4}$$

With boundary condition (2.8.2) this yields

$$\left(\frac{R}{R_{sat}}\right)^3 \sum_{k=0}^{\infty}\left(\frac{R^2}{D_c}\right)^k \frac{2k+2}{(2k+3)!}\frac{d^k c_0}{dt^k}=\frac{c_{sat}}{3}. \qquad (2.8.5)$$

This latter relationship can be expressed in the form

$$c_0-\left(\frac{R_{sat}}{R}\right)^3 c_{sat}=-3\sum_{k=1}^{\infty}\left(\frac{R^2}{D_c}\right)^k \frac{(2k+2)}{(2k+3)!}\frac{d^k c_0}{dt^k}=F(c_0,\ R) \qquad (2.8.6)$$

and its solution sought by the method of iterations:

$$c_0^0(t)=\frac{R_{sat}^3}{R^3(t)}c_{sat},$$

$$c_0^1(t)=\frac{R_{sat}^3 c_{sat}}{R^3(t)}\left[1-3R^3(t)\sum_{k=1}^{\infty}\left(\frac{R^2}{D_c}\right)^k \frac{(2k+2)}{(2k+3)!}\frac{d^k}{dt^k}\left(\frac{1}{R^3(t)}\right)\right]. \qquad (2.8.7)$$

Successive corrections change the coefficients of terms $\left(\frac{R^2}{D_c}\right)$ of increasingly higher order. For this reason, if one restricts oneself only to terms porportional to $\sim\frac{r^2}{D_c}$ truncation of series (2.8.4) after the first two terms enables one to employ only the first approximation with respect to c_0. It follows from (2.8.7) and (2.8.4) that

$$c(r,\ t)=\frac{R_{sat}^3 c_{sat}}{R^3(t)}\left[1+\frac{3}{10}\left(\frac{R^2}{D_c}\right)\frac{1}{R}\frac{dR}{dt}-\frac{1}{2}\left(\frac{r^2}{D_c}\right)\frac{1}{R}\frac{dR}{dt}\right]. \qquad (2.8.8)$$

The concentration at the droplet surface is defined by the expression

$$c(R,\ t)=\frac{R_{sat}^3 c_{sat}}{R^3(t)}\left[1-\frac{1}{5}\left(\frac{R^2}{D_c}\right)\frac{1}{R}\frac{dR}{dt}\right]. \qquad (2.8.9)$$

It is evident that the concentration of the solution is lower at the surface of the growing droplet, which in turn may affect the rate of growth. If the solution is sufficiently dilute, so that one can apply Raoult's law (2.6.9) or the asymptotic form of the latter, then, with consideration of equation (2.8.9), we have

$$\Phi(c_R)=\frac{aR_{sat}^3 c_{sat}}{\rho_2 R^3(t)}\left[1-\frac{1}{5}\left(\frac{R^2}{D_c}\right)\frac{1}{R}\frac{dR}{dt}\right]. \qquad (2.8.10)$$

According to (2.6.13) and (2.4.5), quantities $\Phi(c_R)$, δ_0 and $\frac{\Delta T}{T}$

are much smaller than unity. Therefore, for dilute solutions the equation of droplet growth becomes

$$\frac{dR}{dt}=\frac{\rho_{\infty}D_{v}f_{1}(R,l)}{\rho_{2}R}\times$$

$$\times\frac{\left(\delta_{0}+\frac{ac_{sat}R_{sat}^{3}}{\rho_{2}R^{3}}-\frac{2\sigma}{\rho_{2}R_{v}TR}\right)}{1+\frac{ac_{sat}R_{sat}^{3}f_{1}(R,l)D_{v}\rho_{\infty}}{5\rho_{2}D_{c}R^{2}}+\frac{\rho_{2}LD_{v}f_{1}(R,l)}{k_{1}Tf_{2}(R,l)}\left(\frac{L}{R_{v}T}-1\right)}. \quad (2.8.11)$$

This equation was derived on the basis of a number of assumptions, the most important of which is that $\Phi(c_R)$ can be expressed in the form of (2.8.10). If the latter expression is valid, then $\frac{aR_{sat}^{3}c_{sat}}{\rho_{2}R^{3}(t)}\ll 1$.

If $\frac{\rho_{0}D_{v}}{\rho_{2}D_{c}}\approx 1$, the correction for concentration undersaturation can be neglected. (For near-saturation solutions the contribution of the correction becomes more important.) If corrections for temperature and concentration jumps are also neglected, then

$$\frac{dR}{dt}=\frac{\rho_{\infty}D_{v}}{\rho_{2}R}\frac{\left\{\delta_{0}+\frac{ac_{sat}R_{sat}^{3}}{\rho_{2}R^{3}}-\frac{2\sigma}{\rho_{2}R_{v}TR}\right\}}{1+\frac{\rho_{\infty}LD_{v}}{k_{1}T}\left(\frac{L}{R_{v}T}-1\right)}. \quad (2.8.12)$$

It is equations of this type which are primarily utilized for the study of droplet growth in clouds.

Finally, if we again consider the growth of a droplet of nondilute solution, we must employ a more general equation, such as (2.6.13) with $\Phi(c_R)$ in the form of (2.6.9). Here, the equation of growth becomes highly cumbersome and can be used only for numerical calculations.

A second limiting case which may occur is that of low solute content, when its role can be neglected. The equation for $\frac{dR}{dt}$ then has the form

$$\frac{dR}{dt}=\frac{\rho_{\infty}D_{v}f_{1}(R,l)}{\rho_{2}\left[1+\frac{\rho_{\infty}LD_{v}}{k_{1}T}\left(\frac{L}{R_{v}T}-1\right)\right]}\frac{1}{R}\left(\delta_{0}-\frac{2\sigma}{\rho_{2}R_{v}TR}\right). \quad (2.8.13)$$

9. EFFECT OF FACTORS DISREGARDED IN THE EQUATION OF DROPLET GROWTH BY CONDENSATION (RADIANT ENERGY TRANSFER, ELECTRICAL CHARGES, STEFAN FLOW, THERMAL DIFFUSION, DIFFUSIONAL THERMAL EFFECT)

The equations presented in the preceding section, in spite of their cumbersomeness, were obtained on the basis of a number of assumptions and hence are not altogether general. Some remarks should be made on the processes which can be neglected when reference is had to phase transitions in the atmosphere.

In analyzing droplet growth no consideration was given to radiative transfer. This effect is insignificant in the case at hand, due to the small difference between the droplet and air temperatures. In fact, the radiant heat flux can be expressed in the form

$$Q_1 = 4\pi a r^2 \sigma (T_\infty^4 - T_0^4) \approx 16\pi a r^2 \sigma 4 T^3 \Delta T, \qquad (2.9.1)$$

where σ is the Stefan-Boltzmann constant; a is a factor of the order of unity, describing the deviation from the properties of a perfect blackbody.

The ratio of Q_1 to the conduction flux is given in the simplest case by

$$\frac{Q_1}{Q} \approx \frac{4\sigma T^3}{k_1} r. \qquad (2.9.2)$$

For $T \approx 290°K$, $\frac{Q_1}{Q} \approx 2.23 ar$; this shows that the effect is small for cloud droplets.

When treating growth by condensation, no allowance was made also for the effect of electrical charges. This effect, which (according to the Thomson formula) depends markedly on droplet radius, may play some role in the spontaneous condensation on molecule populations, but is entirely negligible for particles of the order of $1\,\mu$ which form under natural conditions on condensation nuclei. Nevertheless, it is quite frequently dealt with in meteorological literature, although it has no practical importance for atmospheric processes.

A quite important approximation used in the study of the problem at hand is the treating of vapor as some small constituent ($\rho \ll \rho_1$) of the air, so making it possible to regard diffusion in a multicomponent system in a simplified form. For greater accuracy we shall treat air as a binary mixture satisfying the expressions

$$\rho_1 = M_1 n_1, \qquad \rho = Mn,$$
$$\bar{\rho} = \rho + \rho_1, \qquad \overline{\rho v} = \rho v + \rho_1 v_1,$$

where M and M_1 are the molecular weights of vapor and air; n, n_1 and $\bar{n}$ are the numbers of molecules of vapor, air and vapor-air mixture per unit volume; ρ, ρ_1 and $\bar{\rho}$ are the densities of vapor, air, and the vapor-air mixture. In this case, the equation describing the transport of vapor has the form /12/

$$\frac{\partial \rho}{\partial t} + \left(\frac{\partial}{\partial r} + \frac{2}{r}\right)\rho \bar{v} = \left(\frac{\partial}{\partial r} + \frac{2}{r}\right)\left(D^* \frac{\partial \rho}{\partial r} + A \frac{\partial T}{\partial r}\right), \qquad (2.9.3)$$

where

$$\bar{v} = -D_v \frac{M_1}{M\rho_1} \frac{d\rho}{dr}, \qquad D^* = \frac{M_1 \bar{n} D_v}{\bar{\rho}},$$
$$A = (M\bar{n}k_T + \rho)\frac{D^*}{T},$$

and k_T is the thermal diffusion ratio.

The convective transport governed by velocity $\bar{v}$ is due to the Stefan flow, arising due to the appearance of the gradient of partial pressures of gas constituents which are not absorbed and not emitted by the droplet. The relative contribution of $\bar{v}$ to the diffusion flux is defined by the quantity $\frac{M_1\rho}{M\rho_1}$. Atmospheric condensation processes occur at moderate temperatures, so when $\rho \ll \rho_1$, the correction for the Stefan flow (being proportional to the ratio of the concentration of vapor to that of the air) is small. (For example, when $T \approx 20°$ it amounts to about 1%.)

The fact that the water vapor is only a minor constituent of air leads to other simplifications of the problem. Since $\rho \ll \rho_1$ and $M \approx M_1$, $\bar{\rho} \approx \rho_1$ and $\bar{n} \approx n_1$. Therefore

$$D^* = \frac{M_1 \bar{n} D_v}{\bar{\rho}} \approx \frac{M_1 n_1}{\rho_1} D_v = D_v. \qquad (2.9.4)$$

Furthermore

$$A = (M\bar{n}k_T + \rho)\frac{D^*}{T} \approx \frac{D_v}{T}(Mn_1k_T + \rho). \qquad (2.9.5)$$

When $\rho \ll \rho_1$, the thermal diffusion ratio can be expressed in the form /34/

$$k_T = a\frac{\rho}{\rho_1}, \tag{2.9.6}$$

where constant a is determined by the ratio of masses, the molecular structure and molecular interaction. On the whole $|a| \leqslant 1$ and a can change sign. We shall subsequently operate on the assumption that the temperature gradient is due to condensation heat release and is defined by the psychrometric correction. Since the latter is small, by assuming a priori that thermal diffusion makes a small contribution, $\frac{\partial T}{\partial r}$ can be estimated from expressions obtained in section 4 of the present chapter without introducing a correction for thermal diffusion and for the diffusional thermal effect. In that case

$$\frac{\partial T}{\partial r} \approx \frac{D_v L}{k_1}\frac{\partial \rho}{\partial r} = \frac{D_v L}{\varkappa_1 c_p \rho_1}\frac{\partial \rho}{\partial r}. \tag{2.9.7}$$

Employing expressions (2.9.4)–(2.9.6) one can derive the relationship

$$\left(D^* \frac{\partial \rho}{\partial r} + A\frac{\partial T}{\partial r}\right) \approx D_v\left[1 + \frac{D_v L \rho}{\varkappa_1 c_p T \rho_1}\left(1 + a\frac{M}{M_1}\right)\right]\frac{\partial \rho}{\partial r}. \tag{2.9.8}$$

Since $\frac{D_v L}{\varkappa_1 c_p T}\left(1 + a\frac{M}{M_1}\right) \approx 1$, we conclude that the contribution of thermal diffusion is defined by the ratio $\frac{\rho}{\rho_1}$, which for temperatures below 20°C gives a correction not exceeding ~1%. Thus, due to the low vapor content its diffusion equation can be expressed in the usual form and applied to the study of transport processes in vapor-air mixtures.

Similar simplifications can be made also for the heat conduction equation where, due to the smallness of $\frac{\rho}{\rho_1}$, it is also possible to neglect the Stefan flow and the diffusional thermal effect. The simplification consists in the fact that, in spite of the ordered vapor flux, due to the smallness of ratio $\frac{\rho}{\rho_1}$, energy is transported primarily by collisions between molecules of the medium.

10. CHARACTERISTIC VALUES OF PARAMETERS AND THE ROLE OF CORRECTIONS. SIMPLIFIED EQUATION OF DROPLET GROWTH BY CONDENSATION

As shown above, droplet growth by condensation is determined by a number of variables which, for a set of specific conditions, can be regarded as constant. However, the variety of atmospheric processes, the quite wide range of temperatures and pressures over which phase transitions occur, require appropriate selection of the values of these variables. In this connection we shall present some values of principal quantities governing droplet growth by condensation:

$$D_v = (0.22 + 0.0015t^\circ)\frac{p_0}{p}\ \mathrm{cm^2/sec}, \tag{2.10.1}$$

where $p_0 = 760$ mm Hg,

$$L = 595.9 - 0.55t^\circ\ \mathrm{cal/g}, \tag{2.10.2}$$

$$k_1 = (5.79 + 0.19t^\circ)\,10^{-5}\ \mathrm{cal/cm \cdot sec \cdot {}^\circ C}, \tag{2.10.3}$$

$$\sigma_0 = (75.60 - 0.143t^\circ)\ \mathrm{dyne/cm}. \tag{2.10.4}$$

The effect of temperature and pressure on the rate of growth by condensation was examined in detail elsewhere /3, 4/. The role of different factors is described by Tables 1 and 2 and Figures 7–10. The tables and Figure 7 present the maximum errors arising in the description of droplet growth over a 24-hour period. The calculations were carried out for different radii R_0 of the dry salt nucleus. The different corrections were estimated by conducting calculations using the complete equation and using an equation from which the correction in question was omitted. The role of the correction at hand was illustrated by comparing the two results.

On the whole these calculations show that temperature and concentration jumps, as well as the content of solutes and the surface tension forces, are factors of importance for small droplets. For larger droplets characteristic of the cloud spectrum ($R \sim 10\mu$), the role of these corrections becomes much less important, although the effect of the concentration jump may still be felt (provided the condensation coefficient $\alpha \ll 1$).

The role of the heat of condensation is substantial for droplets of any size and can be easily taken into account. Smirnov /25/ found this by comparing a number of proposed formulas for describing condensation growth /42, 48, 22/. It can be concluded that when

TABLE 1. Maximum relative error $\frac{\Delta R}{R}$ (%) due to the use of average constant values of surface tension, thermal conductivity coefficient and heat of condensation

	R_0 μ	+20° C; 0 m			−5° C; 0 m			+20° C; 3200 m			−5° C; 3200 m		
		100%	100.1%	101%	100%	100.1%	101%	100%	100.1%	101%	100%	100.1%	101%
$\sigma=\bar{\sigma}$	0.01	−1.42	−1.49	−3.47	0.861	0.899	1.656	−1.42	−1.49	−3.47	0.861	0.899	1.66
	0.1	−1.51	−1.49	−0.17	0.929	1.27	0.13	−1.51	−1.51	−0.175	0.929	1.34	0.131
	1	−0.770	−0.0605	−0.0128	0.323	0.043	0.089	−0.807	−0.061	−0.013	0.358	0.043	0.009
	10	−0.0091	−0.0055	−0.0012	0.0042	0.0032	0.0008	−0.0096	−0.0055	−0.0012	0.0046	0.0033	0.0008
	100	−0.0001	−0.0001	−0.0001	0.0001	0.0001	0.0001	−0.0002	−0.0001	−0.0001	0.0001	0.0001	0.0001
$k=\bar{k}$	0.01	−0.003	−0.003	−0.004	0.0015	0.0015	0.002	−0.0029	−0.0029	−0.0039	0.0015	0.0016	0.0020
	0.1	−0.075	−0.750	−0.750	0.0450	0.887	0.897	−0.077	−0.833	−0.834	0.052	1.12	1.14
	1	−0.257	−0.748	−0.755	0.273	0.865	0.680	−0.280	−0.827	−0.834	0.332	1.09	1.14
	10	−0.298	−0.531	−0.741	0.350	0.529	0.838	−0.329	−0.596	−0.820	0.442	0.697	1.10
	100	−0.296	−0.317	−0.465	0.344	0.358	0.468	−0.328	−0.352	−0.523	0.440	0.460	0.618
$L=\bar{L}$	0.01	−0.002	−0.002	−0.003	0.0009	0.0009	0.0012	0.0024	−0.0024	−0.0033	0.0009	0.0009	0.0012
	0.1	−0.063	−0.620	−0.630	0.029	0.522	0.528	−0.064	−0.695	−0.696	0.031	0.670	0.670
	1	−0.214	−0.623	−0.629	0.161	0.509	0.401	−0.234	−0.689	−0.695	0.195	0.647	0.669
	10	−0.249	−0.443	−0.617	0.206	0.312	0.504	−0.275	−0.497	−0.684	0.260	0.410	0.645
	100	−0.247	−0.264	−0.388	0.203	0.211	0.275	−0.274	−0.293	−0.436	0.259	0.271	0.363

TABLE 2. Maximum relative error $\frac{\Delta R}{R}$ (%) due to neglecting the concentration jump, surface curvature and heat of condensation

	R_0 μ	+20° C; 0 m			−5° C; 0 m			+20° C; 3200 m			−5° C; 3200 m		
		100%	100.1%	101%	100%	100.1%	101%	100%	100.1%	101%	100%	100.1%	101%
$f_1(r, l) = 1$	0.01	58.0	59.4	74.2	56.4	57.8	73.0	59.0	60.4	76.0	57.8	59.3	75.9
	0.1	43.6	44.2	63.0	59.8	74.6	105.06	46.1	46.8	68.3	65.2	68.0	127.0
	1	9.4	9.6	10.2	16.0	16.0	17.6	10.3	10.4	11.1	19.0	19.2	21.1
	10	1.2	1.2	1.2	2.2	2.2	2.2	1.3	1.3	1.3	2.7	2.7	2.9
	100	0.2	0.2	0.2	0.2	0.2	0.2	0.2	0.2	0.2	0.3	0.3	0.3
$\sigma = 0$	0.01	$1.5 \cdot 10^3$	$4.6 \cdot 10^5$	$1.2 \cdot 10^6$	$1.7 \cdot 10^3$	$3 \cdot 10^5$	$8 \cdot 10^5$	$1.6 \cdot 10^3$	$4.9 \cdot 10^5$	$1.2 \cdot 10^6$	$1.7 \cdot 10^3$	$3.3 \cdot 10^5$	$9.2 \cdot 10^5$
	0.1	440	36.4	5.4	480	51.4	6.7	440	36.7	5.5	470	53.0	6.8
	1	24.2	2.0	0.4	17.0	2.2	0.4	25.4	1.9	0.4	19.0	2.3	0.5
	10	0.2	0.2	0	0.2	0.2	0	0.3	0.2	0	0.2	0.2	0
	100	0	0	0	0	0	0	0	0	0	0	0	0
$L = 0$	0.01	0.2	0.2	0.2	0	0	0.4	0.2	0.2	0.2	0	0	0
	0.1	4.0	83.6	84.2	1.0	24.0	24.4	4.15	112.4	113.5	1.1	33.9	34.7
	1	20.8	83.0	84.2	6.6	23.4	24.4	25.2	111.7	113.5	8.5	33.2	34.7
	10	27.0	60.2	83.0	8.8	24.2	23.4	34.3	82.9	112.0	12.2	21.0	33.5
	100	27.2	30.2	52.0	8.8	9.2	12.6	34.8	39.6	72.0	12.3	13.0	18.5
$f_2(r, l) = 1$	0.01	5.9	7.9	9.3	1.5	2.2	2.6	7.8	7.9	9.3	2.2	2.2	2.6
	0.1	8.2	11.5	22.8	2.4	3.7	8.7	11.2	19.9	23.6	3.6	3.8	9.3
	1	3.7	5.3	6.2	1.3	2.0	2.5	5.6	5.6	6.6	2.2	2.2	3.0
	10	0.6	0.9	1.0	0.3	0.4	0.4	1.0	1.0	1.0	0.5	0.5	0.5
	100	0.1	0.1	0.1	0.0	0.0	0.0	0.1	0.1	0.1	0.1	0.1	0.1

considering cloud droplet growth by condensation one can use in a first approximation the Maxwell equation with a correction for the heat of condensation:

$$\frac{dr}{dt}=\frac{D_v \rho_\infty \delta_0}{\rho_2\left[1+\frac{\rho_\infty L D_v}{k_1 T}\left(\frac{L}{R_v T}-1\right)\right]}\frac{1}{r}. \qquad (2.10.5)$$

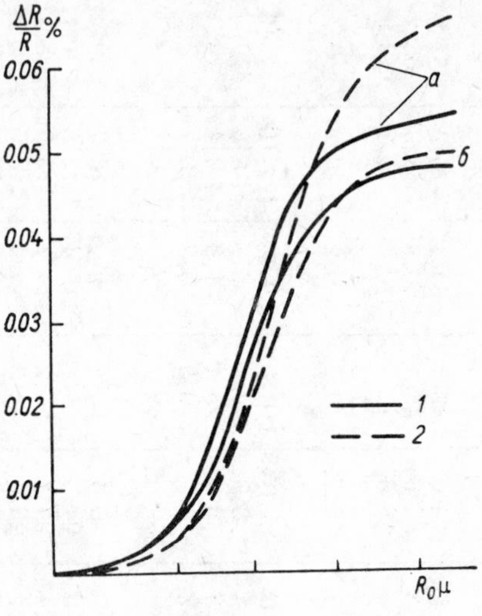

FIGURE 7. Maximum relative errors due to neglecting the nonuniformity of the distribution of the soluble concentration in the droplet ($c_R=\bar{c}$):

R_0 – radius of droplet of saturated solution, $\delta_0 = 0$; a) $p = 510$ mm Hg; b) $p = 760$ mm Hg; 1) $T = 20$°C; 2) $T = -5$°C.

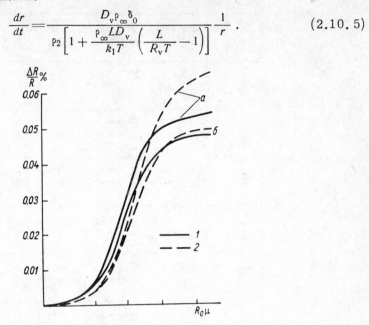

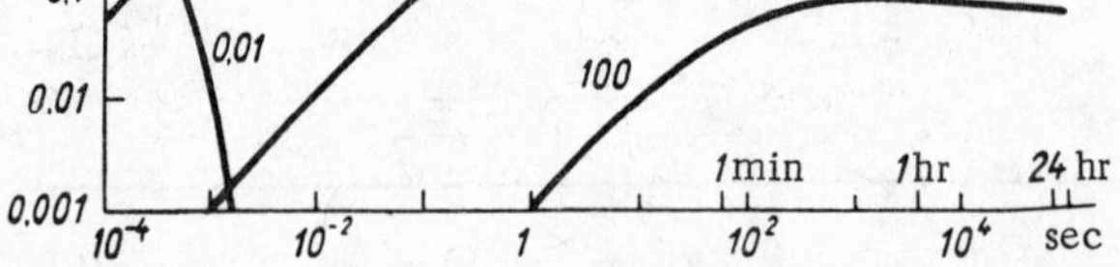

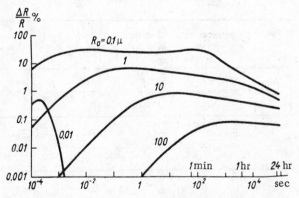

FIGURE 8. Time variation in the error due to neglecting the concentration jump ($T = 20$°C, $p_1 = 760$ mm Hg, $\delta_0 = 10^{-2}$)

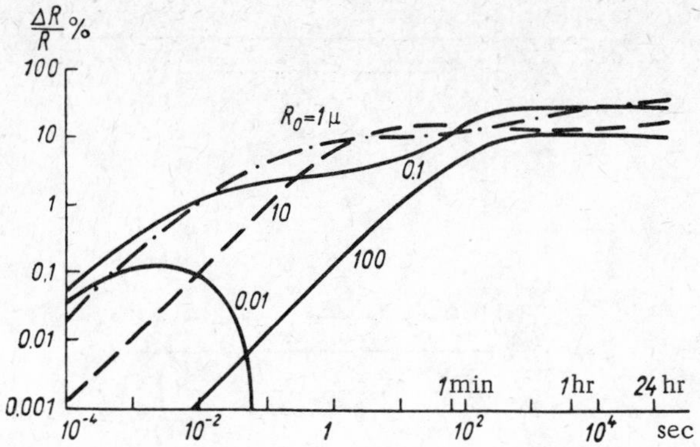

FIGURE 9. Time variation in the error due to neglecting the heat of condensation ($T=10°C$, $p_1=760$ mm Hg, $\delta_0=10^{-2}$)

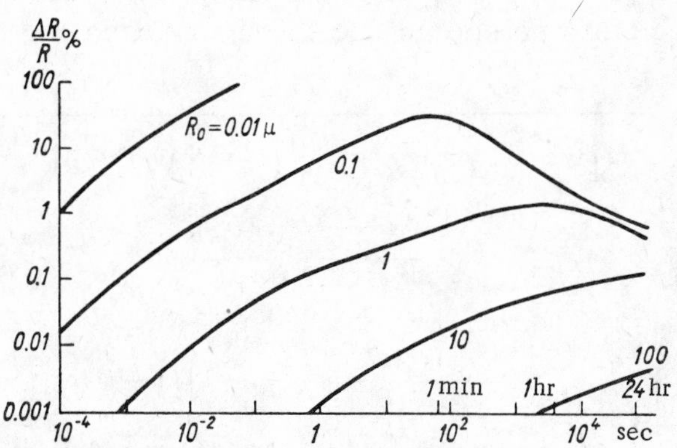

FIGURE 10. Time variation in the error due to neglecting the surface tension ($T=20°C$, $p_1=760$ mm Hg, $\delta_0=10^{-2}$)

In treating droplet formation one must employ a more complicated equation with detailed consideration of the curvature, jumps, and of the effect of solute substances /42, 48, 22, 25, 13/.

As a further refinement of the above expression one can use the approximation of Fuchs /30/ refined by Mazin /22/, who also incorporated a psychrometric correction. The same approximation was obtained elsewhere /13/ by allowing for the temperature jump and using a more exact expression for the coefficients.

An examination of equation (2.8.11) with appropriate simplification and explicit expressions for f_1 and f_2 in the form of (2.6.2) enables the approximating formula to be expressed in the form

$$\frac{dr}{\partial t}=\frac{D_v\rho_\infty}{\rho_2\left[1+\frac{\rho_0 LD_v}{k_1 T}\left(\frac{L}{R_v T}-1\right)\right]}\frac{\delta_0}{r+\xi}, \tag{2.10.6}$$

where

$$\xi=\frac{D_v}{\alpha\bar{v}}\frac{1+\frac{\alpha^2\rho_\infty LD_v}{\omega k_1 T}\left(\frac{L}{R_v T}-1\right)}{1+\frac{\rho_\infty LD_v}{k_1 T}\left(\frac{L}{R_v T}-1\right)}. \tag{2.10.7}$$

It is noteworthy, however, that a formula of this type has a limited range of applicability, since it disregards the effect of salts and surface tension forces, which for small particles have a marked effect on the rate of growth. For the size range over which ξ must be taken into account one should use the approximating formula

$$\frac{dr}{dt}=\frac{D_v\rho_\infty}{\rho_2\left[1+\frac{\rho_\infty LD_v}{k_1 T}\left(\frac{L}{R_v T}-1\right)(1-\Phi(c_R))\exp\left(\frac{B}{r}\right)\right]}\times$$

$$\times\frac{\delta_0-\frac{B}{r}+\Phi(c_R)}{r+\xi_1}, \tag{2.10.8}$$

where

$$\xi_1=\frac{D_v}{\alpha\bar{v}}\frac{1+\frac{\alpha^2\rho_\infty LD_v}{k_1 T}\left(\frac{L}{R_v T}-1\right)(1-\Phi(c_R))}{1+\frac{\rho_\infty LD}{k_1 T}\left(\frac{L}{R_v T}-1\right)(1-\Phi(c_R))}, \tag{2.10.9}$$

$$B=\frac{2\sigma}{\rho_2 R_v T}. \tag{2.10.10}$$

Since $\Phi(c_R)$ is generally small it can be neglected in ξ_1 and one can set $\xi_1=\xi$. In addition, since $\rho_\infty-\rho_0\ll\rho_\infty$ one can replace ρ_∞ by the concentration ρ_0 of saturated vapor. In this case

$$\frac{dr}{dt}=K_3\frac{\delta_0-\frac{B}{r}+\Phi(c_R)}{r+\xi}, \tag{2.10.11}$$

where

$$K_3=\frac{D_v\rho_0}{\rho_2\left[1+\frac{\rho_0 LD_v}{k_1 T}\left(\frac{L}{R_v T}-1\right)\right]}, \tag{2.10.12}$$

$$\xi = \frac{D_v}{\alpha \bar{v}} \frac{1 + \frac{\alpha^2 \rho_0 L D_v}{\omega k_1 T}\left(\frac{L}{R_v T} - 1\right)}{1 + \frac{\rho_0 L D_v}{k_1 T}\left(\frac{L}{R_v T} - 1\right)}. \tag{2.10.13}$$

Analysis shows that equation (2.10.11) describes satisfactorily the growth of droplets over a wide size range and can be employed when considering phase transitions in clouds. It can be simplified by neglecting the effect of $\Phi(c_R)$, B and ξ, the validity of which was proven above. When more exact calculations are needed one should use equations from the preceding sections incorporating the pertinent process in more detail.

Chapter 3

CONDENSATION NUCLEI AND THEIR ROLE IN DROPLET FORMATION

1. CURRENT CONCEPTS OF NUCLEI AS CONDENSATION SITES

In considering the formation of moisture in the atmosphere one must remember, first, that it forms in air which contains a large quantity of small particles, and second, that this formation proceeds rather slowly, since cooling of air resulting in phase transitions generally occurs at a rate not exceeding hundredths of a degree per second. As a result of the first fact condensation starts on impurity particles. The appearance of droplets on these particles under conditions of slow cooling forbids spontaneous condensation, condensation on ions, and also limits the participation of aerosols in the formation of a new phase, permitting only some of the most active of them to participate in its formation.

It can be claimed in the light of current concepts that the formation of droplets in the atmosphere occurs only at particles usually termed condensation nuclei, and that the number of particles participating in droplet formation is much smaller than the total number of particles in the given volume and changes depending on the cooling rate. This circumstance had to be taken into account already in experiments in Wilson chambers, when it was found that on adiabatic expansion of air droplets form on individual particles, and only after some cases of expansion with removal of activated particles do they form on ions. This means that spontaenous condensation is not attainable under ordinary conditions and that it is virtually impossible to create conditions for maintaining vapor in the supersaturated state for a prolonged time.

Thus, not all the condensation nuclei are expended in the formation of droplets. As a rule, even in very pure air very many particles do not participate in droplet formation. Thus particles which actually participate in condensation are termed cloud condensation nuclei.

In order to get a clear idea how the liquid phase forms, it is necessary to investigate in detail the physicochemical properties of atmospheric aerosols, especially those which together establish the hierarchy according to which the particles gradually become droplets. Here particular attention should not be paid to particles which in principle can become condensation nuclei on cooling, but to those which actually become such nuclei. Lately increasingly more data of this kind have appeared. However, available experimental results do not yet suffice for a complete description of droplet formation in the atmosphere.

2. SOME EXPERIMENTAL DATA ON ATMOSPHERIC CONDENSATION NUCLEI

The most thoroughly investigated properties of atmospheric aerosols at present are its geometric characteristics. Although the shape of the particles is not at all near-spherical, by restricting oneself to some effective particle size it becomes possible to classify them by dimensions. It was found that there exists quite a stable size distribution, and the form of this distribution correlates with the origin of the air mass. It becomes possible to utilize two typical distributions: one for marine air masses and the other for continental air /13/. Junge showed that for large and gigantic nuclei* the differential size distribution function obeys the power law

$$n(r) = ar^{-\nu}. \tag{3.2.1}$$

This formula approximates satisfactorily particle spectra in continental air masses (usually $\nu \sim 4$) but is unsatisfactory for marine air. The distribution in the region of Aitken particles is unstable and multimodal /74/.

For the lower troposphere within the continent $\nu = 4$ /23, 30/, due to mixing of a large number of aerosols supplied from different local sources and usually satisfying a lognormal distribution /39/. The origin of the air mass has a marked effect on the concentration, but hardly affects exponent ν of the distribution. Measurements conducted during 1964–1965 in the Alps are given in Table 3.

* In accordance with conventional, but not too convenient, cloud physics terminology, particles with radii below $0.1\,\mu$ are termed Aitken nuclei, particles with radii $0.1-1\,\mu$ are termed large, and those with radii in excess of 1μ are termed gigantic.

TABLE 3

Air mass	$\left(\frac{10^4}{8}\right)^{-1}$ a cm^{-3}	ν
Polar sea	0.561 ± 0.045	3.76 ± 0.07
Sea	6.74 ± 0.39	3.44 ± 0.10
Tropical sea	7.15 ± 0.81	3.47 ± 0.07
Polar	10.0 ± 0.1	3.94 ± 0.08
Polar continental	15.3 ± 2.6	3.81 ± 0.22
Continental	12.7 ± 1.4	3.41 ± 0.06
Moderate	10.64 ± 0.93	3.53 ± 0.42
		ν_{av} = 3.48

In air above the ocean, on the average, $\nu = 3$, but it varies as a function of particle size due to the formation of sea water spray as a result of wind-generated forces /39/. The spray has a wide particle spectrum, from 0.05 to 10μ, depending on wind strength. This distribution is observed over the ocean up to an altitude of 2 km /13/. In the upper troposphere $\nu = 5$, but it also is not constant over the given droplet size range.

The aerosol concentration is determined to a large extent by human activity. For example, it is reported /28/ that in California, in one of the resort regions the following amounts of impurities are ejected daily into the atmosphere:

submicron dust	210 tons
organic compounds	2,159 tons
nitrogen oxides	514 tons
sulfur oxides	429 tons

In Washington, the quantity of man-made aerosols ejected into the atmosphere increased from 500 tons per day in 1925 to 12,000 tons per day in 1965, and began to affect precipitation in the region /31/.

Another important source of atmospheric aerosols are volcanic eruptions /19, 20, 48/ as a result of which aerosol layers with particle radii of $r = 0.1-1\mu$ formed in the stratosphere and upper troposphere at altitudes of 8–15 km /26/. A large quantity of aerosols in the atmosphere is associated with dust storms /61/, which transport dust far into the ocean, and even from Africa over the Atlantic.

The concentration of Aitken nuclei and their size distribution ($0.01-0.1\mu$) /2.44, 56, 57/ are very dependent on the weather. The concentration increases in the presence of direct sunlight, wind, etc. /27, 32/, as well as a result of human activity /47, 60/. In the USA, as a result of human activity the concentration of nuclei in 1964–1965 increased compared with 1928–1931 /15/: twofold in March, fourfold in July, threefold in October, and twofold in November.

Although solid particles in the atmosphere are far from spherical, one can assume that particle shape bears no importance as regards condensation. The latter assumption is valid because, as a rule, large particles which serve as condensation nuclei form populations and do not possess marked asymmetry, and also because hydration of particles, which starts at humidities as low as 30%, also increases their sphericity. The vertical distribution of particles in the troposphere does not usually have a marked effect on the form of the size distribution function and is most evident in the average vertical concentration profile, which decreases exponentially with altitude and tends to a constant value for altitudes in excess of 4 km /11/.

For large particles and condensation nuclei the concentrations increase to an altitude of 300–400 m, where they attain a maximum (apparently associated with inversion) and then decrease /22, 24, 58, 59, 67/. The exponent of the distribution depends on altitude and satisfies the relation

$$\nu=3.2+3.8\cdot 10^{-4}z,$$

where z is the altitude in meters /2.43/. At the given altitude the concentration of nuclei undergoes substantial fluctuations at distances of the order of 1 km /24, 25, 58, 59, 73/. In the ground air layer the vertical variation in concentration N of condensation nuclei is exponential. For higher layers various power and exponential laws have been suggested.

The chemical composition of condensation nuclei is extremely varied. This variety manifests itself not only by the fact that different particles in air samples have different chemical composition, but also that individual particles contain a large number of chemicals. This arises because the formation of the aerosol component is due not only to ejection into the atmosphere of products of combustion, particles originating from the mechanical destruction of surfaces, and from biological and volcanic origin, and so on, but also to subsequent coalescence of atmospheric particles, adsorption of gases, chemical and photochemical reactions. As an

TABLE 4. Results of analysis of dust constituents in Los Angeles smog collected by means of an electrostatic precipitator

Minerals and other inorganic substances (~ 60%)	Water soluble fraction (~ 15%); Nonsoluble fraction (~45%)	Elements identified by an emission spectrograph	
		Silicon	Large quantities (10% and more)
		Aluminum	
		Iron	
		Titanium	Small quantities (1–9%)
		Calcium	
		Magnesium	1%
		Barium	
		Sodium	
		Potassium	
		Lead	Minute quantities (0.1–0.9%)
		Zinc	
		Vanadium	
		Manganese	0.1%
		Nickel	
		Tin	
		Copper	Trace amounts (0.01–0.1%)
		Zirconium	
		Strontium	
		Boron	0.001–0.01%
		Chromium	
		Bismuth	0.001%
		Cobalt	
		Substances identified chemically (%)	
		Silicon (SiO_2)	14.3
		Iron and aluminum	7.8
		Calcium salts (expressed in terms of Ca)	5.2
		Fluorides (expressed in terms of F)	0.05
		Sulfates (expressed in terms of H_2SO_4)	2.5
		Ammonia	0.70
		Nitrates (expressed in terms of HNO_3)	4.8
		Chlorides (expressed in terms of NaCl)	0.26
		Nitrites	0.00
		Sulfites	0.00
		Sodium salts (expressed in terms of NaCl)	4.6
Organic compounds, soluble in organic solvents (~ 10%)		Primarily hydrocarbons, small quantities of organic acids (0.27%) and aldehydes	
Fibers, dust particles, carbon and high-polymeric organic substances (~ 15%)		Peroxides (0.04%) expressed in terms of H_2O_2	
Water and volatile organic substances (~ 15%)			

example /2/, it is of interest to present results of a dust analysis of Los Angeles smog, collected by means of an electrostatic precipitator (Table 4).

The chemical composition of aerosols is determined by their origin and size. For instance, particles more than 1 μ in radius usually consist of nondissolved silicate and carbonate particles /18, 33/, and also of organic residues. The content of soluble substances in such particles (gigantic nuclei) is usually 1–5% /50, 62, 64/; however, during monsoons in India it increases to 26%/62/. Particles 0.1–1 μ in radius (large nuclei) usually contain a larger quantity of soluble substances, primarily ammonium sulfate /33/. The content of soluble substances in such particles may reach 30% /64/. Data on the chemical composition of Aitken nuclei (0.01–0.1 μ) are very sparse. It is assumed that they contain about 20% of soluble substances /50/. It is noteworthy that all the above data on the content of soluble substances in aerosols are not too reliable, since they are based on a determination of only certain soluble constituents (chlorides, sulfates).

Data on the size distribution of individual soluble substances are much more reliable. As a rule, these distributions are lognormal /44, 47, 49, 50, 53, 73/, with a maximum in the 0.1–0.6 μ range. This indicates that they are associated with local sources, usually of man-made origin /44, 47, 73/.

Examination of the relationship between the content of soluble chlorides and the origin of air masses showed that /63/: 1) there are almost no chlorides in marine African tropical, continental Arctic polar, continental polar, continental temperate, continental subtropic and continental African tropical air; 2) there are small quantities of chlorides in marine subtropic, marine polar and marine Arctic air; 3) there are large quantities of chlorides in temperate marine and transformed polar air.

The large variety of chemical compositions of aerosols makes it impossible to make a differentiated allowance for the effect of different substances on the water absorption ability of a particle. Hence one can actually have reference only to average properties of particles which are able to absorb water from air; here it is necessary to consider only the principal of these properties.

One property of this type is the content of soluble salts in particles. Although the drop in water vapor pressure is different above different solutions, its variations are not too large compared with the dependence on the solution concentration. This allows one to limit oneself to consideration of the principal characteristic, which is the content of soluble substances in particles. Observation of the behavior of particles during changes in humidity shows that condensation nuclei in different air samples at high relative humidities behave similarly to salt solution droplets /1, 4/.

It was shown experimentally that hydration can occur starting at humidities of about 30% /10/. The mechanism of this initial hydration is still unknown. However, this process is of no importance from the standpoint of cloud formation since, starting at humidities of 70–80%, there occurs (a more substantial) hydration due to the dissolved substances. In the case of insoluble nuclei it suffices to assume that at humidities close to 100% the particles are coated by a thin water film and to then consider condensation again without allowance for wetting, adsorption and swelling.

If one restricts oneself only to the content of soluble substances in particles, one finds that they are sharply divided into two classes. Particles of marine origin consist almost entirely of soluble substances, while particles of continental origin consist primarily of insoluble substances (70–80%). The fact that continental particles consist of a mixture of soluble and insoluble substances, with their ratio remaining quite stable, is very important, since it enables one to assume, within certain limits, that the structure of condensation nuclei is uniform.

Experimental data /13/ show that the content of soluble substances can vary markedly with particle size and, in addition, it is quite different in particles of the same size. However, if these regularities are known they can in principle always be taken into account in theoretical studies; in some cases they are apparently not important.

The feasibility of a generalized approach to the water condensation capacity of nuclei is indicated by the measured size distribution function of nuclei during variations in humidity, indicating that the particles behave as droplets of a solution. At humidities of about 100%, the particles are already quite markedly hydrated and their sizes are distributed in the order of their droplet formation ability. In considering the nucleation of the liquid phase, the latter fact enables one to use a distribution with respect to some variable, which effectively allows for this capacity. In particular, one can select the nucleus activity as this variable. Frequently, one also uses the supersaturation at which the given particle becomes a droplet.

Extensive studies were recently started on the distribution of condensation nuclei with respect to the supersaturation. Measurements were carried out in the ground layer /4, 37, 38, 42, 70/, as well as in the free atmosphere /5, 16, 46, 65/. Available data on the spectra of condensation nuclei with respect to supersaturation do not as yet suffice for any systematization. However, it is possible to even now draw some conclusions as to the features peculiar to these distributions. The majority of investigators note that over a 0.1–0.2 to 0.5–0.8% supersaturation range the distribution of nuclei can be reasonably approximated by the power function $n(\delta_0)=P\delta_0^l$.

According to Australian measurements, when approximating the distribution by the power law exponent l lies between 1.2 and 1.4 /70, 66/; according to measurements in the Soviet Union and the USA it lies between 2.5 and 3.9 /4, 5/. It is noteworthy that this difference in the value of l may be due not so much to the fact that the measurements were conducted in different air masses, but also because the experimental techniques somewhat differed /3/.

An analysis of 47 measurements in the layer beneath different types of clouds (cumulus, thunderstorm and hail clouds) /46/ shows that the concentration of condensation nuclei active at 0.1% supersaturation ranges from 1–3 up to 250–280 nuclei/cm^3, i.e., approximately hundredfold. The concentration of nuclei active at 1% supersaturation ranges from 80–90 to 1,600–2,200, i.e., approximately 20-fold. Here there is a tendency toward a decrease in l with increasing condensation nuclei concentration.

The same tendency is noted also when studying data on 18 condensation nuclei measurements in the ground layer /38/. This can apparently be attributed to the high variability of the most active part of cloud nuclei. The lowest cloud nuclei concentrations were found in marine air masses, while the highest were observed in continental air /65, 70/. The vertical distribution of nuclei has been studied /5, 6, 65/; the concentration was found to decrease with altitude.

3. EQUILIBRIUM RADIUS OF A NUCLEUS

We now consider the condition of equilibrium of a nucleus consisting of soluble and insoluble parts, and the environment containing vapor. The thermodynamic equilibrium of this kind of system has been studied a number of times /1.4, 51/. For a fully wetted nucleus, the saturated vapor pressure above the particle surface is given by

$$e_r=e_0(T)\exp\left[\frac{2\sigma_s}{\rho_s R_v T r}\right]\left(1-\frac{A_1 m}{r^3-r_T^3}\right), \qquad (3.3.1)$$

where σ_s and ρ_s are the surface tension and density of the solution, respectively; m is the mass of the soluble part of the nucleus; r_T is the radius of the insoluble part of the nucleus; A_1 is a coefficient making allowance for the pressure drop due to molecules of the dissolved substance, dissociation, hydration and other possible effects, and can also be a function of r.

For weak solutions Mason /1.4/ suggested the following expression for A_1:

$$A_1 = \frac{8.6}{M'}, \tag{3.3.2}$$

where M' is the molecular weight of the dissolved substance.

We introduce the quantity

$$C = A_1 m, \tag{3.3.3}$$

which shall be termed the activity of the condensation nucleus /7, 8/. It is first assumed that the hydrated nucleus consists of some central insoluble part and of a solution film enveloping it. In order to provide for possible variants of the ratio of the soluble to the insoluble parts, we assume that the amount of soluble substance is proportional to $r_0^{2(\alpha+1)}$, where r_0 is the radius of the dry nucleus, and α is an exponent characterizing the functional dependence of m on r. When $\alpha = -1$, the amount of soluble substance does not depend on the radius of the dry nucleus, but when $\alpha = \frac{1}{2}$ it is proportional to the volume of the nucleus.

Therefore we shall set

$$C = b r_0^{2(1+\alpha)}, \tag{3.3.4}$$

where b and α are determined by the composition and physicochemical properties of the nucleus.

The effect of the dissolved substance on the saturated vapor pressure manifests itself primarily through the total mass m, slightly less so through the ratio of the soluble and insoluble constituents (corrections for r_T^3) and also through the variation in density and surface tension in the solution. For not too concentrated solutions they are small, while for highly dilute solutions, when the content of solute solutions is not too small, the effect of r_T in equation (3.3.1) can also be neglected.

We shall start on the assumption that the dependence of the quantity

$$B = \frac{2\sigma_s}{\rho_s R_v T} \tag{3.3.5}$$

on the concentration of the solution can be neglected and that $B = \text{const} \approx 1.2 \cdot 10^{-7}$ cm.

Consider the conditions of nucleus equilibrium at humidities close to 100% and above, at supersaturation for which the liquid phase forms in the atmosphere. Here it is assumed that the effect of r_T can be neglected. When $r \gg 10^{-7}$ cm, the exponent of equation (3.3.1) can be expanded in a series and the first two terms retained. We introduce the notation

$$\delta_0 = 1 - \frac{e_0}{e_\infty}, \quad \delta = 1 - \frac{e_r}{e_\infty}, \tag{3.3.6}$$

where δ_0 is the supersaturation of the vapor over a flat water surface, δ is the supersaturation of vapor above the particle, and e is the water vapor pressure at infinity. This definition, in general, differs from the actual supersaturation $\delta = \frac{e_\infty}{e_r} - 1$; however, when $\delta \ll 1$ this difference is negligible. Expressions (3.3.3)–(3.3.5) enable us to derive the expression

$$\frac{1-\delta}{1-\delta_0} = 1 + \frac{B}{r} - \frac{C}{r^3 - r_T^3}. \tag{3.3.7}$$

When subsequently analyzing this relationship it is more convenient to introduce the variable $x = \frac{1}{r}$, in which case

$$\frac{1-\delta}{1-\delta_0} = 1 + Bx - \frac{Cx^3}{1 - \frac{x^3}{x_T^3}}. \tag{3.3.8}$$

Now consider the condition of equilibrium when $\delta_0 = 0$. Since the nucleus can be in equilibrium only at $\delta = 0$, it follows from equation (3.3.8) that

$$Bx\left(\frac{1}{x^3} - \frac{1}{x_T^3}\right) = C. \tag{3.3.9}$$

We are interested in conditions under which x_T has no marked effect on the equilibrium value of x. Without allowance for the insoluble part the latter is given by the expression

$$x_{eq} = \left(\frac{B}{C}\right)^{1/2}. \tag{3.3.10}$$

Equation (3.3.9) yields the condition under which the effect of x_T is insignificant:

$$x_T \gg \left(\frac{B}{C}\right)^{1/2}. \tag{3.3.11}$$

This general equation becomes clearer by making an assumption with respect to C, introduced above in (3.3.4). Then

$$\frac{x_T}{x_0^{1+\alpha}} \gg \left(\frac{B}{b}\right)^{1/2}. \tag{3.3.12}$$

Since $x_T > x_0$, then by requiring that $\frac{x_0}{x_0^{1+\alpha}} \gg \left(\frac{B}{b}\right)^{1/2}$, we only amplify inequality

$$\left(\frac{1}{x_0}\right)^{\alpha} \gg \left(\frac{B}{b}\right)^{1/2}. \tag{3.3.13}$$

This inequality makes it possible to show that in many cases the effect of the insoluble part of the nucleus on the size of the equilibrium radius can be neglected.

Suppose the content of the soluble part is proportional to the droplet volume ($\alpha = \frac{1}{2}$). Then

$$r_0 \gg \frac{1.2 \cdot 10^{-7}}{b}. \tag{3.3.14}$$

Quantity b is proportional to the percentage of the soluble part of the nucleus and in actual cases does not essentially differ from unity (at 20% $b = 0.25$), since the nuclei always contain at least several percents of soluble substances. In accordance with (3.3.14), particles of radius 10^{-5} cm and above always have an equilibrium radius close to that which could be obtained without allowing for the insoluble part, because when δ_0 is close to zero particles of this size are reasonably well hydrated and the effect of r_T can be neglected.

It can be shown that an inequality such as (3.3.14) is also valid when $|\delta_0| \ll 1$. This result is very important, since it enables one to treat the condition of equilibrium of mixed nuclei similarly to the case of fully soluble nuclei. This result is also confirmed by numerous experiments, which showed that during variation in humidity the condensation nuclei behave similarly to droplets of a solution. (This effect can be observed from the variation in visibility.)

Subsequently, we shall employ an approach similar to that used already by Köhler /41/ and base the analysis on the following expression /7/:

$$\frac{1-\delta}{1-\delta_0}=1+Bx-Cx^3, \tag{3.3.15}$$

assuming that (3.3.11) is also valid and that the effect of x_T can be neglected. Although this equation will be examined formally over a wide range of x and δ, the results will be utilized in the region of $|\delta_0| \ll 1$ and over the real range of nucleus sizes, so as not to introduce errors.

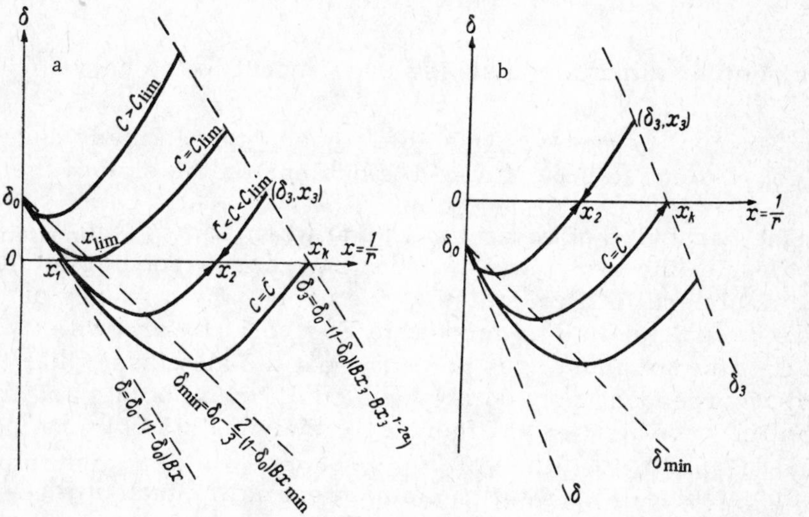

FIGURE 11. Supersaturation δ_0 as a function of droplet size $r=\frac{1}{x}$ for different values of activity C:

a) when $\delta_0>0$; b) when $\delta_0<0$.

We shall examine equation (3.3.15) over the range $x \geqslant 0$. Functions $\delta=\delta(x, \delta_0, C)$ are plotted in Figure 11. The curves of $\delta(x, C)$ represent a family of cubic parabolas with common tangent $\delta=\delta_0-(1-\delta_0)Bx$ at point $(0, \delta_0)$. The locus of the minimum points of these parabolas is the straight line

$$\delta=\delta_0-\frac{2}{3}(1-\delta_0)\,Bx, \tag{3.3.16}$$

and the coordinates of the minimum points are

$$x_{\min}=\sqrt{\frac{B}{3C}}, \tag{3.3.17}$$

$$\delta_{\min}=\delta_0-\frac{2}{3}(1-\delta_0)\,B\sqrt{\frac{B}{3C}}. \tag{3.3.18}$$

If we consider the case $\delta_0>0$ (Figure 11a), it is evident that there exists some limiting value of the activity $C=C_{\lim}$, to which corresponds a parabola touching the abscissa. Expressions (3.3.17)–(3.3.18) yield

$$C_{\lim}=\frac{4B^3}{27}\left(\frac{1-\delta_0}{\delta_0}\right)^2. \tag{3.3.19}$$

The point at which the abscissa is a tangent to the curve $C=C_{\lim}$ is

$$x_{\lim}=\frac{3\delta_0}{2(1-\delta_0)\,B}=\frac{1}{r_{\lim}}. \tag{3.3.20}$$

The parabolas of equation (3.3.15) when $C<C_{\lim}$ intersect the abscissa at the two points x_1 and $x_2>x_1$, corresponding to unstable and stable equilibrium states of the nuclei (the tendency of variations in nucleus size is marked in Figure 11 by arrows). When $C>C_{\lim}$ the parabola does not intersect the abscissa, while the nuclei correspondingly do not have equilibrium points and increase to infinity. When $\delta_0<0$ (Figure 11b) there exists only one point of stable equilibrium, for any C.

Since nuclei with given C cannot be smaller than a predetermined size, the family of parabolas is limited in the region of small $r=\frac{1}{x}$ by some curve. For the nucleus model under study, defined by equations (3.3.4) and (3.3.15) on the assumption that the extreme right values of x_3 are equal to the reciprocal of the dry nucleus radius r_0, the corresponding equation of this curve is

$$\delta_3=\delta_0-(1-\delta_0)\left[Bx_3-bx_3^{1-2\alpha}\right]. \tag{3.3.21}$$

In Figure 11 this curve is represented as a straight line and corresponds to $\alpha=\frac{1}{2}$ or $\alpha=0$. Intermediate values of α result in curves with fractional power dependence on x. Restricting ourselves for brevity to $\alpha = \frac{1}{2}$, it is possible to determine x_k, i.e., the value of x at which $\delta = 0$, from equation (3.3.21):

$$x_k = \frac{b + \frac{\delta_0}{1-\delta_0}}{B}, \tag{3.3.22}$$

and its corresponding activity $\overline{C}$, given by

$$\overline{C} = b\left(\frac{B}{b + \frac{\delta_0}{1-\delta_0}}\right). \tag{3.3.23}$$

The curves in Figure 11 correspond to $x_{lim} < x_k$. Apparently this condition is not always satisfied. When $x_{lim} > x_k$ one must restrict oneself only to a single ascending part of the branch of the parabola for each activity value. The case illustrated in Figure 11 ($x_{lim} < x_k$) is quite general, so we shall consider only it; however, in principle the second version can also exist.

It is seen from (3.3.2) and (3.3.22) that $x_{lim} = x_k$ when $\frac{\delta_0}{1-\delta_0} = 2b$, i.e., the second case ($x_{lim} > x_k$) is attained at very large δ_0, which does not happen in the course of natural cloud genesis. If one considers the tendency toward a variation in the size of particles with a variation in δ when $\delta_0 > 0$, then it is evident that a particle of given activity C over a sufficiently long time will either grow indefinitely, being located to the left of point x_1, or will have size x_2 (if $x_2 < x_k$) or x_3 (if $x_2 > x_3$).

In accordance with this, the droplet spectrum is subdivided into three parts: particles with $C > C_{lim}$ grow indefinitely, particles with $C < C_{lim}$ either grow indefinitely (if $x < x_1$) or have dimensions x_2 or $x_3 = \frac{1}{r_0}$. The boundary separating the zones of growing nuclei (droplets) and nuclei which are in equilibrium ($x = x_2$, $x = x_3$) assumes the value x_{lim}, given by (3.3.20). It is noteworthy that the limiting radius r_{lim} of particles, just as the limiting activity C_{lim} in (3.3.19), is a universal quantity, which does not depend on the particle properties (quantity of the solute, radius of solid nucleus, hygroscopicity factor, etc.) but is determined solely by the value of δ_0.

In this connection it is very convenient to define droplets and nuclei and to establish the boundary between them, taking as such the value at which r equals r_{lim}. (This boundary must be introduced especially for the specific consideration of the kinetics of cloud processes.) Subsequently, we shall treat all particles with $r < r_{\text{lim}}$ as condensation nuclei, the region $x > x_{\text{lim}}$ as the region of condensation nuclei, and all particles with $r > r_{\text{lim}}$ as droplets, with $x < x_{\text{lim}}$ regarded as the droplet region.

It appears that the above definition enables one, to a large extent, to define processes associated with the formation of droplets in the atmosphere and creates favorable conditions for subsequent theoretical study. Since x_{lim} and C_{lim} are functions of δ_0, it is also possible to consider the inverse problem, i.e., to determine δ_{lim} at which a nucleus with given C attains the value x_{lim}. The corresponding expression for δ_{lim} assumes the form

$$\delta_{\text{lim}} = \left[1 + \sqrt{\frac{27C}{4B^3}}\right]^{-1}. \qquad (3.3.24)$$

For particles lying on the x axis ($x = x_2$) the equilibrium radius r_2 is related to the supersaturation, It is therefore of interest to establish this relationship analytically. Setting $\delta = 0$, in equation (3.3.15), we solve the resulting cubic equation. Allowing for the limitation on the minimum size r_0 we obtain

$$r_2 = r_0 \text{ when } C < \overline{C},$$
$$r_2 = \sqrt{\frac{C}{B}}\, f\left(\frac{C}{C_{\text{lim}}}\right) \text{ when } C > \overline{C}, \qquad (3.3.25)$$

where universal function $f\left(\frac{C}{C_{\text{lim}}}\right)$ is defined as follows:

$$\frac{2}{\sqrt{3}} f\left(\frac{C}{C_{\text{lim}}}\right) = \begin{cases} 0 \quad \delta_0 > 0; \ C < C_{\text{lim}};\ x_{\text{lim}} > x_k \\ \cos^{-1}\left(\frac{\pi}{3} - \frac{1}{3}\arccos\sqrt{\frac{C}{C_{\text{lim}}}}\right);\ \delta_0 > 0;\ C < C_{\text{lim}}; \\ \qquad x_{\text{lim}} < x_k \\ \cos^{-1}\left(\frac{1}{3}\arccos\sqrt{\frac{C}{C_{\text{rp}}}}\right);\ \delta_0 < 0;\ C < C_{\text{lim}} \\ \text{ch}^{-1}\left(\frac{1}{3}\operatorname{arcch}\sqrt{\frac{C}{C_{\text{lim}}}}\right);\ \delta_0 < 0;\ C > C_{\text{lim}}. \end{cases}$$

When $\delta_0 < 0$, the concept of C_{lim} has only a formal meaning. The value of C_{lim} is given by expression (3.3.19). When $\delta_0 = 0$, $f\left(\frac{C}{C_{\text{lim}}}\right) = 1$ and $r = \sqrt{\frac{C}{B}}$. It is interesting to note that in the literature one usually examines curves when $\delta = 0$; here the critical radius r_{cr} is defined as the radius corresponding in our notation to $r_{\min}(\delta_0=0)$ /9/. It is easy to show that $r_2(\delta_0=0)=\frac{r_{\min}}{\sqrt{3}}$.

When $\delta_0 < 0$, function $f\left(\frac{C}{C_{\lim}}\right)$ can be satisfactorily approximated by the following expressions:

$$f_1\left(\frac{C}{C_{\lim}}\right)=1-0.153\sqrt{\frac{C}{C_{\lim}}}+0.0192\frac{C}{C_{\lim}} \text{ when } \frac{C}{C_{\lim}}\leqslant 4,$$

$$f_2\left(\frac{C}{C_{\lim}}\right)=\frac{6^{1/2}\left(\frac{C}{C_{\lim}}\right)^{1/6}}{1+2^{2/3}\left(\frac{C}{C_{\lim}}\right)^{1/2}} \text{ when } \frac{C}{C_{\lim}}>4. \tag{3.3.27}$$

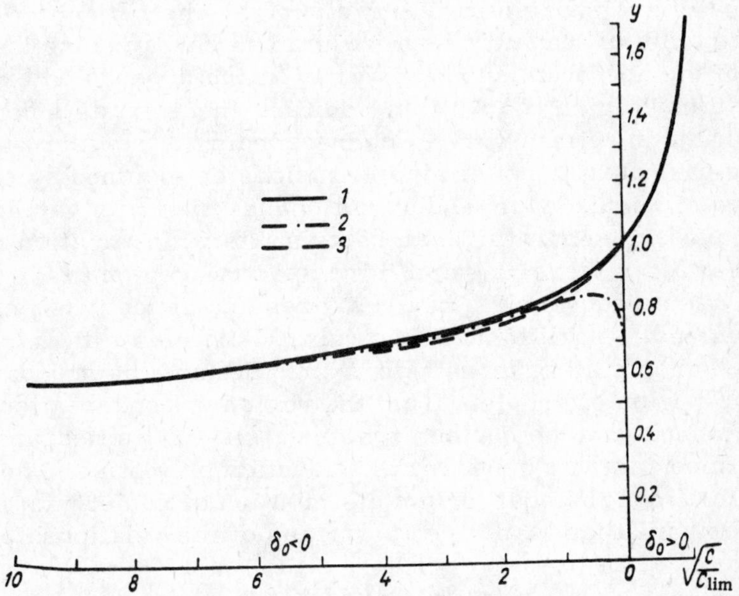

FIGURE 12. Curves of function $f\left(\frac{C}{C_{\lim}}\right)$ (curve 1) characterizing the equilibrium size of particles, and its approximations $f_1\left(\frac{C}{C_{\lim}}\right)$ (curve 2) and $f_2\left(\frac{C}{C_{\lim}}\right)$ (curve 3) as a function of supersaturation δ_0, where

$$\frac{C}{C_{\lim}}=\frac{27\,C}{4\,B^3}\left(\frac{\delta_0}{1-\delta_0}\right)^2.$$

The graphs of function $f\left(\frac{C}{C_{\lim}}\right)$ and its approximations f_1 and f_2 are plotted in Figure 12. These solutions can be used to investigate such important problems as the transformation of the spectrum of condensation nuclei and its integral particles during humidity variations.

4. SPECTRA OF CONDENSATION NUCLEI, THEIR REPRESENTATION AND DISTORTION. SPECTRAL LIMITS WHEN $\delta_0 > 0$

The results obtained in the preceding section make it possible to consider spectra of condensation nuclei and their distortion during variation in supersaturation. The most important of these should be examined again. Analysis shows that for undersaturation ($\delta_0 < 0$) the nuclei are subdivided into two parts. The majority of them reach points of transient equilibrium and characterize the transient part of the spectrum, the behavior of which depends on external conditions (region $x < x_k$). In addition, there exists a conservative part of the spectrum ($x > x_k$) corresponding to smaller particles. These particles do not attain dimensions determined by conditions of dynamic equilibrium and do not change size with variation in δ_0. The boundary separating both parts shifts with variation in δ_0.

When $\delta_0 > 0$ there arises a third spectral region ($x < x_{\lim}$) in which there are no equilibrium nucleus sizes and hence it is impossible to determine the equilibrium spectrum. Particles with $x < x_{\lim}$ were termed droplets and those with $x = x_{\lim}$ defined the boundary separating the region of droplets from the region of condensation nuclei. Thus, when $\delta_0 > 0$ the nucleus spectrum size is limited, and (which is very important) its boundary is a function only of δ_0. The relationships between the equilibrium distribution of nuclei with respect to various variables is attained by means of the relationships

$$n_0(r_0)\,dr_0 = n_c(C)\,dC = n_r(r)\,dr, \tag{3.4.1}$$

where n with some subscript represents the differential function of condensation nuclei distribution with respect to the corresponding variable.

When converting from one distribution to another it suffices to establish the functional relationship between the variables with respect to which the distribution function is given. For example,

$n_c(C)=n_0(r_0(C))\frac{dr_0}{dC}$, whence, having reference to equation (3.3.4) and using the Junge-type distribution $n(r_0)=ar_0^{-\nu}$ as the starting distribution of dry nuclei, we obtain

$$n_c(C)=\frac{a}{2b\,(1+\alpha)}\left(\frac{C}{b}\right)^{-\frac{\nu+1+2\alpha}{2(1+\alpha)}}. \qquad (3.4.2)$$

To find the distribution function with respect to r we return to equation (3.3.15), according to which C under equilibrium conditions ($\delta=0$) can be expressed in terms of x as follows:

$$C=\frac{1}{x^3}\left(Bx-\frac{\delta_0}{1-\delta_0}\right). \qquad (3.4.3)$$

Computation of $\frac{dC}{dr}$ and using equation (3.4.2) yields

$$n_r(r,\ \delta_0)=\frac{a}{1+\alpha}\left(\frac{b}{B}\right)^{\frac{\nu-1}{2(1+\alpha)}}\left(1-\frac{2}{3}\frac{r}{r_{\text{lim}}}\right)^{-\frac{\nu+1+2\alpha}{2(1+\alpha)}}\left(1-\frac{r}{r_{\text{lim}}}\right)r^{-\frac{\nu+\alpha}{1+\alpha}}, \qquad (3.4.4)$$

where

$$r_{\text{lim}}=\frac{2B}{3}\,\frac{1-\delta_0}{\delta_0}.$$

Equation (3.4.4) enables one to easily follow the transformation of the nucleus size distribution function with variation in humidity. This transformation occurs in such a manner that the distribution of dry nuclei, specified in the form of power functions, are reconstructed into power distributions with a different exponent. When $\delta_0=0$, we obtain the power distribution

$$n(r,\ 0)=\frac{a}{1+\alpha}\left(\frac{b}{B}\right)^{\frac{\nu-1}{2(1+\alpha)}}r^{-\frac{\nu+\alpha}{1+\alpha}}. \qquad (3.4.5)$$

When $\alpha=\frac{1}{2}$, the Junge distribution of dry nuclei with exponent $\nu=4$ becomes a power distribution of wet nuclei with exponent 3. It is noteworthy that the resulting distribution occurs only when $r>r_k$ and for $\delta_0>0$ when $r<r_{\text{lim}}$. An example of the distortion of a distribution function with variation in humidity is shown in Figure 13.

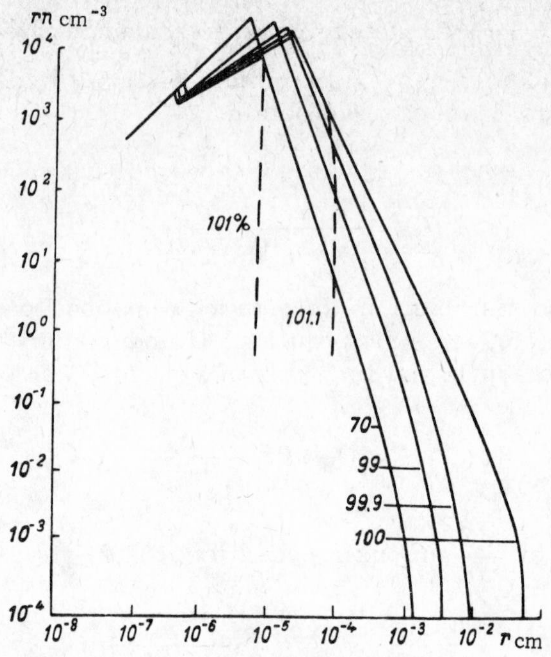

FIGURE 13. Variation in nuclei distribution function with variation in humidity $H=\frac{100\%}{1-\delta_0}$

Of greatest interest is the conversion to the particle spectrum with respect to supersaturation, since it determines the rate of droplet formation in clouds. Here, the term nuclei spectrum with respect to supersaturation is applied to a function $n_\delta(\delta_0)$ which defines the number $n_\delta(\delta_0)\,d\delta_0$ of particles becoming droplets upon increasing the supersaturation from δ_0 to $\delta_0+d\delta_0$. It was shown that C_{lim} is a function of δ_0. For each particle (with activity C) there exists a corresponding value of δ_0 at which it attains the limiting value ($C=C_{\text{lim}}$). Then, by employing the expression $n(C)\,dC\big|_{C=C_{\text{lim}}}=-n_\delta(\delta_0)\,d\delta_0$ one derives

$$n_\delta(\delta_0)=-n_c(C_{\text{lim}}(\delta_0))\frac{dC_{\text{lim}}}{d\delta_0}=$$

$$=\frac{8B^3}{27}\frac{(1-\delta_0)}{\delta_0^3}n_c\left(\frac{4B^3}{27}\frac{(1-\delta_0)^2}{\delta_0^2}\right). \qquad (3.4.6)$$

When

$$n_c(C)=P_1C^{-m}, \tag{3.4.7}$$

the spectrum of nuclei with respect to supersaturation has the form

$$n_\delta(\delta_0)=2P_1\left(\frac{4B^3}{27}\right)^{-m+1}\frac{(1-\delta_0)^{1-2m}}{\delta_0^{3-2m}}\approx 2P_1\times$$
$$\times\left(\frac{4B^3}{27}\right)^{1-m}\delta_0^{2m-3}. \tag{3.4.8}$$

If C and r_0 are uniquely related (e. g., as expressed by equation (3.4.4)), then

$$n_\delta(\delta_0)=P(1-\delta_0)^{-\frac{\nu+\alpha}{1+\alpha}}\delta_0^{\frac{\nu-2-\alpha}{1+\alpha}}\approx P\delta_0^{\frac{\nu-2-\alpha}{1+\alpha}}, \tag{3.4.9}$$

where

$$P=\frac{a}{1+\alpha}\left(\frac{4B^3}{27b}\right)^{\frac{1-\nu}{2(1+\alpha)}}.$$

Equation (3.4.9) shows that for a spectrum $n(r_0)$ having the form of a Junge spectrum ($\nu=4$), when $\alpha=0$ $n_\delta(\delta_0)\sim\delta_0^2$, while when $\alpha=\frac{1}{2}$ $n_\delta(\delta_0)\sim\delta_0$. Experimental measurements of condensation nuclei spectra point to the feasibility of using a power dependence of n_δ on δ_0 /4, 71/.

Distributions with respect to variables δ_0 and C are more universal when considering the transformation of the spectrum with variation in humidity. This is associated with the fact that, by virtue of the inhomogeneity of the distribution of the soluble substance with respect to nuclei, the "dry" spectrum transforms with a rise in humidity not in accordance with the nuclei size r_0 but in accordance with the content of soluble substances. Here, starting with some value of δ_0, the particle dimensions are determined by the content of soluble salts (the fact that the equilibrium size is a weak function of r_0 was proven in section 3 of the present chapter), and subsequently the spectrum is distorted in an orderly manner in the sense that particles with different C have different r and do not grow more rapidly than others.

Consequently, particles of inhomogeneous composition behave as homogeneous starting with some value of δ_0; this results in the distortion of the spectrum identical to the distortion of the droplet spectrum of a pure solution. For this region particle spectra of different composition can be described (starting with some value of

δ_0) by uniform distribution functions, which shall be extensively utilized in the subsequent discussion. On the other hand, direct conversion from the distribution with respect to r_0 to that with respect to C and δ_0 is possible only on the assumption that there exists a unique relationship between r_0 and the amount of soluble substance in the particle.

5. ASSESSMENT OF THE VALIDITY OF THE ASSUMPTION OF EQUILIBRIUM BETWEEN THE NUCLEI AND THE MEDIUM

Under natural conditions, when the external variables change continuously with time, conditions of equilibrium between the particles and the medium are, strictly speaking, not attained. The validity of using equilibrium values of nuclei radii and utilizing equilibrium distributions as points of departure in considering the hydration of nuclei and formation of droplets can be based only on a proof that the characteristic time of establishing this equilibrium is much smaller than the characteristic time of variations in external variables. To estimate the validity of assumptions concerning the existence of equilibrium between the nuclei and the medium, we shall consider the equation governing the growth of a droplet of a solution, expressed in the form of equations (2.10.2):

$$\frac{dr}{dt} = K_3 \frac{\delta(r, \delta_0)}{r + \xi}. \tag{3.5.1}$$

Here, quantity δ is defined in agreement with (3.5.7). In the state of equilibrium, $\delta = 0$ and $\frac{dr}{dt} = 0$. As δ_0 varies, the particle radius at each instant of time differs somewhat from that at equilibrium. Consideration of the parabolas defining δ as a function of r (see Figure 11) shows that they intersect the abscissa at different angles, the angle increasing as the equilibrium size of the particle departs from the limiting value. Since the angle of intersection characterizes the rate of transition to the equilibrium state, then somewhat near the limiting values one should expect a substantial difference between the current and equilibrium values of radii upon variations in external conditions.

With reference to the above we shall find the characteristic time of transition to the state of equilibrium. Near the equilibrium point, where $\delta(r_{eq}, \delta_0) = 0$ (r_{eq} being the equilibrium particle radius), the dependence of δ on r can be expressed as a series in $r - r_{eq}$. In the first approximation

$$\frac{dr}{dt} = K_3 \frac{\left(\delta_0 - \frac{2C}{r_{eq}^3}\right)(r - r_{eq})}{r_{eq}(r_{eq} + \xi)} = \frac{3K_3\left(1 - \frac{r_{lim}}{r_{eq}}\right)\delta_0}{r_{eq}(r_{eq} + \xi)}(r - r_{eq}), \quad (3.5.2)$$

where

$$r_{lim} = \frac{2B}{3\delta_0}, \quad \delta_0 = \frac{B}{r_{eq}} - \frac{C}{r_{eq}^3}.$$

It should be immediately stipulated that the approximation $(\delta(r, \delta_0) \approx \lambda(r - r_{lim}))$ can be used as an estimate of the upper limit of the time for establishing equilibrium at any $\Delta r = r - r_{eq}$. Figure 11 shows that linear extrapolation of the supersaturation, due to the concave shape of the curves, results in underestimated supersaturation or in deviations from the point of equilibrium. This underestimate, in turn, reduces the rate at which the equilibrium position is attained and increases the characteristic time. The solution to equation (3.5.2) has the form

$$r = r_{eq} + [r(0) - r_{eq}] \exp\left(-\frac{t}{\tau}\right), \quad (3.5.3)$$

where τ is the characteristic time for establishing equilibrium, accordingly given by

$$\tau = -\frac{r_{eq}(r_{eq} + \xi)}{3K_3\delta_0}\left(\frac{r_{eq}}{r_{eq} - r_{lim}}\right). \quad (3.5.4)$$

For values of δ_0 close to zero ($|r_{lim}| \gg r_{eq}$),

$$\tau = \frac{r_{eq}^2(r_{eq} + \xi)}{2K_3B}. \quad (3.5.5)$$

Since $K_3 \approx 10^{-6}$ cm^2/sec, we have $\tau \approx 0.4 \cdot 10^6 \frac{r_{eq}^2}{\delta_0}$ sec for not too low values of δ. Hence

$$0.4 \frac{10^{-4}}{|\delta_0|} \text{ sec for } r_{eq} \approx 10^{-5} \text{ cm},$$

$$0.4 \frac{10^{-2}}{|\delta_0|} \text{ sec for } r_{eq} \approx 10^{-4} \text{ cm}.$$

Condensation nuclei at which droplets form lie mainly within this range of sizes. It can therefore be concluded that as external conditions vary with a characteristic time of the order of several seconds, the system is in equilibrium.

In general, one can also estimate the amount by which the radius lags behind that at equilibrium during variation in δ_0. It is seen from equation (3.5.2) that the rate of droplet growth is proportional to $(r - r_{eq})$. Thus during variations in δ_0 resulting in variations in r_{eq}, droplets with r close to r_{eq} will drop behind as regards variation in their size, while those with sufficiently large $(r - r_{eq})$ will overtake them. The boundary separating these two regions is represented by some nucleus radius $\bar{r}$ whose rate of growth equals the rate of variation in r_{eq}. Thus

$$\frac{d\bar{r}}{dt} = \frac{dr_{eq}}{dt}, \tag{3.5.6}$$

whence $\bar{r} = r_{eq} + \Delta r$. We now define quantity Δr characterizing the nucleus lag. Equations (3.5.6) and (3.5.2) yield

$$\frac{dr_{eq}}{dt} = \frac{dr_{eq}}{d\delta_0}\frac{d\delta_0}{dt} = \frac{3K_3\delta_0}{r_{eq}(r_{eq}+\xi)}\left(1 - \frac{r_{lim}}{r_{eq}}\right)\Delta r, \tag{3.5.7}$$

from which it follows that

$$\Delta r = -\frac{r_{eq}^2(r_{eq}+\xi)}{9K_3\delta_0^2\left(\frac{r_{lim}}{r_{eq}} - 1\right)^2}\frac{d\delta_0}{dt}. \tag{3.5.8}$$

By assuming that equilibrium sets in only when $\left|\frac{\Delta r}{r_{eq}}\right| \ll 1$, we can write the following criterion:

$$\left|\frac{d\delta_0}{dt}\right| \ll \frac{9K_3\left(\frac{r_{lim}}{r_{eq}} - 1\right)^2\delta_0^2}{r_{eq}(r_{eq}+\xi)}. \tag{3.5.9}$$

This expression allows one to also obtain estimates of the values of r_{eq} for which the condition of equilibrium is known a priori:

$$\left(\frac{r_{lim} - r_{eq}}{r_{eq}}\right)^2 \gg \frac{r_{eq}(r_{eq}+\xi)}{9K_3\delta_0^2}\left|\frac{d\delta_0}{dt}\right|. \tag{3.5.10}$$

Thus for dimensions far from $r_{\lim}$, when $\left(\frac{r_{\lim}}{r_{eq}}-1\right)\approx 1$ for $r_{eq}\approx$ $\approx 10^{-5}$ cm, the equilibrium conditions set in when the following inequality is satisfied:

$$\left|\frac{d\delta_0}{dt}\right| \ll 2\cdot 10^{-5}\delta_0^2. \qquad (3.5.11)$$

If this inequality is satisfied, then the range of dimensions within which the assumption of equilibrium is valid can be estimated on the basis of inequality (3.5.10).

6. ORDINARY MECHANISM OF DROPLET FORMATION IN THE ATMOSPHERE

Current theories of the formation and growth of droplets on condensation nuclei assume that the genesis of new droplets is associated with a growth in supersaturation and with the consequent variation in the sign of δ (from minus to plus). It is seen from Figure 11a that, as a result of increasing δ, conditions for unlimited growth (passing through $C_{\lim}$, which is equivalent to conversion of a nucleus into a drop) are created primarily for particles with high activity (larger particles). The previously obtained relationships make it possible to establish analytic relationships between $\frac{d\delta_0}{dt}$ and the rate $\frac{dN}{dt}$ of the formation of new droplets.

The regular rate of formation of new droplets can be established with the aid of the nuclei distribution function with respect to limiting supersaturations δ_0, specified by equations (3.4.6), (3.4.8) and (3.4.9). It is clear from the meaning of the problem that in order to determine $\frac{dN}{dt}$ it is necessary to calculate the number of particles lying within the spectral interval δ_0 to $\delta_0+d\delta_0$. Then $dN=n_\delta(\delta_0)\,d\delta_0$ and

$$\frac{dN}{dt}=n_\delta(\delta_0)\frac{d\delta_0}{dt}. \qquad (3.6.1)$$

Equations (3.4.6) and (3.4.9) can be employed to express equation (3.6.1) in the form

$$\frac{dN}{dt}=n_c\left(\frac{4B^3}{27}\left(\frac{1-\delta_0}{\delta_0}\right)^2\right)\frac{8B^3}{27}\,\frac{(1-\delta_0)}{\delta_0^3}\,\frac{d\delta_0}{dt}, \tag{3.6.2}$$

or

$$\frac{dN}{dt}=2P_1\left(\frac{4B^3}{27}\right)^{1-m}\delta_0^{2m-3}\frac{d\delta_0}{dt}. \tag{3.6.2'}$$

The above expressions apply only when δ_0 increases in the region of positive values $\left(\frac{d\delta_0}{dt}>0,\ \delta_0>0\right)$. If $\frac{d\delta_0}{dt}<0$ when $\delta_0>0$, then a reverse transition (from the region of droplets to the region of nuclei) is possible. Apparently, near the boundary there does not exist a perceptible number of droplets, since the equilibrium point $r=r_1$ is a point of unstable equilibrium. Hence, one can set here $\frac{dN}{dt}=0$. However, when the supersaturation varies in a given direction, the region near the boundary can be filled with droplets. In this case

$$\frac{dN}{dt}=f(r_{\lim},\ t)\frac{dr_{\lim}}{d\delta_0}\,\frac{d\delta_0}{dt},$$

where $f(r,\ t)$ is the droplet size distribution function, determined by solving the kinetic equation. The feasibility of an inverse transformation (in spite of the fact that $\delta_0>0$) follows from the following estimate. Let us consider quantity $\frac{d\delta}{dt}$, which we express in the form

$$\frac{d\delta}{dt}=\left(1+\frac{B}{r}-\frac{C}{r^3}\right)\frac{d\delta_0}{dt}+(1-\delta_0)\left(\frac{B}{r^2}-\frac{3C}{r^4}\right)\frac{dr}{dt}. \tag{3.6.3}$$

In accordance with the equation of condensation growth $\frac{dr}{dt}=K_3\frac{\delta}{r+\xi}$, so

$$\frac{d\delta}{dt}=\left(1+\frac{B}{r}-\frac{C}{r^3}\right)\frac{d\delta_0}{dt}+\frac{K_3}{r\,(r+\xi)}\left(\frac{B}{r}-\frac{3C}{r_3}\right)\delta. \tag{3.6.4}$$

In the latter expression the first term on the right-hand side is negative, because $\frac{B}{r}-\frac{C}{r^3}\approx\delta_0\ll 1$ and $\frac{d\delta_0}{dt}<0$, while the second term is determined by the sign of the expression $\left(\frac{B}{r}-\frac{3C}{r^3}\right)$ which, by virtue of the positiveness of r, is determined by the sign of the expression

$$B-\frac{3C}{r^3}=B\left(1-\frac{r_{\min}^2}{r^2}\right). \tag{3.6.5}$$

Quantity $r_{\min}$ is the radius of a particle with given C for a given value of δ_0, at which δ has a minimum (see Figure 11). For larger r the second term in equation (3.6.4) is positive, while for $r<r_{\min}$, which is possible only when $r_{\min}>r_{\lim}$, the second term becomes negative. The multiplier in equation (3.6.5) increases with r and has a minimum at $r=r_{\lim}$. For droplets close to the boundary the second term vanishes ($\delta=0$), by virtue of which

$$\frac{d\delta}{dt}=\frac{d\delta_0}{dt}.$$

For negative $\frac{d\delta_0}{dt}$, this means that in any case some proportion of the droplets with dimensions close to $r_{\lim}$ slows down its growth and the moving boundary is able to overtake them (when $\frac{d\delta_0}{dt}<0$, $\frac{dr_{\lim}}{dt}>0$). Since

$$\frac{dr_{\lim}}{d\delta_0}=-\frac{2B}{3\delta_0^2},$$

$$\frac{dN}{dt}=\frac{2B}{3}f(r_{\lim},\ t)\frac{1}{\delta_0^2}\frac{d\delta_0}{dt}. \tag{3.6.6}$$

The concept of a boundary between nuclei and droplets does not exist for negative δ_0. In this case evaporation should be examined by means of the kinetic equation, describing the behavior of the droplet fraction.

7. FLUCTUATION MECHANISM OF DROPLET FORMATION

The droplet formation mechanism examined in the preceding chapter is not the only one, although it underlies many theoretical studies concerned with the formation of the cloud spectrum /34, 54, 55/. In spite of the fact that it plays the principal role, and hence droplet formation should occur at the boundaries of the cloud (which is indicated by the distribution of droplet concentration), transitions from droplets into nuclei and back within the cloud are theoretically possible and should occur. These transitions are no longer induced by the usual variations in humidity, but statistical transfer from one region to another due to fluctuations. It is possible that such a statistical transfer is of some importance under conditions of very weak variations in the average humidity.

When referring to droplet formation it must be reemphasized that reference is had not to the inception of a new phase, but to the genesis of droplets occurring at humidities above 100%. The appearance of the liquid phase as such on a particle starts already at low humidities (according to some data at 30%) and the mechanism of its formation in this case is not of particular interest. It will be assumed that the particles already contain liquid water which fully envelopes their entire surface, and we shall consider the course of the possible increase on them of the mass of water.

If we examine a vapor-air mixture containing condensation nuclei, possessing some humidity exceeding 100% and subject to constant external conditions, then (as was previously shown) the particle radius assumes an equilibrium value corresponding to the point of stable equilibrium. In this case, there will exist some limiting radius, above which the particles are able to grow indefinitely, i. e., to become droplets. The presence of the point of unstable equilibrium corresponds to the fact that the particles, upon somehow acquiring a quantity of water, already become capable of unlimited growth. Hence this possibility can be realized due to fluctuations in the system, particles being transferred through the forbidden zone to the region where droplets can exist.

This transfer can be investigated within the framework of classical statistical theory as a problem of the fluctuation mechanism of the formation of condensation nuclei. Such a study was carried out for insoluble nuclei /42, 29/, for fully soluble nuclei /41/, and for mixed nuclei /17/. The meaning of this analysis consists in determining the probability of a fluctuation subject to which a particle would move from the point of stable equilibrium to point $r_{u.eq}$ of unstable equilibrium. Since the equilibrium size of a particle is determined by the balance between the number of vapor molecules leaving from and arriving at its surface, the real size at each time differs from that at equilibrium. Smoothing of the equilibrium radius under conditions of dynamic equilibirum can be defined by the expression

$$n(r^3) = n_0(r^3_{eq}) \exp\left(-\frac{\Delta F}{kT}\right), \tag{3.7.1}$$

where ΔF is the deviation of the free energy of a particle with radius r from its value at the point of stable equilibrium, and k is the Boltzmann constant.

The particle flux in the dimensional space in accordance with the continuity equation is defined by the expression

$$I = \frac{3}{4\pi\rho_s}\frac{d}{dr^3}\left(n(r^3)V\right); \tag{3.7.2}$$

here, the rate of variation in the mass of a particle due to capture of water molecules can be determined from kinetic considerations:

$$V = 4\pi r^2 \beta m, \tag{3.7.3}$$

where β is the number of molecules condensing per unit time on unit surface, m is the molecular mass, and ρ_s is the density of the solution.

Since under equilibrium conditions $\frac{d}{dr^3}(n_0(r^3)V) = 0$, equation (3.7.2) can assume the form

$$I = \frac{3n_0(r^3)V}{4\pi\rho_s}\frac{d}{dr^3}\left(\frac{n(r^3)}{n_0(r^3)}\right), \tag{3.7.4}$$

from which it follows that

$$\frac{4\pi}{3}\int\limits_{r^3_{eq}}^{r^3_{u.eq}} \frac{I\rho_s}{n_0(r^3)V}\,dr^3 = \int\limits_{r^3_{eq}}^{r^3_{u.eq}} \frac{d}{dr^3}\left(\frac{n(r^3)}{n_0(r^3)}\right)dr^3. \tag{3.7.5}$$

Further, making use of equation (3.7.1) and restricting ourselves to the steady-state case, when I is constant in time and does not depend on r and when variations in ρ_s are neglected, we obtain

$$I = \frac{\beta n\left(r^3_{eq}\right)m}{\rho_s \int\limits_{r_{eq}}^{r_{u.eq}} \exp\left(\frac{\Delta F}{kT}\right)dr}. \tag{3.7.6}$$

Further simplification of this expression is associated with the expansion and approximate integration of the above equation. If ΔF in the vicinity of $r_{u.eq}$ is given by

$$\Delta F = \Delta F^* + \frac{1}{2}\left(\frac{\partial^2 \Delta F}{\partial r^2}\right)(r - r_{u.eq})^2, \tag{3.7.7}$$

where ΔF^* is the value of ΔF at $r = r_{u.eq}$, and use is made of the fact that $\Delta F\big|_{r=r_{eq}} = 0$, then (3.7.6) yields the following approximate expression for I:

$$I = n(r_{eq}^3)\,\frac{\beta m}{\rho_s}\sqrt{\frac{4\Delta F^*}{\pi kT\,(r_{u.eq} - r)^2}}\,\exp\left(-\frac{\Delta F}{kT}\right), \tag{3.7.8}$$

where the rate of condensation can be defined as

$$\beta = \frac{e}{\sqrt{2\pi mkT}} \tag{3.7.9}$$

(e is the vapor pressure).

Using equation (3.7.8) and taking as the starting point any distribution of equilibrium radii, we can calculate the total rate of droplet formation. Estimates /17/ show that it is small and, practically speaking, droplets can form from nuclei with radii satisfying $0.998\ r_{lim} < r < r_{lim}$ or, upon converting to a distribution with respect to supersaturation, in the region $\delta_{lim} < \delta < \dfrac{\delta_{lim}}{0.998}$.

Estimates for spectra of droplets typical of the atmosphere show that the fraction of these particles in this narrow range is small. This means that this mechanism cannot ensure the actual rates of droplet formation in the atmosphere and it is doubtful whether it makes a perceptible contribution to the formation of droplets during cloud genesis.

8. PULSATION MECHANISM OF DROPLET FORMATION

Particle sizes for which condensation is allowed are quite large (of the order of a micron or a fraction of a micron), and hence fluctuations in the water vapor molecule flux can result only in insignificant variations of nuclei dimensions about the equilibrium value. This allows a small number of them to become transformed from the subcritical state into droplets.

However, there exist in the atmosphere fluctuations with a much greater amplitude of oscillations and which are not induced by molecular processes but by turbulence. These pulsations can also result in the variation of nuclei sizes and similarly produce conditions for droplet formation. This mechanism has been examined and analyzed /7, 8, 45/. We too shall examine the course of pulsation formation of droplets, and shall assume that the average supersaturation does not increase but is maintained at some value $\delta_0 = \text{const}$.

In this case, from the standpoint of common concepts of droplet formation, the appearance of new cloud particles is impossible. However, turbulence results in pulsations in the supersaturation in the cloud and the possibility arises of pulsation transfer of nuclei through the forbidden size ranges. This is accompanied by genesis of new droplets, similar to the phenomenon of particle penetration through a potential barrier. Such a transition was examined by Chandrasekhar for Brownian movement /12/.

The characteristic times of pulsations in v'_z and δ'_0 for the inertial interval have an order of several minutes and the nucleus becomes a droplet after several seconds during variations in supersaturation. It can thus be assumed that the nucleus passes through a barrier, following variations in supersaturation, and it is possible to neglect lag effects. The inverse conversion from the region of droplets to the region of nuclei is much less effective. It can be neglected, since near the boundary of dimensions separating the dropwise fraction from nuclei the droplet concentration is virtually zero (by virtue of the unstable nature of the point of equilibrium for this boundary).

We shall now pass on to a direct investigation of the effect of one-sided transfer of nuclei to the region of droplets. For this we shall first consider the nature of wind speed pulsations governing this process.

The variation in velocity $\mathbf{v}'$ over time Δt is given by the expression

$$\Delta \mathbf{v}' = \int_t^{t+\Delta t} \frac{d\mathbf{v}'}{dt}\, dt = \int_t^{t+\Delta t} \mathbf{w}\, dt. \tag{3.8.1}$$

Acceleration $\mathbf{w}$ is a random variable which is assumed to obey the normal distribution

$$\varphi(\mathbf{w}) = \frac{1}{(2\pi\sigma^2)^{3/2}} \exp\left(-\frac{\mathbf{w}^2}{2\sigma^2}\right). \tag{3.8.2}$$

In accordance with Yaglom /14/

$$\overline{\mathbf{w}}^2=\overline{\left(\frac{d\mathbf{v}}{dt}\right)^2}\approx 3\,\frac{\varepsilon^{3/2}}{\nu_1^{1/2}}, \qquad (3.8.3)$$

where ε is the rate of dissipation of eddy energy and ν_1 is the kinematic viscosity. On the other hand, in line with equation (3.8.2)

$$\overline{(\mathbf{w})^2}=\int_0^\infty \mathbf{w}^2\frac{1}{(2\pi\sigma^2)^{3/2}}\exp\left(-\frac{\mathbf{w}^2}{2\sigma^2}\right)d\mathbf{w}=3\sigma^2,$$

whence it follows that

$$\sigma^2\approx\frac{\varepsilon^{3/2}}{\nu_1^{1/2}}. \qquad (3.8.4)$$

The characteristic time for turbulent pulsations of the acceleration can be taken as

$$\tau=\varkappa\left(\frac{\nu_1}{\varepsilon}\right)^{1/2}, \qquad (3.8.5)$$

where $\varkappa$ is a factor of the order of unity.

Since $\varepsilon\sim 10\ \mathrm{cm^2/sec}$, $\tau\sim 0.1$ sec. Over time $\Delta t\gg\tau$ the velocity increment can be treated as the sum of noncorrelated accelerations.*

$$\Delta\mathbf{v}'(\Delta t)=\int_t^{t+\Delta t}\mathbf{w}\,dt\approx\sum_1^{N=\frac{\Delta t}{\tau}}\mathbf{w}_i\tau. \qquad (3.8.6)$$

The assumed distribution for accelerations in equation (3.8.6) is normal. It therefore follows that the probability distribution function for the velocity increment also obeys a normal law. Hence

$$\psi(\Delta\mathbf{v}',\ \Delta t)=\left(2\pi\sum_1^N\sigma_i^2\tau^2\right)^{-3/2}\exp\left(-\frac{\Delta\mathbf{v}^2}{2\sum_1^N\sigma_i^2\tau^2}\right). \qquad (3.8.7)$$

According to equation (3.8.4)

$$\sum_1^N\sigma_i^2\tau^2=\sigma^2\tau^2N=\sigma^2\tau\,\Delta t.$$

* The expressions presented here and subsequently correspond to a Lagrangian description of the process.

Thus

$$\psi(\Delta\mathbf{v}', \Delta t) = (2\pi\sigma^2\tau\,\Delta t)^{-3/2}\exp\left(-\frac{(\Delta\mathbf{v}')^2}{2\sigma^2\tau\,\Delta t}\right). \qquad (3.8.8)$$

This expression can be rewritten in the more common form encountered in the study of Brownian diffusion:

$$\psi(\Delta\mathbf{v}', \Delta t) = \frac{1}{(4\pi D\,\Delta t)^{3/2}}\exp\left(-\frac{(\Delta\mathbf{v}')^2}{4D\,\Delta t}\right), \qquad (3.8.9)$$

where

$$D = \frac{\varkappa\varepsilon}{2}. \qquad (3.8.10)$$

The meaning of quantity D is close to that of a diffusion coefficient, but equation (3.8.9) characterizes in the case at hand random increments (flights) of velocity, rather than coordinates. It is of interest that $\overline{(\Delta\mathbf{v}')^2}$ computed on the basis of equation (3.8.9) is given by

$$\overline{(\Delta\mathbf{v}')^2} = 3\varkappa\varepsilon\,\Delta t. \qquad (3.8.11)$$

This expression corresponds to the well known Lagrangian structural velocity function /1/, which indicates that our scheme does not contradict current concepts of the theory of turbulence. Equation (3.8.9) makes it possible (as in the theory of Brownian motion) to write the Fokker-Planck equation, not in the configurational space but in the velocity space. Here the velocity probability distribution satisfies the integral equation

$$W(\mathbf{v}', t+\Delta t) = \int_{-\infty}^{\infty} W(v' - \Delta\mathbf{v}', t)\,\psi(\Delta\mathbf{v}', \Delta t)\,d(\Delta\mathbf{v}'). \qquad (3.8.12)$$

Simple transformations of this equation yield an expression for W analogous to the diffusion equation (but in the space of velocities $\mathbf{v}'$):

$$\frac{dW}{dt} = D\,\Delta_{\mathbf{v}'} W. \qquad (3.8.13)$$

A similar equation was used (without proof) by Obukhov /9/ to describe turbulence in Lagrangian variables.

We shall treat the steady-state case, when for the probability flux density j in the direction of increasing v_z one can set

$$j = D\frac{\partial W}{\partial v_z'}. \tag{3.8.14}$$

This flux can be computed on the assumption that W has a normal velocity distribution:

$$W(v_z') = \left[2\pi\overline{(v_z')^2}\right]^{-1/2} \exp\left(-\frac{(v_z')^2}{2\overline{(v_z')^2}}\right). \tag{3.8.15}$$

It follows that

$$j(v_z') = \frac{Dv_z'}{(2\pi)^{1/2}\left[\overline{(v_z')^2}\right]^{3/2}} \exp\left[-\frac{v_z'^2}{2\overline{(v_z')^2}}\right]. \tag{3.8.16}$$

The latter expression gives the probability density flux for increasing the velocity of a unit volume of air by the amount v_z'. The probability of increasing the supersaturation in a unit volume of air can be determined by employing an equation relating the supersaturation to the vertical velocities:

$$\delta_0 = A(\bar{v}_z + v_z'), \tag{3.8.17}$$

where*

$$A = \frac{c_p(\gamma_a - \gamma_{w.a})\rho_1}{LK_3F_1}.$$

Knowing the condensation nuclei distribution function with respect to limiting supersaturation $n\delta_0$, one can easily construct from (3.8.17) the nuclei distribution function with respect to the velocities of vertical pulsations, corresponding to these limiting supersaturations:

$$n_v(v_z) = An_\delta(\delta_0(v_z)) = An_\delta(\bar{\delta}_0 + Av_z'), \tag{3.8.18}$$

where $\bar{\delta}_0 = A\bar{v}_z$.

If one knows the nuclei distribution function over limiting vertical velocity pulsations (3.8.18) and the expression for the probability density flux for increasing v_z', it is possible to derive the rate of droplet formation from nuclei in a unit volume for the given value of δ_0.

* This expression is derived in Chapter 5.

For droplets forming from nuclei during vertical pulsations in v'_z per unit time over interval dv'_z,

$$\frac{dN}{dt}\,dv'_z = \frac{Dv'_z n_\delta(\delta_0)}{(2\pi)^{1/2}\left[\overline{(v'_z)^2}\right]^{3/2}} \exp\left(-\frac{(v'_z)^2}{2\overline{(v'_z)^2}}\right) dv'_z, \tag{3.8.19}$$

while the total number $\overline{\Phi}'$ of droplets forming in unit volume per unit time is determined by the integral over all $v'_z > 0$:

$$\overline{\Phi}' = \frac{AD}{(2\pi)^{1/2}\left[\overline{(v'_z)^2}\right]^{3/2}} \int_0^\infty v'_z n(\bar{\delta}_0 + Av'_z) \exp\left[-\frac{(v'_z)^2}{2\overline{(v'_z)^2}}\right] dv'_z. \tag{3.8.20}$$

If we convert from variable v'_z to δ'_0 in the integrand, then the expression for $\overline{\Phi}'$ assumes the form

$$\overline{\Phi}' = \frac{D}{(2\pi)^{1/2} A\left[\overline{(v'_z)^2}\right]^{3/2}} \int_0^\infty \delta'_0 n_\delta(\delta) \exp\left[-\frac{(\delta'_0)^2}{2A^2\overline{(v'_z)^2}}\right] d\delta'_0. \tag{3.8.21}$$

Since $\delta_0 = \bar{\delta}_0 + \delta'_0$, equation (3.8.21) can be expressed as

$$\overline{\Phi}' = \frac{D}{(2\pi)^{1/2} A\left[\overline{(v'_z)^2}\right]^{3/2}} \int_{\bar{\delta}_0}^\infty (\delta_0 - \bar{\delta}_0)\, n_\delta(\delta_0) \exp\left[-\frac{(\delta_0 - \bar{\delta}_0)^2}{2A^2\overline{(v'_z)^2}}\right] d\delta_0. \tag{3.8.22}$$

We shall estimate $\overline{\Phi}'$ on the basis of the above nuclei distribution function $n_\delta(\delta_0) = P\delta_0^{\frac{\nu-2-\alpha}{1+\alpha}}$:

$$\overline{\Phi}' = S \int_{\bar{\delta}_0}^\infty (\delta_0 - \bar{\delta}_0)\, \delta_0^{\frac{\nu-2-\alpha}{1+\alpha}} \exp\left[-\frac{(\delta_0 - \bar{\delta}_0)^2}{2A^2\overline{(v'_z)^2}}\right] d\delta_0, \tag{3.8.23}$$

where

$$S = \frac{D\rho}{(2\pi)^{1/2} A\left[\overline{(v'_z)^2}\right]^{3/2}}. \tag{3.8.24}$$

In general, the integral in (3.8.23) reduces to an incomplete gamma function. As regards the spectrum of condensation nuclei, $\nu = 4$ when $\alpha = 0$ and $\alpha = \frac{1}{2}$, the exponent of δ_0 in equation (3.8.23) is equal to 2 and 1, respectively, and integration yields

$$\overline{\Phi}' = SA^2\overline{(v_z')^2}\left\{\bar{\delta}_0 + A\left[\frac{\pi}{2}\overline{(v_z')^2}\right]^{1/2}\right\} \text{when } \alpha = \frac{1}{2}, \tag{3.8.25}$$

$$\overline{\Phi}' = SA^2\overline{(v_z')^2}\left\{\bar{\delta}_0 + A\left[2\pi\overline{(v_z')^2}\right]^{1/2} + 2A^2\overline{(v_z')^2}\right\} \text{when } \alpha = 0. \tag{3.8.26}$$

To estimate the rate $\overline{\Phi}'$ of droplet formation, we take into consideration that in stratus $\overline{v_z} \approx 1-3$ cm/sec, while $[\overline{(v_z')^2}]^{1/2} \approx 30-50$ cm/sec; $A \approx 5 \cdot 10^{-6}$ cm/sec.

If the nucleus is assumed to comprise 20% of soluble substances with molecular weight ~60 and specific weight 2 g/cm^3, then $\alpha = \frac{1}{2}$, and the activity of the nucleus is

$$C = 0.25 r_0^3,$$

whence $b = 0.25$.

The expression for quantity P entering equation (3.8.24) was obtained previously:

$$P = \frac{a}{1+\alpha}\left(\frac{4B^3}{27b}\right)^{\frac{1-\nu}{2(1+\alpha)}}.$$

According to data of Junge, $a \approx 10^4$; hence $P \approx 10^{10}$. At these values, for nuclei containing 20% of soluble substances

$$\overline{\Phi}' \approx 4 \text{ sec}^{-1} \cdot \text{cm}^{-3}.$$

Similar estimates for completely insoluble nuclei show that

$$\overline{\Phi}' = 10^{-3} \text{ sec}^{-1} \cdot \text{cm}^{-3}.$$

Such a sharp reduction in $\overline{\Phi}'$ on changing from partially soluble to completely insoluble nuclei is natural, since in the latter case a much greater increase in δ_0 is needed for an unbounded growth of the particle. It should also be noted that the calculations yield only an order of magnitude of the flux of particles which become droplets due to supersaturation fluctuations. As the concentration of nuclei with dimensions adjoining the boundary $r_{\text{lim}}(\delta_0)$ is thinned out, this flux decreases.

However, the above estimates show that the pulsation mechanism of droplet formation must be taken into account when constructing the theory of cloud genesis. For a more correct analysis of pulsation formation of droplets it is necessary to allow for thinning out of the nuclei spectrum and the process of spectrum distortion should be examined within the framework of the kinetic equation.

Alongside the above pulsation mechanism of droplet formation, there should exist a pulsation mechanism governing the conversions of droplets into nuclei. Apparently, it is of no importance for clouds, since the process occurs against the background of $\delta_0 > 0$, which results in thinning out of the droplet spectrum directly in the region of dimensions close to the limiting size (unstable nature of the equilibrium point). However, when $\delta_0 = 0$, which occurs in various experimental facilities for artificial fog formation, this mechanism can be extremely effective.

Chapter 4

KINETICS OF THE INITIAL CONDENSATION STAGE

1. EQUATIONS GOVERNING THE DROPLET FORMATION PROCESS AND THEIR SIMPLIFICATION

The transformation of nuclei into droplets and the initial development of the resulting droplet spectrum is a peculiar process. This peculiarity is due to the strong effect of the feedback, as a result of which the number of forming droplets is a function of the spectrum of condensation nuclei and the cooling rate. The variation in the droplet distribution function has a specific nature, since new droplets are created in addition to the intensive growth of already existing droplets.

These circumstances are to some extent the reason for the desire to examine separately the initial stage of the cloud spectrum formation. This stage could be disregarded, as in a number of numerical calculations /21, 23, 26/. However, it has been shown that this generalization results in the loss of interesting information and greatly reduces the accuracy.

It is assumed in formulating the principal equation of kinetics of the initial condensation stage that the mutual effect of droplets can be taken into account by altering the average values of external variables, which are determined with consideration of balance requirements. The question as to the validity of this assumption and the limitations it involves is not simple. It will be treated in part in the following chapter. Here we shall at present restrict ourselves to noting that this assumption is the weak point of the theory presented below, although there is a basis for assuming that the actual description of this process in this manner is quite accurate.

We introduce the droplet distribution function $f(r, t)$ and assume that it satisfies the equation of balance of the number of particles:

$$\frac{\partial f}{\partial t}+\frac{\partial}{\partial r}\left(\frac{dr}{dt} f(r, t)\right)=\Psi(r, t). \qquad (4.1.1)$$

Function $\Psi(r, t)$ characterizes the operation of a source, which results in the appearance or disappearance of droplets in the volume. This form automatically assumes spatial homogeneity, neglect of sedimentation and a number of other effects. It should, however, be stipulated that in some cases a time-dependent process described by equation (4.1.1) can be interpreted in spatial terms, such as in the case of updrafts of a nonmixing air mass, when z and t are uniquely related by the relationship

$$z=z_0+v_z t,$$

and the insignificance of effects associated with sedimentation makes it possible to neglect the spatial derivative. Equations of this type are used quite extensively in studies of condensation processes /3, 15, 16/ and hence we shall omit the proof. Equation (4.1.1) contains the rate of growth by condensation, which must be determined. This question was considered in great detail in Chapter 2, and hence we shall restrict ourselves here only to a simplified form of the equation for $\frac{dr}{dt}$ in accordance with equation (2.10.11) /2.13/:

$$\frac{dr}{dt}=K_3\frac{\delta_0-\frac{B}{r}+\Phi(c)}{r+\xi}, \tag{4.1.2}$$

where

$$K_3=\frac{D_v\rho_0}{\rho_2\left[1+\frac{\rho_0 L D_v}{k_1 T}\left(\frac{L}{R_v T}-1\right)\right]},$$

$$B=\frac{2\sigma}{\rho_2 R_v T},$$

$$\xi=\frac{D_v}{\alpha\bar{\nu}}\,\frac{1+\frac{\alpha^2}{\omega}\frac{\rho_0 L D_v}{k_1 T}\left(\frac{L}{R_v T}-1\right)}{1+\frac{\rho_0 L D_v}{k_1 T}\left(\frac{L}{R_v T}-1\right)},$$

$$\bar{\nu}=\sqrt{\frac{R_v T}{2\pi}},$$

ρ_0, ρ_2 and ρ_1 are the densities of saturated vapor, water and air, respectively; k_1 is the thermal conductivity of air; α is the condensation coefficient; ω is the thermal accommodation coefficient; $\Phi(c)$ is a function characterizing the drop in saturated vapor pressure due to soluble substances with surface concentration c. In order to close system of equations (4.1.1) and (4.1.2), we shall determine the variation in δ_0 due to external variables and the transport of vapor to droplets. Since $\delta_0 = \left(1 - \frac{\rho_0}{\rho}\right)$,

$$\frac{d\delta_0}{dt} = \frac{\rho_0}{\rho^2}\frac{d\rho}{dt} - \frac{1}{\rho}\frac{d\rho_0}{dt}, \tag{4.1.3}$$

where ρ_0 is a function of temperature. Hence, using the Clausius-Clapeyron relation we derive

$$\frac{d\rho_0}{dt} = \frac{d\rho_0}{dT}\frac{dT}{dt} = \frac{\rho_0}{T}\left(\frac{L}{R_v T} - 1\right)\frac{dT}{dt}. \tag{4.1.4}$$

We shall determine $\frac{d\rho}{dt}$ from the continuity equation for the air-vapor mixture, within which the vapor condenses. If we neglect the volume of the liquid phase, then, utilizing the spatial homogeneity of the problem,

$$\frac{\partial\bar{\rho}}{\partial t} + \operatorname{div}\bar{\rho}\mathbf{v} = -I, \tag{4.1.5}$$

where I is the vapor flux to the droplet, while the mixture density is $\bar{\rho} = \rho_1 + \rho$. In the first approximation, if diffusion of air is neglected,

$$\frac{d\rho_1}{dt} + \rho_1 \operatorname{div}\mathbf{v} = 0, \tag{4.1.6}$$

from which it follows that

$$\frac{d\rho}{dt} + \rho \operatorname{div}\mathbf{v} = -I. \tag{4.1.7}$$

If div $\mathbf{v}$ is defined by equation (4.1.6), then

$$\frac{d}{dt}\left(\frac{\rho}{\rho_1}\right) = -\frac{I}{\rho_1}. \tag{4.1.8}$$

To determine derivative $\frac{d\rho_1}{dt}$ we shall use the equation of state in the form

$$\frac{d\rho_1}{dt} = \frac{1}{R_a T}\frac{dp_1}{dt} - \frac{\rho_1}{T}\frac{dT}{dt}, \tag{4.1.9}$$

where R_a is the gas constant for air.

Equations (4.1.3), (4.1.4), (4.1.8) and (4.1.9) yield

$$\frac{1}{1-\delta_0}\frac{d\delta_0}{dt}=\frac{d\ln p_1}{dt}-\frac{L}{R_v T}\frac{d\ln T}{dt}-\frac{I}{\rho}. \tag{4.1.10}$$

By definition, I can be expressed in the form

$$I=4\pi\rho_2\int_0^\infty r^2\frac{dr}{dt}f(r,\ t)\,dr. \tag{4.1.11}$$

The above system of equations (4.1.1), (4.1.2), (4.1.10) and (4.1.11) should be supplemented by the equation of state of air, the governing relationships for p_1 or T, and the heat balance equation relating the variation in ρ_1 and T.

To consider the simplest model of droplet formation we shall assume that this process occurs over a sufficiently short period and can be treated within the framework of the regular condensation model. We shall write the heat balance equation neglecting effects due to radiation, heat transfer and mixing. Unlike the wet-adiabatic process, flux I of vapor to the droplets is in equilibrium and is determined by the supersaturation δ_0. Thus the heat balance equation becomes

$$\rho_1 c_p\frac{dT}{dt}=\frac{dp_1}{dt}+LI. \tag{4.1.12}$$

The relationship between $\frac{dT}{dt}$ and $\frac{dp_1}{dt}$ in various situations can also be determined differently: during radiation cooling one must consider the heat loss, but assume $\frac{dp_1}{dt}\approx 0$; during mixing of two different masses new assumptions must be made. Note that allowance must be made for the nonadiabaticity of atmospheric processes and, depending on the conditions at hand, one or another assumption must be used regarding the relationship between T and p_1.

In particular, the kinetics of phase transitions was considered on the assumption that the process is isobaric /9/. In the atmosphere, variations in T and p_1 should be taken into account more rigorously and this should be remembered when employing equation (4.1.12). Finally, we shall assume that the formation of droplets from nuclei occurs by means of ordinary growth in δ_0, and by using the nuclei distribution function with respect to supersaturations we shall express $\Psi(r, t)$ in the form

$$\Psi(r,\ t)=n(\delta_0)\frac{d\delta_0}{dt}\,\delta\left(r-\frac{2B}{3\delta_0}\right), \tag{4.1.13}$$

where $\delta\left(r-\frac{2B}{3\delta_0}\right)$ is a delta function.

The system of equations describing the kinetics of the initial condensation stage thus becomes

$$\begin{gathered}
\frac{\partial f}{\partial t}+\frac{\partial}{\partial r}\left(\frac{dr}{dt}f\right)=n(\delta_0)\frac{d\delta_0}{dt}\,\delta\left(r-\frac{2B}{3\delta_0}\right),\\
\frac{dr}{dt}=K_3\frac{\delta_0-\frac{B}{r}+\Phi(c)}{r+\xi},\\
\frac{1}{1-\delta_0}\frac{d\delta_0}{dt}=\left(1-\frac{M}{M_1}\frac{L}{c_pT}\right)\frac{d\ln p_1}{dt}-\left(1+\frac{L^2\rho}{R_vT^2c_p\rho_1}\right)\frac{I}{\rho},\\
I=4\pi\rho_2\int\limits_{\frac{2B}{3\delta_0}}^{\infty}r^2\frac{dr}{dt}f(r,\ t)\,dr,
\end{gathered} \tag{4.1.14}$$

where M and M_1 are, respectively, the molecular weights of the vapor and air.

In the last equation the lower limit was specified by assuming that when $\delta_0>0$ the spectrum can be divided into two parts: nuclei and droplets. Here the nuclei are in equilibrium, and the absorption on them of vapor can be neglected $\left(\frac{dr}{dt}=0\text{ for nuclei}\right)$, while $r_{\text{lim}}\approx\frac{2B}{3\delta_0}$. In general, one can forgo this assumption and not divide the spectrum into droplets and nuclei. In this case integration is carried out from zero, the right-hand side in the first equation of the system vanishes, and the initial distribution used is now the size spectrum of the nuclei.

2. EQUATION DEFINING THE TIME VARIATION OF THE SUPERSATURATION

The system of equations derived in the preceding section is very complicated and can only be solved numerically. In order to analyze the effect of various variables it is very useful to consider the problem in a simplified form. Before making these simplifications we undertake the following transformations. It will be assumed that it was possible to formally integrate the droplet growth equation in (4.1.14) and that the solution to this equation is some function

$$t_0 = t_0(r,\ t,\ \delta_0(t)), \tag{4.2.1}$$

where t_0 is the time of droplet genesis, determined by

$$r_0 = r_{\lim} = \frac{2B}{3\delta_0(t_0)}.$$

The first of equations (4.1.14), describing the deformation of the droplet distribution function, can also be formally integrated and its solution given by

$$f(r,\ t) = n(\delta_0(t_0)) \frac{d\delta_0(t_0)}{dt_0} \frac{dt_0(r,\ t)}{dr}, \tag{4.2.2}$$

where t_0 is a function of r and t in accordance with equation (4.2.1).

The formal nature of the integration consists in the fact that the behavior of $\delta_0(t)$ is assumed to be given, while actually it is determined by a separate equation, which is also a function of $f(r,\ t)$. However, these formal integrals make it possible to write in closed form one equation for δ_0. The solution of the latter equation enables one to obtain the solution for t_0 and $f(r,\ t)$ from equations (4.2.1) and (4.2.2):

$$\frac{1}{1-\delta_0} \frac{d\delta_0}{dt} = \left(1 - \frac{ML}{M_1 c_p T}\right) \frac{d \ln p_1}{dt} - \left(1 + \frac{L^2 \rho}{R_v c_p T^2 \rho_1}\right) \frac{4\pi \rho_2 K_3}{\rho} \times$$
$$\times \left\{ \delta_0(t) \int_{\frac{2B}{3\delta_0(t)}}^{\infty} \frac{r^2}{r+\xi} n(\delta_0(t_0)) \frac{d\delta_0(t_0)}{dt_0} \frac{dt_0}{dr} dr - \right.$$
$$\left. - \int_{\frac{2B}{3\delta_0(t)}}^{\infty} \frac{r^2}{r+\xi} \left[\frac{B}{r} - \Phi(c)\right] n(\delta_0(t_0)) \frac{d\delta_0(t_0)}{dt_0} \frac{dt_0(r,\ t)}{dr} dr \right\}. \tag{4.2.3}$$

It should be stipulated that equation (4.2.3), just as system of equations (4.1.14), is valid only when $\frac{d\delta_0}{dt} > 0$, since only in this case can the right-hand side of the first equation of the system be represented in this form. For a decrease in δ_0, if the number of droplets does not decrease, the lower limit in the integrals of equation (4.2.3) is fixed and $\delta_0(t)$ should be replaced by its maximum value.

This circumstance will be taken into account in the subsequent discussion.

We introduce the following model when examining the course of droplet formation.

a) The droplets form due to expansion and to the corresponding cooling of air rising at constant velocity:

$$\frac{dp_1}{dt} = \frac{\partial p_1}{\partial t} + v_i \frac{\partial p_1}{\partial x_i} \approx \frac{\partial p_1}{\partial t} + v_z \frac{\partial p_1}{\partial z}. \tag{4.2.4}$$

b) The air pressure is constant in time and is distributed vertically in accordance with the law of statics:

$$\frac{\partial p_1}{\partial t} = 0, \quad \frac{\partial p_1}{\partial z} = -g\rho_1. \tag{4.2.5}$$

c) The distribution of condensation nuclei with respect to supersaturation is defined by the power law

$$n(\delta_0) = P\delta_0^l. \tag{4.2.6}$$

d) The equation of condensation growth is considered disregarding corrections for surface tension, hygroscopicity, jumps in vapor concentration and in temperature:

$$\frac{dr}{dt} = \frac{K_3}{r}\delta_0. \tag{4.2.7}$$

The correction for heat of condensation is substantial for any dimensions and is taken into account by coefficient K_3. In this case equation (4.2.7) is easily integrated to yield

$$r^2 = \frac{4B^2}{9\delta_0^2(t_0)} + 2K_3\int_{t_0}^{t} \delta_0(t)\,dt. \tag{4.2.8}$$

e) We shall assume that the air rises reasonably slowly, so that always $\delta_0 \ll 1$. In this case

$$1 - \delta_0 \approx 1, \quad \rho \approx \rho_0. \tag{4.2.9}$$

Before considering equation (4.2.3) note that the most important of all the above assumptions is that the equation of droplet growth can be described by a Maxwellian equation. This results in overestimating the rate of droplet growth; hence any refinement will reduce it. Since consideration of ξ is relatively simple, the correction for the jumps will be made during the calculations. As to quantity $\left(\frac{B}{r} - \Phi(c)\right)$, within the framework of the theory considered here it is as yet impossible to take it into account, although apparently this is a more substantial correction than that for ξ.

We introduce the following notation:

$$y(t) = \int_0^t \delta_0(t)\,dt, \tag{4.2.10}$$

$$K_1 = \left(\frac{ML}{M_1 c_p T} - 1\right)\frac{v_z}{p_1}, \tag{4.2.11}$$

$$K_2 = 4\pi K_3 \frac{\rho_2}{\rho_0}\left(1 + \frac{L^2 \rho_0}{R_v c_p T^2 \rho_1}\right). \tag{4.2.12}$$

It is assumed that over the time range under study K_1 and K_2 remain constant. Here we have already employed assumption (4.2.9). Then, with consideration of the above assumptions, equation (4.2.3) yields

$$y''(t) = K_1 - PK_2 y'(t) \int_0^{\bar{t}} \left\{2K_3 [y(t) - y(t_0)] + \right.$$
$$\left. + \frac{4B^2}{9y'(t_0)^2}\right\}^{1/2} [y'(t_0)]^l y''(t_0)\,dt_0, \tag{4.2.13}$$

where

$$\bar{t} = \begin{cases} t & t < t_m, \\ t_m & t \geqslant t_m, \end{cases}$$

t_m being the time required to attain maximum supersaturation.

Since the correction for ξ should generally improve the results, we shall present an equation making allowance for the concentration and temperature jumps. It follows from the droplet growth equation that

$$(r+\xi)^2 = (r_0+\xi)^2 + 2K_3 [y(t) - y(t_0)]. \tag{4.2.14}$$

Noting the identity $\frac{r^2}{r+\xi} = (r-\xi) + \frac{\xi^2}{(r+\xi)}$ and employing equation (4.2.14), we can derive from equation (4.2.3)

$$y''(t)=K_1-PK_2y'(t)\int\limits_0^{\bar{t}}\left\{\left[2K_3\left(y(t)-y(t_0)\right)+\left(\frac{2B}{3y'(t_0)}-\xi\right)^2\right]^{1/2}-\right.$$
$$\left.-2\xi+\frac{\xi^2}{\left[2K_3\left(y(t)-y(t_0)\right)+\left(\frac{2B}{3y'(t_0)}-\xi\right)^2\right]^{1/2}}\right\}[y'(t_0)]^l\,y''(t_0)\,dt_0. \quad (4.2.15)$$

Since equation (4.2.15) also overestimates the rate of droplet growth, one can expect a drop in the supersaturation compared with its actual value. When using the complete growth equation it is impossible to write separately the equation for δ_0 in closed form. Therefore δ_0 should be estimated from an expression underestimating the actual rate of droplet growth.

At the instant of droplet formation

$$\delta_0(t_0)=\frac{B}{r_0}-\Phi(c) \quad (4.2.16)$$

and during subsequent times, $\delta_0(t_0)>\frac{B}{r}-\Phi(c)$. It is thus possible to express the equation of droplet growth in the form

$$\frac{dr}{dt}=K_3\frac{\delta_0(t)-\delta_0(t_0)}{r+\xi}, \quad (4.2.17)$$

integration of which yields

$$(r+\xi)^2=(r_0+\xi)^2+2K_3[y(t)-y(t_0)]-2K_3y(t_0)(t-t_0). \quad (4.2.18)$$

This expression enables one to write the equation majorizing the variation in supersaturation:

$$y''(t)=K_1-PK_2y'(t)\int\limits_0^{\bar{t}}\left(\theta(t,\ t_0)-2\xi+\frac{\xi^2}{\theta(t,\ t_0)}\right)\times$$
$$\times[y'(t_0)]^l\,y''(t_0)\,dt_0, \quad (4.2.19)$$

where

$$\theta(t,\ t_0)=\left\{2K_3[y(t)-y(t_0)]-2K_3y(t_0)(t-t_0)+\left(\frac{2B}{3y'(t_0)}-\xi\right)^2\right\}^{1/2}.$$

3. ANALYTICAL STUDY OF THE KINETICS OF THE INITIAL CONDENSATION STAGE

The equation describing the variation in supersaturation with time is an integrodifferential nonlinear equation and it does not appear possible to obtain its exact analytic solution. Nevertheless, an analytic study of even its simplest version is very sensible, since it enables one to find the characteristic properties of the solution and its dependence on the principal variables. An attempt at such an analysis was made by Twomey /16/, and later more thoroughly by Sedunov /13/. In line with these studies we consider equation (4.2.13) which in terms of the notation

$$K_4 = PK_2(2K_3)^{1/2}, \quad K_5 = \frac{2B}{9K_3} \tag{4.3.1}$$

assumes the form

$$y''(t) = K_1 - K_4 y'(t) \int_0^t \left\{ y(t) - y(t_0) + \frac{K_5}{[y'(t_0)]^2} \right\}^{1/2} \times \\ \times [y'(t_0)]^l y''(t_0)\, dt_0. \tag{4.3.2}$$

Note in the first place that $y'(t) \geqslant 0$ for all t; $y'(t)$ increases over the range $[0, t_m]$ (the curve corresponding to it is convex), attains a maximum at the point $t = t_m$, and increases almost linearly when $t \ll t_m$. When $t > t_m$, $y'(t)$ decreases monotonically and approaches zero asymptotically. Even in this simplified form equation (4.3.2) is quite complex, so we shall estimate the effect of the initial droplet size on the course of the process. An approximate solution to equation (4.3.2) can be obtained by substituting into its right-hand side the quantity

$$y' = K_1 t \tag{4.3.3}$$

and correspondingly $y'' = K_1$ and $y = K_1 \frac{t^2}{2}$.

We introduce the following inequality:

$$[y(t) - y(t_0)]^{1/2} \leqslant \left[y(t) - y(t_0) + \frac{K_5}{(y'(t_0))} \right]^{1/2} \leqslant \\ \leqslant [y(t) - y(t_0)]^{1/2} + \frac{K_5^{1/2}}{y'(t_0)}. \tag{4.3.4}$$

Then, substituting both its parts for the expression contained in brackets in the integrand in equation (4.3.2) and making use of equation (4.3.3), we derive the two approximate solutions

$$y_1''(t)=K_1-2^{-3/2}B\left(\frac{l+1}{2},\ \frac{3}{2}\right)K_1^{l+\frac{5}{2}}K_4t^{l+3}$$
$$y_2''(t)=y_1''(t)-\frac{1}{l}K_1^{l+1}K_4K_5^{-1/2}t^{l+1}, \qquad (4.3.5)$$

where

$$B\left(\frac{l+1}{2},\ \frac{3}{2}\right)=2\int_0^1(1-x^2)^{1/2}x^l\,dx \text{ is a beta function.}$$

The condition under which the initial droplet radius is small becomes $\left|\frac{y_1'-y_2'}{y_1'}\right|\ll 1$. This quantity attains a maximum for some t corresponding to the maximum of y_1'. Integration of both equations and evaluation of t_m yields

$$\frac{(l+4)\cdot 2^{\frac{3(l+1)}{2(l+3)}}}{l(l+2)(l+3)\left[B\left(\frac{l+1}{2},\ \frac{3}{2}\right)\right]^{\frac{l+1}{l+3}}}K_1^{\frac{l-3}{2(l+3)}}K_4^{\frac{2}{l+3}}K_5^{\frac{1}{2}}\ll 1. \qquad (4.3.6)$$

In particular, when $l=1$ condition (4.3.6) reduces to the form

$$\frac{K_4K_5}{\sqrt{K_1}}\ll 1. \qquad (4.3.7)$$

Since condition (4.3.6) can be satisfied in some real processes, we shall conduct our subsequent discussion without considering the initial size. After this simplification equation (4.3.2) can be reduced by an order and its integration yields

$$y'(t)=K_1t-\frac{2}{3}K_4\int_0^{\bar{t}}[y(t)-y(t_0)]^{3/2}[y'(t_0)]^l\,y''(t_0)\,dt_0. \qquad (4.3.8)$$

The approximate solution $y'(t)$ located below the actual value (the lower majorant) can be taken as the solution which is obtained upon substituting, respectively, equation (4.3.3) instead of the unknown functions in the integrand. In this case

$$[y(t)-y(t_0)] \leqslant \frac{K_1}{2}(t^2-t_0^2);$$

$$y'(t_0) \leqslant K_1 t_0; \quad y''(t_0) \leqslant K_1. \tag{4.3.9}$$

This substitution overestimates the value of the integral and hence results in the lower majorant curve, the equation of which is easily derived from equation (4.3.8):

$$y_L'(t) = K_1 t - \frac{B\left(\frac{l+1}{2}, \frac{5}{2}\right)}{6\sqrt{2}} K_1^{\frac{2l+5}{2}} K_4 t^{4+l}, \tag{4.3.10}$$

where $B(\mu, \nu)$ is a beta function.

The value of t_1 at which the lower majorant attains its maximum is

$$t_1 = \left[\frac{6\sqrt{2}}{(4+l)\, B\left(\frac{l+1}{2}, \frac{5}{2}\right) K_1^{\frac{2l+3}{2}} K_4}\right]^{\frac{1}{l+3}}, \tag{4.3.11}$$

while the maximum value of $y_L'(t_1)$ is given by

$$y_L'(t_1) = \frac{3+l}{4+l} K_1 t_1. \tag{4.3.12}$$

When $l=1$, $B\left(1, \frac{5}{2}\right) = \frac{2}{5}$ and expressions (4.3.11) and (4.3.12) simplify to

$$t_1 = \left(\frac{18}{K_1^5 K_4^2}\right)^{1/8}, \tag{4.3.13}$$

$$y_L'(t_1) = \frac{4}{5} K_1 t_1 = \frac{4}{5}\left(\frac{18 K_1^3}{K_4^2}\right)^{1/8}. \tag{4.3.14}$$

With the aid of (4.3.11) we can reduce equation (4.3.10) to the more convenient form

$$y_L(t) = K_1 t \left[1 - \frac{1}{(4+l)}\left(\frac{t}{t_1}\right)^{3+l}\right]. \tag{4.3.15}$$

It is noteworthy that a refinement of the solution can in principle also be obtained by the iteration method. However, the next approximation results again in complicated integrals.

We now pass on to the construction of the upper majorant. Twomey /16/ obtained this very roughly, so we shall approximate the integrand as follows. We shall assume that $y'(t)$ in the integrand of equation (4.3.8) varies linearly from zero to $y'_2(t_2)$, where t_2 is the time to attain the maximum, while $y'_U(t_2)$ is the maximum value of the upper majorant. Then

$$y''(t) = \frac{y'_U(t_2)}{t_2}, \quad y'(t) = \frac{y'_U(t_2)}{t_2} t, \quad y''(t) = \frac{y'_U(t_2)}{t_2} \frac{t^2}{2}. \qquad (4.3.16)$$

We shall show that such a substitution yields the upper majorant. Upon substituting equation (4.3.16), the integral in equation (4.3.8) is found to be greater than zero. Therefore $y'_U(t) < K_1 t$. This means that

$$\alpha = \frac{y'(t_2)}{t_2} < K_1. \qquad (4.3.17)$$

Consider the behavior of $y'(t)$ and $y'_U(t)$ at near-zero values of t, when the integrand contains functions $y'(t)$ linear in t but with different gradients $(t \to 0,\ y'(t) \to K_1(t))$. It can be shown that the real solution will pass below the majorizing solution. We shall show that the majorizing curve cannot intersect the curve of the exact solution. We shall assume the converse, assuming that at τ, $y'(\tau) = y'_U(\tau)$. Since the majorant is convex, $\dfrac{y'_U(\tau)}{\tau} = \alpha_1 > \alpha$.

If we substitute the auxiliary approximation $y_a(t) = \alpha_1 \dfrac{t^2}{2}$, $y'_a(t) = \alpha_1 t$, $y''_a(t) = \alpha_1$ into the integrand in equation (4.3.8), the resulting curve $\tilde{y}'(t)$ will pass below $y'_U(t)$, since the coefficient α_1 of the linear approximation is greater than α. It will be shown that the exact solution should not intersect curve $\tilde{y}(t)$, but should pass below it. Consider the integral in (4.3.8). Since the exact solution is a convex curve, while $y'_a(t) = \alpha_1 t$ is the equation of a straight line and $y'(\tau) = y'_a(\tau) = \alpha_1 \tau$, it is evident that

$$[y(t) - y(t_0)] > [y_a(t) - y_a(t_0)].$$

Further, since

$$\int_0^\tau [y'(t_0)]^l\, y''(t_0)\, dt_0 = \int_0^\tau [y'_a(t_0)]^l\, y''_a(t_0)\, dt_0,$$

it is clear that the integral of the exact solution yields a higher value and accordingly curve $y'(t)$ of the exact solution should pass below $\tilde{y}(t)$ and $y'(\tau) < \tilde{y}'(\tau)$. We then have a contradiction, so proving the contention that $y'(t)$ and $y'_U(t)$ do not intersect.

Equation (4.3.16) enables one to easily obtain from equation (4.3.8)

$$y'_U(t) = K_1 t - \frac{K_4}{6\sqrt{2}} B\left(\frac{l+1}{2}, \frac{5}{2}\right)\left[\frac{y'_U(t_2)}{t_2}\right]^{\frac{5+2l}{2}} t^{4+l}. \quad (4.3.18)$$

If this equation is differentiated with respect to t and the second derivative set equal to zero, we find the relationship between $y'(t_2)$ at its maximum and t_2. This relationship and equation (4.3.18) yield

$$y'_U(t_2) = \left(\frac{4+l}{3+l}\right)^{\frac{5+2l}{6+2l}} y'_L(t_1),$$

$$t_2 = \left(\frac{4+l}{3+l}\right)^{\frac{5+2l}{6+2l}} t_1,$$

$$y'_U(t) = K_1 t\left[1 - \frac{1}{4+l}\left(\frac{t}{t_2}\right)^{3+l}\right].$$

The ratio of the maximum of the upper majorant to the maximum of the lower majorant is 1.215 for $l=1$ and decreases with increasing l. Thus the above approximation is quite satisfactory, especially as for calculations one can use an approximate solution composed of the two majorants.

We now pass on to consider the process when $t > t_m$. In this case equation (4.3.8) assumes the form

$$y'(t) = K_1 t - \frac{2}{3} K_4 \int_0^{t_m} [y(t) - y(t_0)]^{3/2} [y'(t_0)]^l y''(t_0)\, dt_0. \quad (4.3.22)$$

Integration is carried out from zero to t_m, so functions $y(t_0)$, $y'(t_0)$ and $y''(t_0)$ can be assumed known. This equation is also not solved in general form. For t close to t_m it is possible to construct a series solution in $(t - t_m)$. Simple calculations yield the expression

$$y'(t) = y'(t_m) - a[y'(t_m)]^2 (t - t_m)^2 + \ldots, \quad (4.3.23)$$

where

$$a = \frac{K_4}{4} \int_0^{t_m} [y(t_m) - y(t_0)]^{1/2} [y'(t_0)]^l y''(t_0)\, dt_0.$$

Unlike the increasing part, the drop in the curve is slower, following a quadratic law. It is of greatest interest to obtain the asymptotic equation at large t. Starting with the assumption that $y(t) \to \infty$ when $t \to \infty$ (which is, physically, fully substantiated), equation (4.3.21) is transformed to the form

$$y'(t) = K_1 t - \frac{2K_4}{3(l+1)} [y'(t_m)]^{l+1} [y(t)]^{3/2}. \qquad (4.3.24)$$

Hence for large t

$$y(t) \approx \left\{ \frac{3(l+1) K_1}{2K_4 [y'(t_m)]^{l+1}} \right\}^{2/3} t^{2/3}, \qquad (4.3.25)$$

$$y'(t) \approx \frac{2}{3} \left\{ \frac{3(l+1) K_1}{2K_4 [y'(t_m)]^{l+1}} \right\}^{2/3} t^{-1/3}. \qquad (4.3.26)$$

As the cloud develops, the supersaturation was thus shown to decrease after attaining a maximum, and at sufficiently large t it is proportional to $t^{-1/3}$. An expression such as (4.3.26) characterizes the appearance of quasi-equilibrium between the vapor and droplets, since the supersaturation is no longer determined by a differential equation but by the requirement that the fluxes are equal. The time elapsing from the start of condensation to the onset of quasi-equilibrium (transition to asymptotic behavior expressed by equation (4.3.26)) will be termed the initial stage of condensation in a cloud. The asymptotic variation in supersaturation as a function of time, expressed by equation (4.3.26), cannot be regarded as very important, since as the cloud develops, other mechanisms of droplet growth are triggered and these alter the kinetics of the process. Apparently coalescence, having the effect of reducing the effective surface of droplets, should result in slowing down the reduction in $y'(t)$ with time.

The above discussion makes it possible to pass on to a consideration of the formation and deformation of the cloud spectrum. First we shall calculate the concentration of the droplets which form. This concentration can be easily found by integrating the nuclei distribution function with respect to supersaturation:

$$N = \int_0^{y'(t_m)} n(\delta_0)\, d\delta_0 = \frac{P}{l+1} [y(t_m)]^{l+1}. \qquad (4.3.27)$$

Making use of the dependence of $y(t_m)$ on v_z and P, we can write

$$N \sim P^{\frac{2}{3+l}} v_z^{\frac{3(l+1)}{2(l+3)}}. \qquad (4.3.28)$$

Calculations yielded not only the concentration of the droplets which formed, but also the formation of the distribution function at the initial stage. If when $t<t_m$ we use the approximate expression $y'(t)=K_1t\left[1-\frac{1}{5}\left(\frac{t}{t_m}\right)^4\right]$, the droplet distribution function is easily derived by formally solving equation (4.3.11) for $f(r, t)$. On the condition that $\delta_0(t)$ corresponds to the approximate solution, the first integral in equation (4.3.27) has the form

$$r^2=K_1K_3\left[t^2\left(1-\frac{t^4}{15t_m^4}\right)-t_0^2\left(1-\frac{t_0^4}{15t_m^4}\right)\right]+\\+\frac{2K_3K_5}{K_1^2t_0^2\left(1-\frac{t^4}{5t_m^4}\right)}. \qquad (4.3.29)$$

Setting

$$1-\frac{t^4}{15t_m^4}\approx 1,\qquad \frac{2K_3K_5}{K_1^2t_0^2\left(1-\frac{t^4}{5t_m^4}\right)}\approx\frac{2K_3K_5}{K_1^2t_0^2},$$

we arrive at an equation which can be solved for t_0. In this case

$$t_0^2=\frac{1}{2}\left(t^2-\frac{r^2}{K_1K_3}\right)+\sqrt{\frac{1}{4}\left(t^2-\frac{r^2}{K_1K_3}\right)^2+\frac{2K_5}{K_1^3}}, \qquad (4.3.30)$$

while the distribution function can be expressed in the form

$$f(r, t)=\frac{K_1P}{K_3}\left\{1-\frac{1}{t_m^4}\left[\frac{1}{2}\left(t^2-\frac{r^2}{K_1K_3}\right)+\right.\right.\\\left.\left.+\sqrt{\frac{1}{4}\left(t^2-\frac{r^2}{K_1K_3}\right)^2+\frac{2K_5}{K_1^3}}\right]^2\right\}r, \qquad (4.3.31)$$

where

$$0\leqslant t\leqslant t_m,\qquad \frac{\sqrt{2K_1K_5}}{K_1+\sqrt{1-\frac{t^4}{5t_m^4}}}<r\leqslant\sqrt{K_1K_3}\,t.$$

It is noteworthy that the fact that the initial size is incorporated in equation (4.3.31), while it is not considered when determining $y'(t)$, is not contradictory, since the effect of the initial size, characterizing the integral properties of droplets, can be insignificant when calculating the total vapor flux and significant when studying the distribution function. If the initial size is neglected, equation (4.3.31) reduces to the simpler form

$$f(r,\ t) = \frac{K_1 P}{K_3}\left[1 - \frac{\left(t^2 - \frac{r^2}{K_1 K_3}\right)^2}{t_m^4}\right] r. \tag{4.3.32}$$

The form of the distribution function for different times is illustrated in Figure 14.

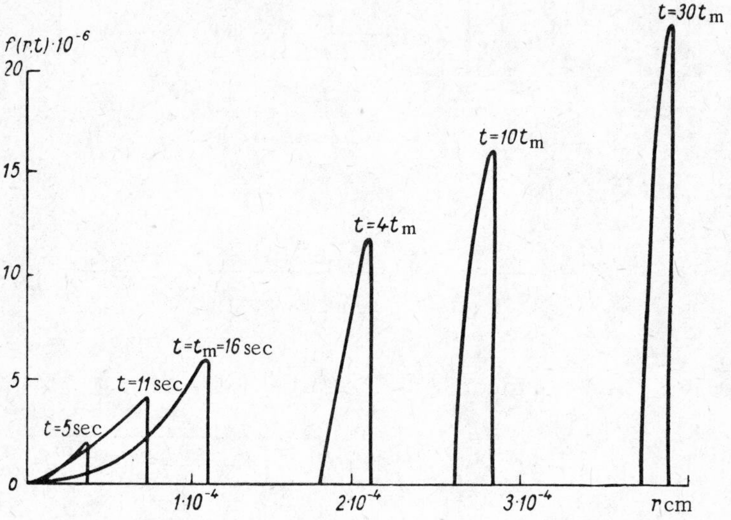

FIGURE 14. Droplet distribution function $f(r,\ t)$ for different times t:

$t_m = 5.7$ cm; $p = 0.5 \cdot 10^{10}$ cm^{-3}; $K_1 v_z = 2.25 \cdot 10^{-5}$ sec^{-1}; $K_3 = 2 \cdot 10^{-8}$ cm^2/sec; $K_4 = 6 \cdot 10^7$ sec$^{-3/2}$.

In the same approximation, one can derive the droplet distribution function when l differs from unity:

$$f(r,\ t) = \frac{PK_1^l}{K_3}\left(t^2 - \frac{r^2}{K_1 K_3}\right)^{\frac{l-1}{2}}\left[1 - \frac{\left(t^2 - \frac{r^2}{K_1 K_3}\right)^{\frac{l+3}{2}}}{(4+l)\, t_m^{3+l}}\right]^{\frac{l-1}{2}} \times$$
$$\times\left[1 - \frac{\left(t^2 - \frac{r^2}{K_1 K_3}\right)^{\frac{l+3}{2}}}{t_m^{l+3}}\right] r. \tag{4.3.33}$$

These results show that the width of the distribution function (the most important characteristic of the initial spectrum) is determined not only by the difference in the size of the activated condensation nuclei, but also by the course of the initial stage of the process, which depends on the entire ensemble of variables. The most active nuclei, which are converted into droplets, start to grow rapidly, while the growth of less active nuclei is inhibited and the last droplets form only after time t_m. The difference in the squares of the dimensions of the forming droplets is hence determined not only by the difference in r_0^2, but also by quantity $2K_3y(t_m)$, the values of which can yield a perceptibly larger contribution.

As was previously noted, the distribution function can be represented by expressions (4.3.31)–(4.3.33) only when $t<t_m$. For reasonably large t, when it is possible to employ an asymptotic equation for $y(t)$, the form of the distribution function can be easily established. When $t>t_m$ new droplets do not form. Therefore, if we base ourselves on the distribution function when $t=t_m$ we obtain

$$f(r,\ t)=f(r_m,\ t_m)\frac{dr_m}{dr}. \tag{4.3.34}$$

Utilization of (4.3.12) and (4.3.33) hence yields

$$f(r,\ t)=\frac{PK_1^l}{K_3}[\varphi(r,\ t)]^{\frac{l-1}{2}}\left\{1-\frac{[\varphi(r,\ t)]^{\frac{l+3}{2}}}{(4+l)\,t_m^{l+3}}\right\}^{\frac{l-1}{2}}\times$$
$$\times\left\{1-\frac{[\varphi(r,\ t)]^{\frac{l+3}{2}}}{t_m^{l+3}}\right\}r, \tag{4.3.35}$$

where

$$\varphi(r,\ t)=t_m^2-\frac{r^2}{K_1K_3}+\frac{2\left[Et^{2/3}-y(t_m)\right]}{K_1},$$
$$E=\left\{\frac{3(l+1)K_1}{2K_4[y'(t_m)]^{l+1}}\right\}^{2/3}.$$

When $l=1$,

$$f(r,\ t)=\frac{PK_1}{K_3}\left(1-\frac{\varphi^2(r,\ t)}{t_m^4}\right)r. \tag{4.3.36}$$

The form of the distribution function for different times is represented on the right-hand side of Figure 14. Since the maximum and minimum values of r^2 are given by

$$r_{max}^2=2EK_3t^{2/3}+K_1K_3t_m^2-2K_3y(t_m),$$
$$r_{min}^2=2EK_3t^{2/3}-2K_3y(t_m), \tag{4.3.37}$$

it is evident that

$$r_{\max}-r_{\min}=\frac{K_1K_3t_m^2}{2\sqrt{2EK_3t^{2/3}-2K_3y\,(t_m)}}\approx\frac{K_1K_3^{1/2}t_m^2}{2\sqrt{2E}}t^{-1/3}. \qquad (4.3.38)$$

As expected, the distribution function narrows down as $t^{-1/3}$, while the droplet radius varies as $t^{1/3}$.

In conclusion, note that the initial condensation stage determines not only the inception of the cloud as a whole, but also affects its subsequent development. This is because new droplets in a developing cloud can appear on its boundaries, and condensation processes in some region near the boundary can be investigated on the basis of the previous concepts.

4. RESULTS OF NUMERICAL CALCULATIONS OF THE KINETICS OF THE INITIAL STAGE OF CONDENSATION

Equations such as (4.2.13) and (4.2.15) have been treated elsewhere in extensive detail /2.13, 13, 14, 3, 10, 8/. It is of interest to examine the results obtained in these studies. For the result to be as general as possible, we shall transform equation (4.2.15) in such a manner as to reduce the number of variables to a minimum.

The following transformation of variables is introduced:

$$y=\beta z, \quad t=\gamma\tau, \qquad (4.4.1)$$

where

$$\beta=K_1\left(\frac{1}{K_1^{\frac{2l+3}{2}}K_4}\right)^{\frac{2}{l+3}}, \qquad (4.4.2)$$

$$\gamma=\left(\frac{1}{K_1^{\frac{2l+3}{2}}K_4}\right)^{\frac{1}{l+3}}. \qquad (4.4.3)$$

Equation (4.2.15) then reduces to the form

$$z''(\tau)=1-\int_0^{\bar{\tau}}\left\{\sqrt{z(\tau)-z(\tau_0)+\left(\frac{a}{z'(\tau_0)}-b\right)^2}-\right.$$

$$\left.-2b+\frac{b^2}{\sqrt{z(\tau)-z(\tau_0)+\left(\frac{a}{z'(\tau_0)}-b\right)^2}}\right\}[z'(\tau_0)]^l\,z'(\tau_0)\,d\tau_0, \qquad (4.4.4)$$

where

$$a = \frac{\sqrt{2}E\gamma}{3K_3^{1/2}\beta^{3/2}} = \frac{\sqrt{2}E\left(K_1^{\frac{2l+3}{2}}K_4\right)^{\frac{3}{l+3}}}{3K_1^{3/2}K_3^{1/2}}, \qquad (4.4.5)$$

$$b = \frac{\xi}{\sqrt{2}\,K_3^{1/2}\beta^{1/2}} = \frac{\xi\left(K_1^{\frac{2l+3}{2}}K_4\right)^{\frac{1}{l+3}}}{\sqrt{2}K_1^{1/2}K_3^{1/2}}, \qquad (4.4.6)$$

$$\tau = \begin{cases} \tau & \text{when } \tau < \tau_m \\ \tau_m & \text{when } \tau \geqslant \tau_m. \end{cases}$$

Equation (4.4.4) is a function of the three variables l, a and b (l characterizes the nuclei spectrum, a the effect of the initial droplet sizes, and b the effect of concentration and temperature jumps). Unfortunately, its solution in complete form was not found and hence we shall present results obtained for particular cases. When a and b are equal to zero, the form of function $z'(\tau)$ at $l = 2, \frac{3}{2}, 1, \frac{1}{2}$, and $\frac{1}{3}$ is shown in Figure 15. As expected, initially $z'(r)$ increases linearly, then its growth is rapidly retarded, and at $\tau \approx 1.8$ it attains a maximum after which it starts to decrease slowly. This curve, in fact, illustrates the time variation of the supersaturation.

Examination of the $z'(\tau)$ curves shows that, after attaining a maximum, each curve decreases more slowly than it grew; the formation of new droplets ceases, as if one of the vapor absorption mechanisms were switched off. It is possible to pass on to an analytic description of the process at this stage, because the curves approach their asymptotes, defined by the equation

$$z'_{as}(\tau) = A\tau^{-1/3}, \qquad (4.4.7)$$

where

$$A = \frac{2}{3}\left\{\frac{3(l+1)}{2\,[z'(\tau_m)]^{l+1}}\right\}^{3/2}\tau^{-1/3}.$$

Calculations (Figure 16) show that $z'(\tau)$ is approximated satisfactorily by this asymptotic formula starting already with $\tau \approx 4\tau_m$.

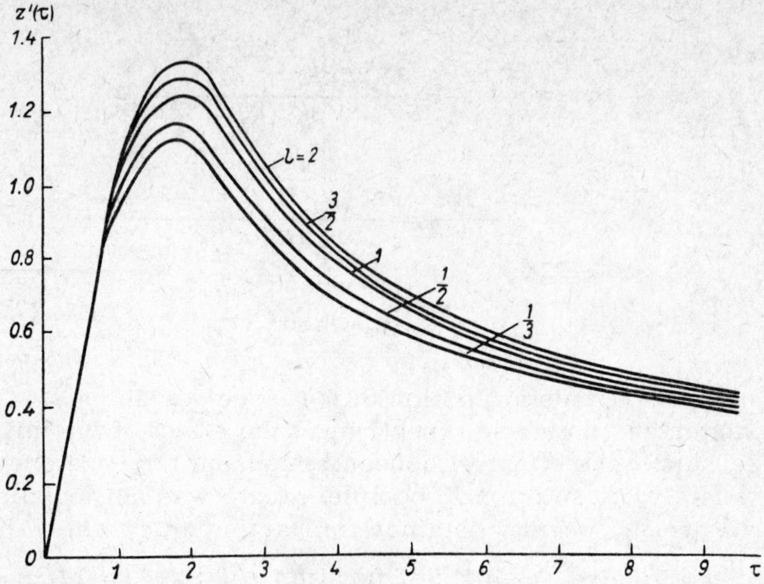

FIGURE 15. Graph of function $z'(\tau)$ for different values of l; $a=0$, $b=0$.

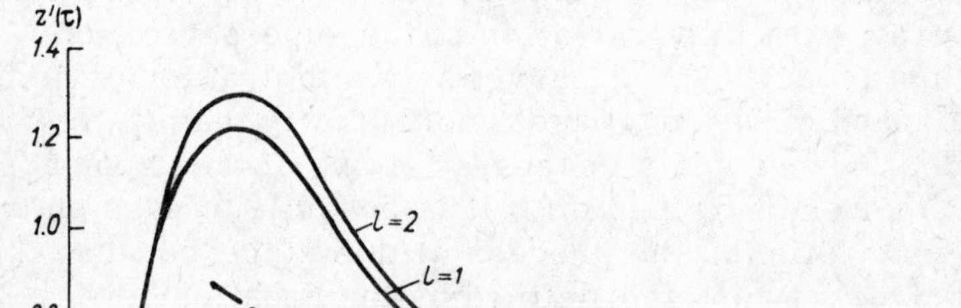

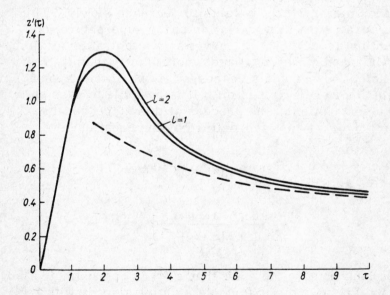

FIGURE 16. Graph of function $z'(\tau)$ and its asymptotic behavior (dashed curve); $a=0$, $b=0$.

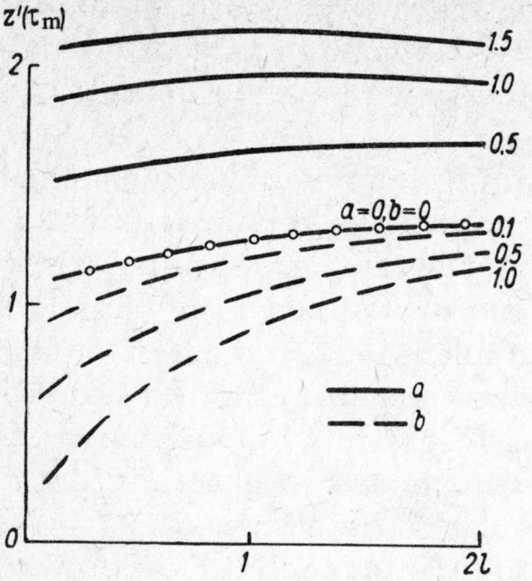

FIGURE 17. Curves of $z'(\tau_m)$ as a function of l for different a and b

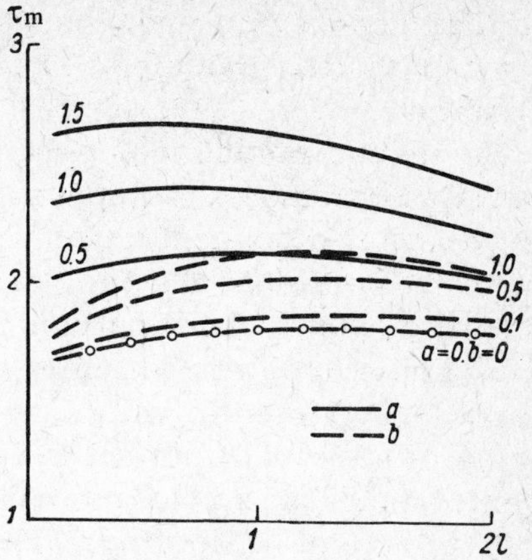

FIGURE 18. Curves of τ_m as a function of l for different a and b

Finally, Figures 17 and 18 show the results of computing $z'(\tau_m)$ and τ_m for nonzero a and b. Note that the time to attain the maximum depends little on the value of l. As to $z'(\tau_m)$, here the dependence on l manifests itself more strongly. On the whole, the results of numerical calculations when $a=0$ and $b=0$ are approximated quite satisfactorily by the analytical solutions presented earlier.

5. EXPERIMENTS ON THE INITIAL CONDENSATION STAGE

The process of droplet formation during cooling of air and formation of the cloud spectrum at the initial development stage was investigated not only theoretically. This process was recently studied in the course of the formation and development of cumulus /17, 23, 24, 3.76, 25, 26/ and some quite thorough experiments were conducted under laboratory conditions /4–7, 22/. The results of laboratory experiments and their comparison with theoretical calculations demand separate consideration.

The formation of the droplet spectrum was studied in a large 3,000-m^3 chamber in which the air expansion was controlled to produce a temperature drop corresponding to the cooling of the air mass rising at velocities from several centimeters to several meters per second. Here, due to the large volume of the chamber, the thermodynamic process was near-adiabatic during several minutes and the modeled vertical velocity was approximately constant.

The experiment involved measuring the spectrum of condensation nuclei with respect to supersaturation until the formation of the fog, as well as the concentration and droplet size distribution. Throughout the experiment the temperature and pressure in the chamber were recorded. The instrumentation used /1, 12/ made it possible to measure droplets which grew to sizes greater than 2μ in diameter. Over time t_m (which, according to estimates, does not exceed tenths of a second) not all the droplets succeed in growing to a size greater than 2μ, so their concentration was determined 10–20 t_m after the onset of cooling. This experimental technique allowed one to establish the dependence of the concentration of the droplets of the forming fog on the rate of air cooling and to determine the effect of the parameters of the power distribution of condensation nuclei with respect to supersaturation on the concentration of the formed droplets.

The experimentally obtained dependence of the droplet concentration N on the rate of air cooling, expressed in terms of updraft velocity v_z (varying from 15 to 120 cm/sec), is shown in Figure 19. It is evident that in both series of experiments carried out for quite different condensation nuclei spectra with respect to supersaturation the droplet concentration increases markedly with cooling rate. In the first series of experiments the concentration of condensation nuclei was substantially smaller than in the second, since l in the distribution of nuclei with respect to supersaturation had higher values in the first series.

The theoretically found dependence of droplet concentration on the cooling rate and condensation nuclei parameters have thus been qualitatively confirmed. In the experiments all the quantities governing the droplet concentration (P, l and v_z) were varied, so we compared the experimental data with the results of computing droplet concentrations from equations making allowance for the effect of initial droplet sizes and the effect of jumps in the vapor concentration and temperature on the droplet growth by condensation /7/. A comparison of experimental and calculated data is shown in Figure 20.

In the case of complete agreement between experimental and theoretical droplet concentrations, the corresponding values of $\frac{N}{N_{cal}}$ should fall about a line with ordinate equal to unity. Actually

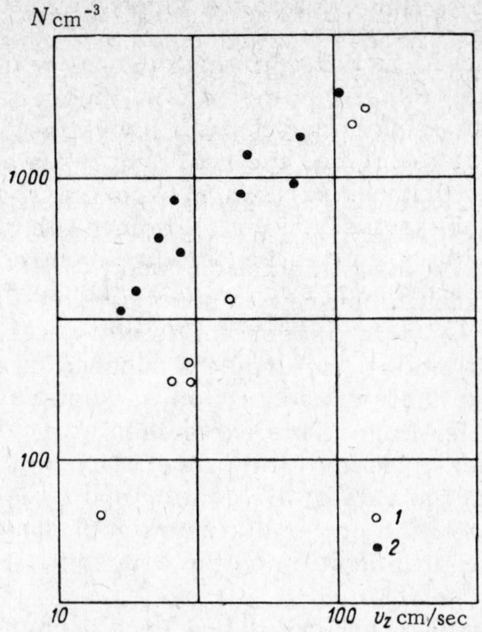

FIGURE 19. Determination of the concentration of fog droplets forming in a chamber at different air cooling rates:

1) first series of experiments at lower concentration of cloud condensation nuclei; 2) second series of experiments at higher concentration of cloud condensation nuclei.

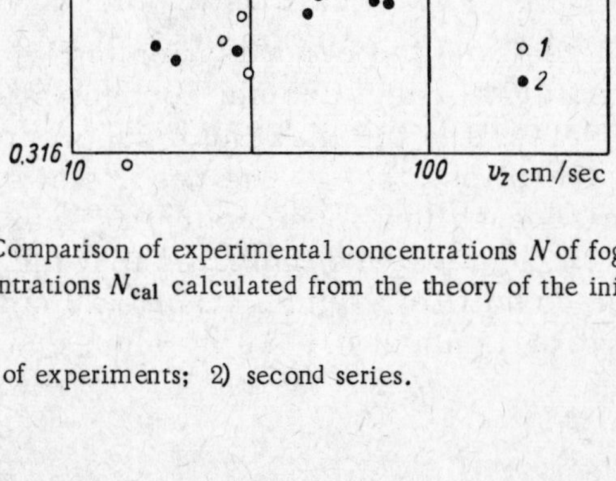

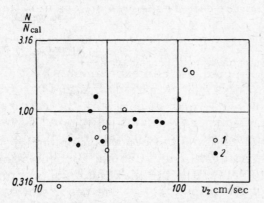

FIGURE 20. Comparison of experimental concentrations N of fog droplets with droplet concentrations N_{cal} calculated from the theory of the initial condensation stage:

1) first series of experiments; 2) second series.

the values of $\frac{N}{N_{\text{cal}}}$ have a marked scatter (the rms scatter is 0.44) and some systematic increase in this quantity with v_z. In spite of this difference between experimental and theoretical droplet concentrations, it can be assumed that the above theory of the initial condensation stage describes the real processes quite satisfactorily. It should be noted that comparison of experimental and theoretical results, using expressions making allowance for the equation of droplet growth without correction for the psychrometric temperature of the droplet and jumps in the vapor concentration and temperature, did not yield satisfactory results /5/.

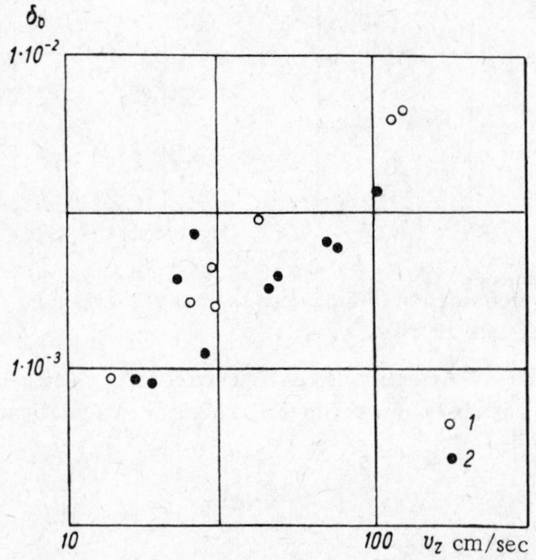

FIGURE 21. Determination of the maximum supersaturation δ_0 attained in experiments with fog formation in a chamber:

1) first series of experiments; 2) second series.

From available data on the condensation nuclei spectrum with respect to supersaturation and droplet concentrations of forming fog, it is easy to determine the maximum supersaturation arising at the initial condensation stage. The results of such a determination of maximum supersaturations occurring in experiments are shown in Figure 21. The figure indicates that the maximum supersaturation increases with v_z. When $v_z = 15-20$ cm/sec the maximum supersaturation is about $0.1 \cdot 10^{-2}$; when $v_z = 100-200$ cm/sec it increases to $0.6 \cdot 10^{-2}$. Here, at higher concentrations of condensation nuclei (second series of experiments), the supersaturation at these values of v_z was smaller in the majority of experiments.

6. METHOD OF ESTIMATING THE MAXIMUM ATTAINABLE SUPERSATURATION

One of the principal variables determining droplet formation and the deformation of their distribution function is the supersaturation which, according to estimates, is very small and most likely does not exceed tenths of a percent. Unfortunately, no direct methods for measuring such small supersaturations are presently available, and hence one can judge about the supersaturation during droplet formation in clouds only on the basis of indirect experiments or theoretical estimates.

It is noteworthy that in theoretical calculations of supersaturation one uses directly quantities such as the rate of cooling (ascent) of the air mass and the nuclei spectrum with respect to supersaturation. These quantities themselves are determined with insufficient accuracy. For example, the upward velocity of the air mass during the formation of stratus is determined from theoretical considerations and has not yet been measured. Published data indicate that instruments for measuring nuclei spectrum with respect to supersaturation are still imperfect and this technique requires further refinement and analysis /20/. It follows that even when a good theoretical model for calculating the supersaturation is available, one cannot be sure of the reliability of the corresponding results.

We now consider a method for estimating supersaturation proposed elsewhere /2/. It is known that at humidities in excess of 70% the nuclei become hydrated, while at humidities in excess of 100% some of these hydrated nuclei become capable of unlimited growth, and cloud droplets form on them. If we use the previously considered model of condensation nuclei, then the limiting radius of these hydrated droplets is governed by the equations

$$\varphi = 1 - \frac{1}{1-\delta_0} \exp\left(-\frac{B}{r_{\lim}}\right),$$

$$(1-\varphi)\frac{B}{r_{\lim}^2} = \frac{3r_{\lim}^2 \varphi^2}{aR_c^3}, \tag{4.6.1}$$

where

$$B=\frac{2\sigma}{\rho_s R_v T}, \qquad \varphi=\frac{aR_c^3}{\left[r_{\lim}^3-R_0^3+(1-b)\,R_c^3\right]},$$

σ is the surface tension of the solution, ρ_s is the density of the solution, R_v is the gas constant for the vapor, T is the temperature, R_0 and R_c are the radius of the dry nucleus and the equivalent radius of its soluble part, respectively, a and b are some constants selected empirically and making allowance for the ability of various substances to reduce the saturated vapor pressure above the solution, and δ_0 is the supersaturation of vapor above a flat water surface.

TABLE 5. Limiting radius $r_{\lim}$ of hydrated nuclei (μ) for supersaturation δ_m (%) (numerator) and for supersaturation $\delta_0 = 0$ (denominator)

G	δ_m						
	0.01	0.02	0.05	0.1	0.2	0.5	1
0.01	7.18 / 4.17	3.60 / 2.10	1.45 / 0.861	0.730 / 0.445	0.371 / 0.234	0.153 / 0.104	0.0794 / 0.0571
0.05	7.17 / 4.15	3.59 / 2.08	1.44 / 0.835	0.719 / 0.421	0.361 / 0.214	0.146 / 0.0894	0.0740 / 0.0471
0.1	7.17 / 4.14	3.58 / 2.07	1.43 / 0.832	0.718 / 0.418	0.359 / 0.211	0.145 / 0.0866	0.0729 / 0.0449
0.5	7.17 / 4.14	3.58 / 2.07	1.43 / 0.829	0.717 / 0.415	0.359 / 0.208	0.144 / 0.0841	0.0718 / 0.0426
1.0	7.17 / 4.14	3.58 / 2.07	1.43 / 0.829	0.717 / 0.415	0.358 / 0.208	0.143 / 0.0837	0.0717 / 0.0422
Equation (4.6.2) / Equation (4.6.5)	7.17 / 4.14	3.58 / 2.07	1.43 / 0.828	0.717 / 0.414	0.359 / 0.207	0.143 / 0.0828	0.0717 / 0.0414

Table 5 lists the calculated values of $r_{\lim}$ for nuclei whose soluble part consists of sodium chloride for different values of $G=\frac{m_c}{m_0}$ (m_c is the mass of soluble substance in the nucleus while m_0 is the total mass of the dry nucleus). Constants a and b were taken from /2.2/. For comparison, the table also tabulates values of $r_{\lim}$ obtained from the simplified expression

$$r_{\text{lim}} = \frac{4\sigma}{3\rho_s R_v T \delta_0} \approx 0.72 \cdot 10^{-7} \frac{1}{\delta_0} \text{ cm.} \qquad (4.6.2)$$

It is seen from Table 5 that the maximum error in using simplified equation (4.6.2) does not exceed 10%. Since supersaturations below 1% are more probable for atmospheric conditions, the error in determining r_{lim} (or δ_0) will be even less.

The comparatively weak dependence of r_{lim} on the content and chemistry of the soluble part of the nuclei (which follows from equation (4.6.2) and is confirmed by calculation data presented in Table 5) yields the very important conclusion that for atmospheric condensation nuclei containing a wide range of various chemical compounds in various proportions, it is possible for positive supersaturations ($\delta_0 > 0$) to determine the actual supersaturation δ_0 only from the measured value of r_{lim}.

If the droplet formation in a cloud is studied as a function of time, then at the initial stage the supersaturation increases, attains some maximum, and then gradually decreases. Since the rise in supersaturation is accompanied by the formation of new droplets due to successive utilization of increasingly less active nuclei, the maximum supersaturation determines the number of forming droplets. Upon reduction in δ_0, the droplet spectrum divides itself into two parts, one of which corresponds to droplets which continue to grow in spite of the reduction in δ_0 while the other corresponds to hydrated nuclei, which start shrinking in size. Here the distribution function acquires a depressed segment, which widens with time. The feasibility of the existence of such a distribution has been pointed out many times in the literature; however, due to difficulties in measuring small particles, very little data are available about this part of the spectrum.

An exception to this is the work by Deloncle /18/, in which he presents measurements of particles up to tenths of a micron in size obtained by a high-sensitivity photoelectric counter. Measurements in stratocumulus (Figure 22) yield spectrum with the aforementioned depressed segment for sizes between 0.43 and 0.55μ which, according to equation (4.6.2), corresponds to supersaturations of 0.13–0.17%. This result is highly sensible and conforms to theoretical concepts.

It was mentioned previously that supersaturation which varies with time attains its maximum δ_m, and then slowly decreases. The size of hydrated nuclei which are unable to grow into cloud droplets also decreases in the course of a reduction in supersaturation and is determined by the supersaturation prevailing at the given time.

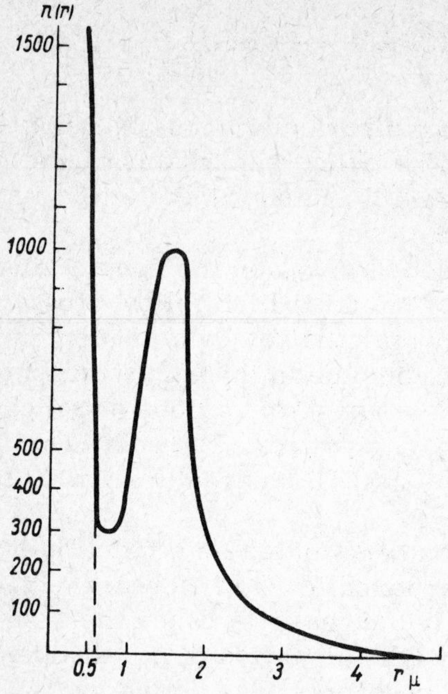

FIGURE 22. Particle size distribution in stratocumulus on 8 December 1961 /20/; $r_{lim} \approx 0.55\mu$, $\delta_0 \approx 0.13\%$.

The equilibrium radius of the hydrated nucleus is given by the expression

$$r_{eq} = \sqrt{\frac{C}{B}}\, f\left(\frac{C}{C_{lim}}\right), \tag{4.6.3}$$

where f is some function, C is the activity of the nucleus, B is a characteristic quantity defining the effect of surface tension forces, while C_{lim} characterizes the activity of nuclei which become droplets at δ_0:

$$C_{lim} = \frac{4B^3}{27}\left(\frac{1-\delta_0}{\delta_0}\right)^2. \tag{4.6.4}$$

If the deformation of the droplet spectrum is examined after attaining the maximum supersaturation δ_m, r_{lim} will correspond precisely to those nuclei whose activity is C_{lim} at the time of attaining maximum supersaturation. Then, remembering that $\delta_0 \ll 1$, by taking function f in explicit form we obtain from equations (4.6.3) and (4.6.4) for $\delta_0 \geqslant 0$

$$r_{\lim}(\delta_0, \delta_m) = \frac{2B}{3\sqrt{3}\,\delta_m} f\left(\frac{\delta_0^2}{\delta_m^2}\right) = \frac{B}{3\delta_m \cos\left(\frac{\pi}{3} - \frac{1}{3}\arccos\frac{\delta_0}{\delta_m}\right)} =$$

$$= \frac{r_{\lim}(\delta_m)}{2\cos\left(\frac{\pi}{3} - \frac{1}{3}\arccos\frac{\delta_0}{\delta_m}\right)}. \qquad (4.6.5)$$

The equation defining the equilibrium of $r_{\lim}(\delta_0, \delta_m)$ can also be solved for δ_m:

$$\delta_m = \frac{2B\sqrt{B}}{3r_{\lim}(\delta_0, \delta_m)\sqrt{3\,[B - \delta_0 r_{\lim}(\delta_0, \delta_m)]}}. \qquad (4.6.6)$$

The unknown quantity in (4.6.5) and (4.6.6) is δ_0, which is the supersaturation at the time of measuring $r_{\lim}$. However, it is evident that $\frac{r_{\lim}(\delta_0, \delta_m)}{r_{\lim}(\delta_m)}$ and δ_m depend quite weakly on the values of δ_0, since the factor which is a function of δ_0 lies between 1 and $\frac{1}{\sqrt{3}} \approx 0.58$ as δ_0 varies from δ_m to zero. This means that if $r_{\lim}$ is determined by direct measurements at a somewhat smaller supersaturation, the maximum supersaturation estimated from formula (4.6.2) will be greater than the true supersaturation by not more than 73%. This accuracy is reasonable, since we are not referring to the determination of a quantity of the order of δ_m. In principle, the accuracy in determining δ_m can be improved by measuring the limiting radius under some controlled conditions when δ_0 is known. The feasibility of the practical utilization of (4.6.5) and (4.6.6) depends on the validity of the nuclei model used.

To check the applicability of equation (4.6.5), the variation in $r_{\lim}(\delta_0, \delta_m)$ was calculated for a reduction in supersaturation with a more exact incorporation of the effect of the dissolved substance on the saturated vapor pressure above the solution at different weight contents G of the dissolved substance in the nucleus (see the numerators in Table 5). The results of calculations presented in Table 5 (numerators) point to satisfactory agreement with the values of $r_{\lim}(\delta_0, \delta_m)$ calculated from equation (4.6.5).

Note that the use of simplified equation (4.6.2) results in underestimating the value of δ_m by approximately 30%, while the use of equation (4.6.5) overestimates the maximum supersaturation, so that the total error should not exceed 50%.

The above discussion leads to the following conclusions.

1) The content of soluble substances in the nuclei and their chemical composition have virtually no effect on the size of the

limiting radius, determining the feasibility of converting hydrated nuclei into droplets.

2) The maximum supersaturation δ_m in the course of cloud genesis can be determined from the upper boundary of the finely dispersed part of the spectrum.

3) Quantity δ_m can be estimated with reasonable accuracy from equation (4.6.2).

4) The error in determining δ_m can be found from equations (4.6.5) and (4.6.6).

The above method of estimating the maximum supersaturation from the measured particle spectrum is of great importance in the investigation of processes occurring in clouds, since this eliminates the use of data on the nuclei spectrum with respect to supersaturation and the rate of air mass cooling.

Chapter 5

GROWTH OF DROPLET POPULATIONS BY ORDINARY CONDENSATION

1. KINETIC EQUATION OF ORDINARY CONDENSATION

In considering condensation processes, we do not usually deal with the growth of a single droplet but of an ensemble of particles. If the particles are not individually singled out in any way, which frequently is the case, it is more convenient to consider the deformation of the entire ensemble as a whole. A rigorous description of this process is very complicated, since in essence we are dealing here with a many-body problem.

In meteorology, a treatment of the interaction of diffusion fields of droplets is generally based on balance considerations and on the assumption concerning the existence of some average supersaturation in whose field each individual droplet grows. This approach is justified by the fact that the volume occupied by droplets and by their immediate vicinity (where the vapor concentration is quite low) is much smaller than the total volume, i. e., the average particle size is much smaller than the average distance between them. Although this condition is fulfilled in all atmospheric processes, it must nevertheless be conceded that a sufficiently rigorous justification of this approach has not yet been obtained and that the limits of applicability of the theory have not been established.

It should furthermore be remembered that local inhomogeneities produced by droplets can result in a number of effects which in principle cannot be taken into account in examining the process on the basis of balance considerations. This question has been examined thoroughly so far only by Stepanov /6/, but is also dealt with in the simplest case.

In general form the problem should be formulated on the basis of heat and mass transfer equations:

$$c_p \rho_1 \frac{dT}{dt} = \frac{dp_1}{dt} + k_1 \Delta T + \varepsilon_1,$$

$$\frac{d\rho}{dt} = D_v \Delta\rho + \frac{\rho}{p_1}\frac{dp_1}{dt} - \frac{\rho_1}{T}\frac{dT}{dt}, \tag{5.1.1}$$

where ε is the radiant heat transfer, while the remaining notation is the same as above. The boundary conditions should be specified at the droplet surface and at the boundary of the volume in the form

$$\rho(\mathbf{r}) = \rho_0(T)\big|_{\mathbf{r}=\mathbf{r}_i + R_i\boldsymbol{\alpha}},$$

$$\left(D_v L \frac{\partial\rho}{\partial r} + k_1 \frac{\partial T}{\partial r}\right)\Bigg|_{\mathbf{r}=\mathbf{r}_i + R_i\boldsymbol{\alpha}} = 0,$$

where r_i are the droplet center coordinates, R_i the droplet radii, and $\boldsymbol{\alpha}$ is a unit vector in an arbitrary direction. The diffusive transport of heat and vapor through the boundaries of the volume is assumed to be zero.

Function $\rho_0(T)$, which defines the saturated vapor pressure above the droplet surface, can be specified by the Clausius-Clapeyron relation, if no corrections are made. A direct solution to the problem is difficult because the vapor field, which determines the vapor flux to the individual droplets, is in turn formed not only by the sources, but also by the flow to the droplets. This problem was not solved in the rigorous formulation, and it does not appear possible to solve it in a reasonably general form.

One transformation enabling one to consider (to some approximation) the condensation process in a polydisperse droplet system is to simplify the starting equations by averaging. As averaging scale L one should select a quantity much smaller than the inhomogeneity scale L_1 of the system as a whole, but on the other hand substantially exceeding the interdroplet distance, so that the flow of vapor to the droplets can be expressed by a sufficiently smooth function. This gives rise to the following limitations on the applicability of the balance equation:

$$\frac{1}{\sqrt[3]{n}} \ll L \ll L_1. \tag{5.1.2}$$

When these conditions are not satisfied, the question arises whether it is at all possible to describe the variation in the mass of liquid droplets in a volume by means of the balance equation. This averaging is equivalent to smoothing the vapor sinks over some space with dimension L. For the homogeneous problem such averaging with allowance for boundary conditions yields the equations

$$\rho_1 c_p \frac{dT}{dt} = \frac{dp_1}{dt} + LI + \varepsilon_1,$$

$$\frac{d\rho}{dt} = I + \frac{\rho}{p_1}\frac{dp_1}{dt} - \frac{\rho}{T}\frac{dT}{dt} \tag{5.1.3}$$

(the averaging sign has been omitted), where

$$I = \frac{D_v}{V_L}\iiint\limits_{V_L} \Delta\rho\, d\mathbf{r} = \frac{4\pi D_v}{V_L}\sum_{i=1}^{N} R_i^2 \nabla\rho\big|_{\mathbf{r}=\mathbf{r}_i + R_i\boldsymbol{\alpha}}.$$

The volume integral is reduced by means of the Gauss theorem to an integral over all the droplet surfaces and over the outer boundary of volume V_L which, subject to the condition of spatial inhomogeneity, results in the summation of all the fluxes over all the droplets within V_L. Since $\nabla\rho$ is unknown, such an averaging cannot yield perceptible results. The feasibility of correctly determining $\nabla\rho$ is very promising when the droplet concentration is low, when the diffusion fields of droplets do not affect one another directly, but act against some common background, such as the average value of the vapor pressure obtained as a result of this operation.

The feasibility of applying this approach is determined by the condition

$$R \ll \frac{1}{n^{1/3}}, \tag{5.1.4}$$

where R is the root-mean-cube droplet radius, while n is the droplet concentration, In this case the vapor field near each droplet is not distorted, while the interaction between droplets can be incorporated by boundary conditions which, when (5.1.4) is satisfied, can be specified at infinity, since this is virtually equivalent to specifying them at some distance of the order of $n^{-1/3}$.

For the spherically symmetrical problem

$$\rho(r) = c_1 + \frac{c^2}{r}, \quad \nabla\rho = \frac{\rho(l) - \rho(R)}{R}\left(\frac{l}{l-R}\right). \tag{5.1.5}$$

When $l \gg R$, the flux can be derived from the expression for the flux to a sphere in infinite space. In accordance with equation (5.1.3) and assuming (5.1.5),

$$I = \frac{4\pi D_v}{V_L} \sum_{i=1}^{N} R_i [\rho(l) - \rho(R_i)]. \tag{5.1.6}$$

If the value of I is known, it is easy to estimate the characteristic time over which the excess vapor is absorbed by the system:

$$\tau = \frac{1}{4\pi D_v \bar{R} n} \tag{5.1.7}$$

(here $n = \frac{N}{V_2}$ has the meaning of concentration, provided V_L is sufficiently large).

The characteristic time governing the removal of vapor from the system actually limits that droplet population which participates in absorbing vapor from some vicinity. Since the characteristic scale of a diffusion phenomenon is determined by the expression $l = \sqrt{4D_v t}$, expression (5.1.7) yields

$$l \approx \frac{1}{\sqrt{\pi \bar{R} n}}. \tag{5.1.8}$$

Quantity l thus determines the scale of that cell within which the condensation process occurs collectively.

It follows from elementary estimates that the averaging scale L in deriving the balance equations should not be smaller than l (i.e., $L \geqslant l$), which means that equation (5.1.3) is valid only for systems with inhomogeneity scale $L_1 \gg l$. On the other hand, for the fluctuations of variables in a volume of the order of l^3 not to be large, it is necessary that the number of particles be sufficiently large:

$$nl^3 = \frac{1}{\pi \bar{R} \sqrt{\pi \bar{R} n}} \gg 1. \tag{5.1.9}$$

In addition, consideration must be given also to time limitations. Processes with $T \geqslant \tau$ can be described by means of the balance equation, while those with $T \ll \tau$ cannot be so described. As for processes with scale smaller than l, they result in the interaction of fewer droplets, which is accordingly reflected by the structure of the vapor field.

If we restrict ourselves to processes with space and time characteristics satisfying the above conditions, then the heat and vapor balance equations can be used for considering phase transitions in disperse systems. The same conclusion was reached by Stepanov /6/ who employed a more rigorous approach from the standpoint of droplet interaction. We shall not consider here the actual derivation of the balance equations, due to its complexity, but we only note that it is carried out to an approximation within which the operation of water droplets as sinks of finite size is replaced by their operation as point sinks of the same strength. (The sources are not distributed over the space, but situated together.)

The applicability of balance equations allows the growth of a droplet population to be treated in the hydrodynamic approximation. If the particles are characterized by some distribution function $f(r, t)$, then it is possible to treat the deformation of the entire ensemble of particles as a whole. For simplicity, we shall restrict ourselves to the homogeneous case (the extension to the inhomogeneous case with scale $L_1 \gg l$ is trivial.) The existence of some background supersaturation, determined from the balance equation, makes it possible to treat the variation in r as a unique continuous function t and r.

The meaning of the hydrodynamic approximation consists in assuming that particles of different size do not overtake one another while growing (in the hydrodynamic sense, this means that the paths of individual particles do not intersect). Then, on assumption that the selected particle population continuously changes its properties and interacts with other populations only as with a background, the continuity equation for an n-particle distribution function yields the equation for the single-particle distribution function:

$$\frac{df}{dt} = -f \frac{\partial}{\partial r} \dot{r}, \qquad (5.1.10)$$

or

$$\frac{\partial f}{\partial t} + \frac{\partial}{\partial r} (\dot{r} f) = 0. \qquad (5.1.11)$$

This equation, called the kinetic equation, is used quite extensively when investigating the deformation of the distribution function /1, 2/. Equation (5.1.11) should be supplemented by the droplet growth equation

$$\frac{dr}{dt}=K_3\frac{\delta_0-\frac{B}{r}+\Phi(c)}{r+\xi}\tag{5.1.12}$$

and the equation obtained by simultaneously solving equations (5.1.1):

$$\frac{d\delta_0}{dt}=\frac{d}{dt}\ln p_1-\frac{L}{R_vT}\frac{d\ln T}{dt}-$$

$$-4\pi K_3\frac{\rho_2}{\rho_0}\int_0^\infty\left[r^2\delta_0-rB+r^2\Phi(c)\right]\frac{f(r)}{r+\xi}\,dr.\tag{5.1.13}$$

In this form equations (5.1.11)–(5.1.13) describe the variation of the droplet distribution function in the system, provided the time variation of p_1 and T is known. It usually suffices to determine the variation in one variable (or to write the corresponding equation), while the variation in the other can be derived from the equation of state using the quasi-static approximation.

2. GROWTH AND EVAPORATION OF A POPULATION OF MONODISPERSE DROPLETS

Processes of evaporation and condensation in monodisperse aerosols are simplest as regards theoretical research. In this case it is sufficient to consider only two equations – the droplet growth equation and the vapor balance equation in the system:

$$\frac{dr}{dt}=K_3\frac{\delta_0-\frac{B}{r}+\Phi(c)}{r+\xi},$$

$$\frac{d\delta_0}{dt}=\frac{d}{dt}\ln p_1-\frac{L}{R_vT}\frac{d\ln T}{dt}-$$

$$-4\pi\frac{\rho_2}{\rho_0}K_3\left[\frac{r^2\delta_0}{r+\xi}-\frac{r\left(B-r\Phi(c)\right)}{r+\xi}\right].\tag{5.2.1}$$

If the condensation or evaporation is considered during cooling or heating at a constant rate, then the effect of external sources, expressed in terms of derivatives with respect to pressure and temperature, can be taken into account in the form of some process constant. (In Chapter 4, during a similar discussion, it was represented by the constant K_1.) The second equation then assumes the form

$$\frac{d\delta_0}{dt}=K_1-K_2\left(\frac{r^2}{r+\xi}\delta_0-\frac{rB-r^2\Phi(c)}{r+\xi}\right). \tag{5.2.2}$$

One solution of system of equations (5.2.1) with allowance for the previous assumption can be easily obtained by adding both equations of the system, but first multiplied by an appropriate factor. This yields

$$\delta_0+\frac{K_2}{3K_3}r^3=K_1t+C_1, \tag{5.2.3}$$

where C_1 is some constant, determined from initial conditions. This expression enables one to write the differential equation governing $r(t)$ or $\delta_0(t)$:

$$r'=\frac{K^3(K_1t+C_1)}{r+\xi}-K_3\frac{\left[\frac{K_2r^3}{3K_3}+\frac{B}{r}-\Phi(c)\right]}{r+\xi}. \tag{5.2.4}$$

This equation is too complicated for direct integration, but can be easily evaluated numerically.

We shall restrict ourselves to an approximate solution. Since $\frac{K_2}{K_3}\approx 10^5\ \text{cm}^{-3}$, the first term in brackets in equation (5.2.4) is much greater than the sum of the other two, so the latter sum will be disregarded. (Actually, this is an assumption regarding the fact that the water accumulated in droplets, upon complete evaporation, results in a much greater supersaturation than the correction for δ_0 due to hygroscopicity and surface tension.) In this case

$$(r+\xi)r'=K_3(K_1t+C_1)-\frac{1}{3}K_2r^3. \tag{5.2.5}$$

The asymptotic form of equation (5.2.5) corresponds to the quasi-steady regime and is determined by setting the right-hand side equal to zero. Hence

$$r=\left[\frac{3K_3}{K_2}(K_1t+C_1)\right]^{1/3}. \tag{5.2.6}$$

In the next approximation it is possible to make allowance for the effect of r' by the usual technique of substituting the value of r from equation (5.2.6) into the right-hand side of equation (5.2.5). In the quasi-steady approximation the value of δ_0 from equation (5.2.2) can be determined similarly:

$$\delta_0 = \frac{K_1}{K_2}\,\frac{(r+\xi)}{r^2} + \left[\frac{B}{r} - \Phi(c)\right]. \tag{5.2.7}$$

Substitution of r from equation (5.2.6) into equation (5.2.7) yields the variation of δ_0 in the quasi-steady approximation. Here, neglect of corrections for hygroscopicity and surface tension will not be justified, since both these terms are generally of commensurable magnitude.

It was thus shown that in the quasi-steady approximation the ensemble of particles changes its mass linearly with time, irrespective of corrections governing the growth rate of an individual particle by condensation. However, here the supersaturation depends markedly on these corrections, so compensating the different influences affecting the rate of vapor transport to an individual particle.

The compensation of the different corrections is, from the physical point of view, a result of the fact that for systems containing a reasonably large number of particles the excess of vapor released upon cooling of the air stops accumulating after some time and is transferred directly to the droplets. In this case (existence of quasi-steady conditions), if the droplets are equal, the rate of their growth is determined simply by the rate at which excess vapor is supplied to the system (it is assumed that $\delta_0 \ll 1$), and hence does not depend on the form of the equation and accordingly on the different corrections. In the case of a polydisperse droplet distribution, corrections which depend on r make themselves felt, as a result of which the vapor is redistributed between the droplets but the total flux does not change.

The conditions governing the applicability of these approximations can be easily obtained by requiring that each term in the right-hand sides of equations (5.2.5) and (5.2.2) be much larger than the quantity in the left-hand side. It follows that

$$t \gg K_2 r_0. \tag{5.2.8}$$

These are precisely the usual conditions for transformation to the quasi-steady regime.

It is of interest to examine the case of instantaneous release or absorption of heat and the reaction of a system of monodisperse particles:

$$\frac{d}{dt}\ln p_1-\frac{L}{R_v T}\frac{d}{dt}\ln T=Q_0\delta(t). \tag{5.2.9}$$

Then, similarly to equation (5.2.3),

$$\delta_0+\frac{K_2}{3K_3}(r^3-r_0^3)=Q_0, \tag{5.2.10}$$

while the equation for r becomes

$$r'=\frac{K_3}{r+\xi}\left[Q_0-\frac{K_2}{3K_3}(r^3-r_0^3)-\left(\frac{B}{r}-\Phi(c)\right)\right]. \tag{5.2.11}$$

This equation, with separable variables, can be integrated formally to yield

$$t=\frac{1}{K_3}\int_{r_0}^{r}\frac{(r+\xi)\,dr}{Q_0-\frac{K_2}{3K_3}(r^3-r_0^3)-\left(\frac{B}{r}-\Phi(c)\right)}. \tag{5.2.12}$$

It is evident that even in the simplest case, when the initial particle size distribution is described by a delta function, the question of droplet size variation is highly complicated and cannot be solved without simplifying assumptions. In this connection, when examining any behavior of a more general type in calculations we shall employ the droplet growth equation in a simpler form, with allowance only for thermal corrections.

3. THE PACKET QUESTION AND THE PROBLEM OF SPECTRUM NARROWING

A very characteristic example, which can be used for examining any distortion in the distribution function and which makes it possible to obtain reasonably simple relations, is the case when the initial distribution is truncated for small and large values of r and the function is specified only in the region $(r_{01},\ r_{02})$. The system of equations describing this process can be expressed as follows:

$$\frac{\partial f}{\partial t}+\frac{\partial}{\partial r}\left(\frac{dr}{dt}f\right)=0,$$

$$\frac{dr}{dt}=K_3\frac{\delta_0-\frac{B}{r}+\Phi(c)}{r+\xi},$$

$$\frac{d\delta_0}{dt}=\frac{d}{dt}\ln p_1-\frac{L}{R_vT}\frac{d\ln T}{dt}-$$

$$-K_2\delta_0\int\limits_{r_1(t)}^{r_2(t)}\frac{r^2f(r)}{r+\xi}dr+K_2\int\limits_{r_1(t)}^{r_2(t)}\frac{[rB-r^2\Phi(c)]}{r+\xi}f(r)\,dr. \tag{5.3.1}$$

In general, this system of equations, though not complicated, cannot be solved exactly. In this connection we shall deal with several particular cases.

1. The supersaturation is maintained at some constant value ($\delta_0=$ const). In this case the last of equations (5.3.1) can be neglected and one can solve a system consisting of the first two equations alone.

If we set

$$\frac{1}{K_3}\int\frac{(r+\xi)\,dr}{\delta_0-\frac{B}{r}+\Phi(c)}=\Psi(r), \tag{5.3.2}$$

the second of the equations yields

$$\Psi(r)-\Psi(r_0)=t, \tag{5.3.3}$$

using which we arrive at the following equation for function f (with consideration of the fact that $\Psi(r)$ is a monotonically increasing function and hence $\Psi'(r)\neq 0$):

$$\frac{\partial f}{\partial t}+\frac{\partial}{\partial r}\left(\frac{f}{\Psi'(r)}\right)=0. \tag{5.3.4}$$

The transformation

$$\varphi(x,\ t)=f(r,\ t)\frac{dr}{dx}=\frac{f(r,\ t)}{\Psi'(r)}, \tag{5.3.5}$$

where $x=\Psi(r)$, yields the equation

$$\frac{\partial\varphi}{\partial t}+\frac{\partial\varphi}{\partial x}=0, \tag{5.3.6}$$

the solution of which is

$$\varphi = \Phi(x - t), \tag{5.3.7}$$

where Φ is some arbitrary function determined from initial conditions. If $\varphi = \varphi_0(x)$ at $t = 0$, the solution can be written in the form

$$\varphi = \varphi_0(x - t). \tag{5.3.8}$$

Function $f(r, t)$ can be expressed as

$$f(r, t) = \Psi'(r)\varphi_0(\Psi(r) - t). \tag{5.3.9}$$

Of greatest interest is the case when the form of the distribution function retains a constant analytic form and only the boundaries of the region, cutting off a given section from the analytic section, move. The possibility of the existence of a self-preserving distribution follows from equation (5.3.8). If $\varphi_0 =$ const, function φ is independent of time and is also a constant quantity. In terms of variables (r, t) function $\bar{f}(r)$, defining the dependence on the radius, assumes the form

$$\bar{f}(r) = A\Psi'(r) = \frac{A}{K_3} \frac{r + \xi}{\delta_0 - \frac{B}{r} + \Phi(c)}. \tag{5.3.10}$$

The shape of the curve will be defined by this analytic expression while the boundaries will move in accordance with the equation of droplet growth at the boundary points. Hence

$$f(r, t) = \frac{A}{K_3} \frac{r + \xi}{\left(\delta_0 - \frac{B}{r} + \Phi(c)\right)} \theta(r - r_1(t))\,\theta(r_2(t) - r), \tag{5.3.11}$$

where

$$\theta(x) = \begin{cases} 1 & \text{when} \quad x > 0 \\ 0 & \text{when} \quad x < 0, \end{cases}$$

A is determined from normalization conditions, $r_1(t)$ and $r_2(t)$ are derived from equation (5.3.3). The variation in the distribution function, satisfying conditions (5.3.9), is illustrated in Figure 23. It is clear that widening or narrowing of the spectrum is determined by the shape of curve $\bar{f}(r)$: as it increases the condition of droplet conservation results in narrowing of the spectrum, while when it decreases the boundary widens. The separation between the regions where the spectrum narrows and widens is defined by the condition

$$\Psi''(\bar{r})=0. \tag{5.3.12}$$

For dilute solutions, Raoult's law enables one to set $\Phi(c)=\frac{C}{r^3}$. It follows from equation (5.3.12) that

$$\delta_0-2\left(\frac{B}{r}-\frac{2C}{r^3}\right)-\frac{\xi}{r}\left(\frac{B}{r}-\frac{3C}{r^3}\right)\bigg|_{r=\bar{r}}=0. \tag{5.3.13}$$

In particular, for droplets of pure water $\bar{r}$ can be derived analytically in the form

$$\bar{r}=\frac{B}{\delta_0}\left(1+\sqrt{1+\frac{\xi\delta_0}{B}}\right). \tag{5.3.14}$$

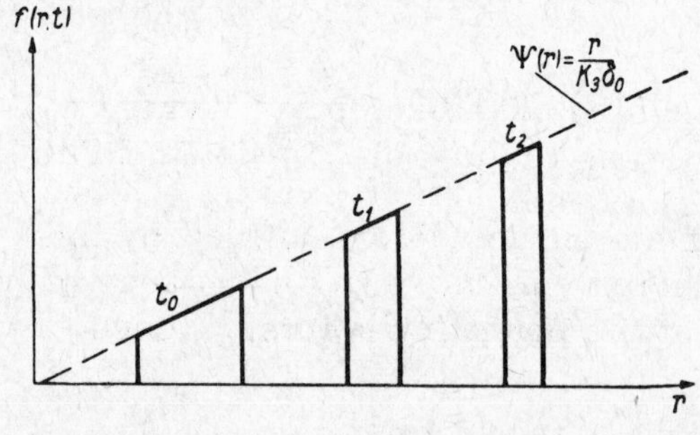

FIGURE 23. Time variation of the distribution function when the shape of the distribution satisfies the self-preserving condition $t_0<t_1<t_2$

The question of narrowing or widening of the droplet spectrum is not so trivial, and situations are possible when for sufficiently small supersaturation the spectrum widens (such as the case of large $\bar{r}$).

The above results, (5.3.13) and (5.3.14), are of general importance, since they are based on an examination of the droplet growth equation and are therefore valid for any distribution function. Direct examination of the equation of droplet growth (when $\delta_0 \neq$ const) yields the following condition:

$$\left(\delta_0 - \frac{B}{r} + \frac{C}{r^3}\right)\left[\delta_0 - 2\left(\frac{B}{r} - \frac{2C}{r^3}\right) - \right.$$

$$\left. - \frac{\xi}{r}\left(\frac{B}{r} - \frac{3C}{r^3}\right)\right] = \frac{(r+\xi)^2}{K_3} \frac{d\delta_0}{dt}, \tag{5.3.15}$$

which shows that $\bar{r}$ is a function of time.

We now consider the second case, the analysis of which is of some interest when investigating the distortion in the distribution function. Suppose the initial distribution in terms of variables r, t is Π-shaped. Since the problem of finding $\Psi(r)$ in explicit form yields cumbersome expressions, we restrict ourselves to the case when no allowance is made for hygroscopicity and surface tension. Then

$$\Psi(r) = \frac{1}{2K_3\delta_0}(r+\xi)^2. \tag{5.3.16}$$

On the assumption that $f(r, 0) = A\theta(r - r_1(0))\theta(r_2(0) - r)$, the initial distribution in terms of variable x has the form

$$\varphi_0(x) = \frac{AK_3\delta_0}{r+\xi} = \frac{AK_3\delta_0}{\sqrt{2K_3\delta_0 x}}. \tag{5.3.17}$$

(The fact that the size of the region is limited will be taken into account on converting to variable r.) In line with (5.3.8), the solution to the problem becomes

$$\varphi(x, t) = A\sqrt{\frac{K_3\delta_0}{2(x-t)}}, \tag{5.3.18}$$

while the distribution function is

$$f(r, t) = \frac{A(r+\xi)}{\sqrt{(r+\xi)^2 - 2K_3\delta_0 t}}\theta(r - r_1(t))\theta(r_2(t) - r), \tag{5.3.19}$$

where

$$r_{1,2} = -\xi + \sqrt{2K_3\delta_0 t + [r_{1,2}(0) + \xi]^2}.$$

An examination of the behavior of $f(r, t)$ shows that the distribution function is distorted: over the segment $r_1(t) < r < r_2(t)$ it changes from a flat curve into a monotonically decreasing curve; the curvature increases with time. A graph of this function is presented in Figure 24.

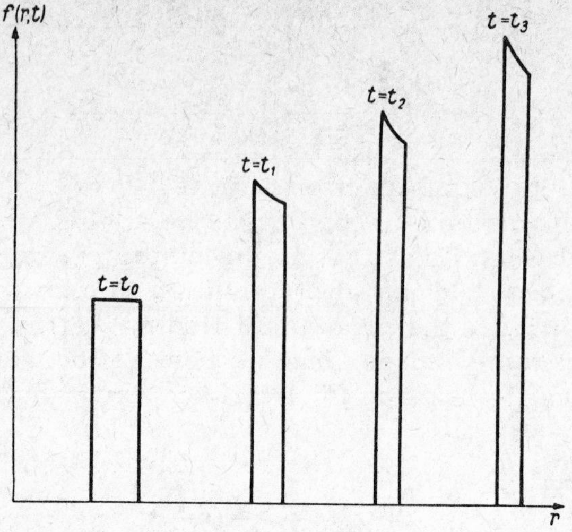

FIGURE 24. Distortion of the Π-shaped droplet distribution during its growth $(t_0 < t_1 < t_2)$

2. Consider the distortion in the distribution function when δ_0 is some function of time. Due to the need of expressing the integral of the droplet growth equation in explicit form, we shall again neglect corrections for surface tension and hygroscopicity. In this case, integration of equation (5.2.1) yields

$$(r+\xi)^2-(r_0+\xi)^2=2K_3\int_0^t \delta_0(t)\,dt. \tag{5.3.20}$$

The equation defining the distortion in the distribution function is

$$\frac{\partial f}{\partial \tau}+\frac{\partial}{\partial r}\left(\frac{f}{\Psi'(r)}\right)=0, \tag{5.3.21}$$

where

$$\tau=2K_3\int_0^t \delta_0(t)\,dt,$$

$$\Psi(r)=(r+\xi)^2.$$

The subsequent procedure for finding a solution is similar to that considered above. In terms of the variables $x=\Psi(r)$, τ

for $\varphi(x,\ t)=\dfrac{f(r,\ t)}{\Psi'(r)}$, the solution has the form of equation (5.3.8) with the corresponding distribution function

$$f(r,\ t)=\Psi'(r)\,\varphi_0\left(\Psi(r)-2K_3\int_0^t \delta_0(t)\,dt\right). \tag{5.3.22}$$

If the initial distribution is Π-shaped with respect to variable x, then

$$f(r,\ t)=A(r+\xi)\,\theta(r-r_1(t))\,\theta(r_2(t)-r), \tag{5.3.23}$$

where

$$r_{1,2}(t)=-\xi+\sqrt{\tau+[r_{1,2}(0)+\xi]^2}. \tag{5.3.24}$$

If the initial distribution is Π-shaped with respect to variable r, then

$$f(r,\ t)=\frac{A(r+\xi)}{\left[(r+\xi)^2-2K_3\int_0^t \delta_0(t)\,dt\right]^{1/2}}\,\theta(r-r_1(t))\,\theta(r_2(t)-r), \tag{5.3.25}$$

where $r_{1,2}(t)$ is given by equation (5.3.24). The graph of $f(r,\ t)$ will be similar to that describing the variation in f for constant δ_0, if in the first case one introduces a transformation with respect to t using τ as the time variable.

3. Finally, consider the case when the variation in supersaturation is caused by the operation of external sources $z(t)$, i. e., by transfer to droplets in accordance with the third of equations (5.3.1). It will again be assumed that the droplet growth is considered without corrections for B, $\Phi(c)$ and ξ. Then, taking δ_0 as some unknown function of time, it is possible to derive a formal solution to the system comprising the first two of equations (5.3.1) and to obtain an expression for δ_0. With the aid of the above results we set

$$f(r,\ t)=2r\Phi_0(r^2-2K_3y(t)),$$

$$y''(t)=z(t)-K_2y'\int_{r_1(t)}^{r_2(t)} rf(r,\ t)\,dr,$$

$$r_{1,2}(t)=[r_{1,2}^2(0)+2K_3y(t)]^{1/2}. \tag{5.3.26}$$

It is evident that vapor transfer to the droplets does not affect the shape of the spectrum and, upon introducing the transformation $\tau=2K_3y(t)$, function $f(r, t)$ varies similarly to the previously examined cases. However, the rate of droplet [size] variation with time should be treated separately.

For a П-shaped distribution with respect to variable x, $f(r, t)= =2r\theta(r_2(t)-r)\theta(r-r_1(t))$, while quantity $y(t)$ governing the variation in $r_{1,2}(t)$ should be found by solving the equation

$$y''(t)=z(t)-\frac{2}{3}K_2y'(t)\{[r_2^2(0)+2K_3y(t)]^{3/2}-$$
$$-[r_1^2(0)+2K_3y(t)]^{3/2}\}. \quad (5.3.27)$$

On the assumption of quasi-steadiness $y''(t)\ll z(t)$ this equation can be integrated to yield

$$K_3\int_0^t z(t)\,dt=\frac{2}{15}\{[r_2^2(0)+2K_3y(t)]^{5/2}-[r_1^2(0)+2K_3y(t)]^{5/2}\}. \quad (5.3.28)$$

By singling out $y(t)$ in explicit form, it is possible to obtain an expression for the moving boundaries $r_{1,2}(t)$. The case of a П-shaped distribution of r is much more complicated and can be considered only after introducing certain specifications. It will not be treated here.

4. An item of particular interest is the study of the variation in the shape of the distribution curve described by function $f(r, t)$. The distortion in the distribution curve can be investigated as follows. In accordance with equation (5.3.9), the derivative of $f(r, t)$ with respect to r (characterizing the slope of the distribution curve) is given by

$$\frac{\partial f(r, t)}{\partial r}=\Psi''(r)\varphi_0(\Psi(r)-t)+\Psi'^2(r)\varphi_0'(\Psi(r)-t). \quad (5.3.29)$$

Evaporation or condensation result in shifting the distribution function, so the total time derivative of $\frac{\partial f}{\partial r}$ must be obtained in order to determine the variation in the slope of the curve. Since

$$\frac{d}{dt}=\frac{\partial}{\partial t}+\frac{dr}{dt}\frac{\partial}{\partial r}=\frac{\partial}{\partial t}+\frac{1}{\Psi'(r)}\frac{\partial}{\partial r} \quad (5.3.30)$$

and

$$\frac{d}{dt}[\Psi(r)-t]=\left[\frac{1}{\Psi'(r)}\Psi'(r)-1\right]\equiv 0, \tag{5.3.31}$$

we obtain

$$\frac{d}{dt}\frac{\partial f}{\partial r}=[\Psi'''(r)\varphi_0(\Psi(r)-t)+2\Psi'(r)\Psi''(r)\varphi_0'(\Psi(r)-t)]\frac{dr}{dt}. \tag{5.3.32}$$

Derivative $\frac{dr}{dt}$ describes the course of the processes (whether we are dealing with evaporation or condensation), and hence the distortion in $f(r, t)$ is defined by the expression in brackets; here $\varphi_0(\Psi(r)-t)=\varphi_0(\Psi(r_0))$ is the initial distribution, while $\Psi(r)$ is the integral of the droplet growth equation. The above expression enables one to easily analyze the distortion in the droplet distribution function. As an illustration, consider the case $\Psi(r)=\lambda(r+\xi)^2$, in which case

$$\frac{d}{dt}\frac{\partial f}{\partial r}=4\lambda^2(r+\xi)\varphi_0'(\Psi(r_0))\frac{dr}{dt}. \tag{5.3.33}$$

Suppose $\varphi_0=$ const (case of Π-shaped distribution with respect to x). Since $\varphi_0'\equiv 0$, $\frac{d}{dt}\frac{\partial f}{\partial r}\equiv 0$, which was obtained previously. The distribution retains its shape. If, however, $\varphi_0=b+ax$, then

$$\frac{d}{dt}\frac{\partial f}{\partial r}=4\lambda^2(r+\xi)a\frac{dr}{dt}. \tag{5.3.34}$$

It is evident that the sign of $\frac{d}{dt}\frac{\partial f}{\partial r}$ is determined by the sign of a. If $a>0$, then when $\frac{dr}{dt}>0$ the slope increases, and the profile of the distribution becomes more accentuated. If $a<0$, then when $\frac{dr}{dt}>0$ the value of $\frac{d}{dt}\frac{\partial f}{\partial r}$ decreases, which also results in making the distribution more accentuated but sloping with opposite sign. This means that the distribution of $\varphi_0=$ const is unstable and any disturbances can result in its sharp distortion. In the course of condensation the maxima at points on an initially smooth distribution curve may also become sharper at points corresponding to $\varphi_0'=0$.

4. DROPLET EVAPORATION AND GROWTH IN THE CASE OF AN ARBITRARY DISTRIBUTION FUNCTION

It was shown in the preceding section that even for quite simple starting distribution functions their distortion in time is described in quite a complicated manner and, without simplifying assumptions, it cannot be investigated analytically. For this reason problems of the growth of a droplet population are (with some exceptions /1, 2/) examined on the basis of numerical solutions /3–5/.

The analytical study of the distortion of a distribution which differs initially from zero over the entire region defined by $r > 0$ and which has a continuous derivative, involves a different mathematical approach to the problem of evaporation and condensation. The existence of a boundary at $r = 0$ means that in the problem of growth by condensation one must consider the motion of the boundary or allow uncontrolled formation of new droplets (first order equation for $f(r, t)$). Only when the formation of new droplets does not have a marked effect on the process is it possible to employ formal methods of solution in the region $r > 0$.

The problem of droplet evaporation is simpler. Their disappearance is due to the fact that particles pass through the interface separating droplets from nuclei. This process can be easily taken into account and hence the problem with stationary boundaries is physically correct. The evaporation of a polydisperse fog in the Maxwellian approximation was investigated in detail elsewhere /1, 2/, but without allowance for external sources. Following these studies and making allowance for thermal effects by means of coefficient K_3, we consider the distortion of the distribution function in the presence of an influx or removal of heat from the system.

In terms of variables x and τ, we have in general form

$$\varphi(x, \tau) = \varphi_0(x - \tau)$$

and accordingly, in terms of variables r and t (when $x = \Psi(r) = r^2$, $r = 2K_3 \int_0^\tau \delta_0(t)\, dt$)

$$f(r, t) = \frac{r}{\left(r^2 - 2K_3 \int_0^t \delta_0(t)\, dt\right)^{1/2}} f_0\left[\left(r^2 - 2K_3 \int_0^t \delta_0(t)\, dt\right)^{1/2}\right]. \quad (5.4.1)$$

The entire difficulty in determining the behavior of $f(r, t)$ consists in finding the explicit distribution of δ_0 as a function of time from the expression

$$\tau''=2K_3\left(\frac{d}{dt}\ln p_1-\frac{L}{R_vT}\frac{d\ln T}{dt}\right)-K_2\tau'\int\limits_{\sqrt{-\tau}}^{\infty}(r^2+\tau)^{1/2}f_0(r)\,dr. \quad (5.4.2)$$

Note that for evaporating droplets $\tau<0$ ($\delta_0<0$), hence the lower limit of the integral in (5.4.2) is positive and actually characterizes the reduction in the number of particles in the system. Equation (5.4.2) allows a reduction of order:

$$\tau'=2K_3\int\limits_0^t\left(\frac{d}{dt}\ln p_1-\frac{L}{R_vT}\frac{d\ln T}{dt}\right)dt-$$

$$-\frac{2K_2}{3}\int\limits_{\sqrt{-\tau}}^{\infty}(r^2+\tau)^{3/2}f_0(r)\,dr. \quad (5.4.3)$$

With unchanged external conditions the first term on the right is constant. The growth of droplets can be examined similarly. In this case the droplet distribution function is described by solution (5.4.1) multiplied by the theta function

$$\theta(r^2-\tau).$$

The equation for τ is more simple, since it disregards any variation in the number of particles:

$$\tau''=2K_3\left(\frac{d\ln p_1}{dt}-\frac{L}{R_vT}\frac{d\ln T}{dt}\right)-K_2\tau'\int\limits_0^{\infty}(r^2+\tau)^{1/2}f_0(r)\,dr. \quad (5.4.4)$$

The variation in the number of particles in the system during evaporation can also be calculated easily with the aid of (5.4.1):

$$n(t)=\int\limits_0^{\infty}f(r,t)\,dr=\int\limits_{\sqrt{-\tau}}^{\infty}f_0(r)\,dr. \quad (5.4.5)$$

Consequently, $\frac{dn}{dt}=\frac{-\tau'}{2(-\tau)^{3/2}}f_0(\sqrt{-\tau})$ is determined by the time variation in τ and by the dependence of the initial distribution on r.

Since the particle size distribution function can have a continuous time derivative over the entire region of sizes only during evaporation, we shall consider the feasibility of retaining the form of the distribution curve while the total number of particles decreases. The feasibility of the existence of such a distribution, which would retain its form, is of great interest. In terms of variables x and τ, the distribution function satisfies the equation

$$\frac{\partial \varphi}{\partial \tau}+\frac{\partial \varphi}{\partial x}=0. \tag{5.4.6}$$

It follows from the existence of a solution $\varphi=X(x)T(\tau)$ that

$$X=C\exp(-sx),$$
$$T=\exp s\tau, \tag{5.4.7}$$

where s is some parameter independent of time. Since $\varphi(x,\ 0)=$ $=\varphi_0(x)=X(x)$, the initial distribution, retaining its form, should be expressible as $\varphi_0(x)=C_1\exp(-sx)$, which yields the following distribution with respect to r:

$$f_0(r)=Cr\exp(-sr^2). \tag{5.4.8}$$

Thus

$$f(r,\ t)=Cr\exp[-s(r^2-\tau)], \tag{5.4.9}$$

where the time-dependence of τ is defined by

$$\tau''=2K_3\left(\frac{d\ln p_1}{dt}-\frac{L}{R_vT}\frac{d\ln T}{dt}\right)-C\frac{\sqrt{\pi}K_2}{4s^{3/2}}\tau'\exp(s\tau). \tag{5.4.10}$$

The solution to this equation can often be obtained easily. In particular, in the quasi-steady approximation (τ'' in equation (5.4.10) can be neglected) we set

$$\exp(s\tau)=1+\frac{8}{\sqrt{\pi}}\frac{K_3}{CK_2}s^{5/2}\int_0^t\left(\frac{d\ln p_1}{dt}-\frac{L}{R_vT}\frac{d\ln T}{dt}\right)dt. \tag{5.4.11}$$

On the basis of these assumptions

$$f(r,\ t)=\left[C+\frac{8}{\sqrt{\pi}}\frac{K_3}{K_2}s^{5/2}\int_0^t\left(\frac{d\ln p_1}{dt}-\right.\right.$$
$$\left.\left.-\frac{L}{R_vT}\frac{d\ln T}{dt}\right)dt\right]r\exp(-sr^2). \tag{5.4.12}$$

During uniform heating $\frac{d\ln p_1}{dt}-\frac{L}{R_vT}\frac{d\ln T}{dt}=-K_1=\text{const}$, in which case

$$f(r,\ t)=\left[C-\frac{8}{\sqrt{\pi}}\frac{K_1K_3}{K_2}s^{5/2}t\right]r\exp(-sr^2). \tag{5.4.13}$$

The growth of a population of droplets can be treated similarly. Solution $f(r,\ t)$ in this case will also have the form of function (5.4.9), the absence of particles in the region of small dimensions will be taken into account by additional multiplication by function $\theta[(r^2-\tau)^{1/2}]$, and the equation for τ will be

$$\tau''=2K_3\left(\frac{d}{dt}\ln p_1-\frac{L}{R_vT}\frac{d\ln T}{dt}\right)-\frac{CK_2}{2s^{3/2}}\tau'\Gamma\left(\frac{3}{2},\ s\tau\right)\exp(s\tau). \tag{5.4.14}$$

Equation (5.4.14) can be solved approximately for a number of cases of practical interest. For instance, if the starting distribution can be extrapolated by an expression such as (5.4.8), the subsequent behavior of the system can be investigated analytically with reasonable accuracy.

The feasibility of the stable existence of some form of the distribution and of a simpler analytic investigation of it allows one to approach the development of a technique for solving the problem. This would involve expanding the starting function in terms of spectral functions of self-similar systems of the above type.

If the starting distribution of φ_0 with respect to x can be expressed as

$$\varphi_0(x)=\sum_{n=1}^{N}C_n\exp(-s_nx), \tag{5.4.15}$$

then the solution to the equation can assume the form

$$\varphi(x,\ \tau)=\sum_{1}^{N}C_n\exp[-s_n(x-\tau)], \tag{5.4.16}$$

where τ in the case of evaporation is determined by solving the equation

$$\tau''=2K_3\left(\frac{d\ln p_1}{dt}-\frac{L}{R_vT}\frac{d\ln T}{dt}\right)-$$
$$-\frac{\sqrt{\pi}K_2}{4}\tau'\sum_{n=1}^{N}\frac{C_n}{s_n^{3/2}}\exp(s_n\tau) \tag{5.4.17}$$

and the equation

$$\tau''=2K_3\left(\frac{d\ln p_1}{dt}-\frac{L}{R_vT}\frac{d\ln T}{dt}\right)-\frac{K_2}{2}\tau'\sum_{n=1}^{N}\frac{C_n}{s_n^{3/2}}\Gamma\left(\frac{3}{2},\ s_n\tau\right) \quad (5.4.18)$$

in the case of the growth of a droplet population, Here equation (5.4.16) should be multiplied by $\theta(x-\tau)$. These equations can be solved quite easily in a number of cases, or at least investigated.

Finally, an arbitrary distribution can be represented in the form of an integral

$$\varphi_0(x)=\int_0^\infty A(s)\exp(-sx)\,dx. \quad (5.4.19)$$

The feasibility of this representation is related to the existence of a Laplace transform with respect to function $\varphi_0(x)$. Then

$$\varphi(x,\ \tau)=\int_0^\infty A(s)\exp[-s(x-\tau)]\,ds, \quad (5.4.20)$$

where τ during evaporation is defined by the equation

$$\tau''=2K_3\left(\frac{d\ln p_1}{dt}-\frac{L}{R_vT}\frac{d\ln T}{dt}\right)-$$

$$-\frac{\sqrt{\pi}}{4}K_2\tau'\int_0^\infty s^{-3/2}A(s)\exp(s\tau), \quad (5.4.21)$$

while during condensation

$$\tau''=2K_3\left(\frac{d\ln p_1}{dt}-\frac{L}{R_vT}\frac{d\ln T}{dt}\right)-$$

$$-\frac{K_2}{2}\tau'\int_0^\infty s^{-3/2}A(s)\Gamma\left(\frac{3}{2},\ s\tau\right)ds; \quad (5.4.22)$$

here, equation (5.4.20) should be multiplied by function $\theta(x-\tau)$.

In some cases the time-dependence of τ can be established analytically from equations (5.4.21) and (5.4.22). In the quasi-steady approximation, in particular for evaporation,

$$\int_0^\infty s^{-5/2}A(s)\exp(-s\tau)\,ds=$$

$$=\frac{8}{\sqrt{\pi}}\frac{K_3}{K_2}\int_0^t\left[\frac{d\ln p_1}{dt}-\frac{L}{R_vT}\frac{d\ln T}{dt}\right]dt, \quad (5.4.23)$$

whence for given $A(s)$ one can establish an explicit dependence of τ on time.

The case of condensation is more complicated, although here too approximate solutions can be found. At present, the most extensively used analytic expression for describing the droplet distribution is the gamma distribution:

$$f_0(r) = Cr^\alpha \exp(-r\omega). \tag{5.4.24}$$

In terms of variable x this is $\varphi_0(x) = \frac{C}{2} x^{\frac{\alpha-1}{2}} e^{-\omega\sqrt{x}}$. The spectral distribution of such a function with respect to eigenfunctions of the problem yields the expression

$$A(s) = \frac{C}{2}\sqrt{\frac{2}{\pi}}\,(2s)^{-\frac{\alpha-1}{2}} \exp\left(-\frac{\omega^2}{2s}\right) D_{\alpha-2}\left(\frac{\omega}{2\sqrt{s}}\right), \tag{5.4.25}$$

where $D_{\alpha-2}$ is the parabolic cylinder function.

Distributions such as

$$f_0(r) = Cr^\alpha \exp(-r^2\omega) \tag{5.4.26}$$

yield much simpler expressions. Relations of this type are recommended in the study of growth by condensation or evaporation. In this case

$$A(s) = \frac{C}{r}\Gamma\left(\frac{\alpha+1}{2}\right)(s+\omega)^{-\frac{\alpha+1}{2}}. \tag{5.4.27}$$

The use of spectra expansions in the study of the kinetics of condensation processes apparently yields satisfactory conditions for obtaining approximate solutions and hence is highly promising for specific problems.

Chapter 6

TURBULENCE AND FLUCTUATIONS IN ATMOSPHERIC VARIABLES

1. TURBULENCE AND ITS ROLE IN PRODUCING MICROINHOMOGENEITIES

One of the most characteristic features of the atmosphere is that it exists in a state of turbulent motion. This means that the wind speeds at different points in space and at different times can differ not only due to inhomogeneity or unsteadiness of the flow, but also due to fluctuations in the velocity field, which obeys some random laws. The velocity field in turbulent flow has been and is being investigated by many scientists.

Though it would appear that the velocity field does not concern us directly, by virtue of fluctuations in the velocity field the atmospheric variables, which are in one way or another associated with atmospheric motions, should also undergo random fluctuations. This can play an important role in considering certain atmospheric phenomena which govern the formation and development of clouds.

At present the most thoroughly explored problem is that of fluctuations in the conservative passive impurity. Passive impurity is a term applied to an impurity which does not affect the dynamic turbulence regime. An impurity, the concentration of which (or some other property equivalent to the concentration) does not change during the motion of a given volume element in space, is termed conservative. The question of fluctuations in the conservative passive admixture is of general and extremely great importance, since a large number of very important atmospheric variables, such as temperature, humidity and wind speed, can be treated with sufficient accuracy as a conservative passive impurity.

The question of the microstructure of the concentration of a conservative passive impurity was first examined by Obukhov /13/, who used the temperature field as an illustration, and then in more detail elsewhere /18, 8/. These ideas were most fruitfully developed by Tatarskii /16/, who considered the effect of fluctuation phenomena on the propagation of waves in the turbulent atmosphere.

In the light of current concepts the process resulting in the fluctuation of a given meteorological variable can be treated as follows. Let quantity c characterize the concentration of some conservative passive impurity, and for simplicity let the mean value of c be a function of only one coordinate z, say. We shall examine the value of c at levels z_1 and z_2.

As a result of turbulent mixing parcels of air from level z_2 will be shifted to level z_1, and conversely. Thus each level will contain parcels of air characterized by $c(z_1)$ and $c(z_2)$. Owing to such mixing the mean values will change so as to reduce the difference between them which, in turn, will result in smoothing out the mean concentration profile. On the other hand, the variety of values at each level increases, as well as the local gradients of c. Due to this increase in local gradients there sets in at some stage the smoothing-out mechanism of molecular diffusion, which eliminates the appearance of infinite gradients.

The fundamentals governing the theory of fluctuations in an passive impurity will be treated on the basis of the cited reference. As a measure of the inhomogeneity of c in volume V, we introduce some quantity P^* given by

$$P^* = \frac{1}{2}\int\limits_V (\overline{c'})^2 dV, \tag{6.1.1}$$

where $c' = c - \overline{c}$. Hence the variation in P^* can be derived from the continuity equation for c. For incompressible flow the equation of continuity for c has the form

$$\frac{\partial c}{\partial t} + \frac{\partial}{\partial x_i}\left(v_i c - D\frac{\partial c}{\partial x_i}\right) = 0, \tag{6.1.2}$$

where v_i is a component of the air velocity while D is the coefficient of molecular diffusion.

The equation for $\overline{c}$ is derived from equation (6.1.2) by averaging:

$$\frac{\partial \overline{c}}{\partial t} + \frac{\partial}{\partial x_i}\left(\overline{v}_i \overline{c} + \overline{v_i' c'} - D\frac{\partial \overline{c}}{\partial x_i}\right) = 0. \tag{6.1.3}$$

Subtraction of equation (6.1.3) from equation (6.1.2) yields

$$\frac{\partial c'}{\partial t} + \frac{\partial}{\partial x_i}\left(\overline{v}_i c' + v_i' \overline{c} + v_i' c' - \overline{v_i' c'} - D\frac{\partial c'}{\partial x_i}\right) = 0, \tag{6.1.4}$$

where $v'_i = v_i - \overline{v_i}$.

If equation (6.1.4) is multiplied by c' and simple transformations performed, we obtain

$$\frac{\partial}{\partial t}\left(\frac{c'^2}{2}\right) + \operatorname{div}\left(\frac{\mathbf{v}c'^2}{2} - Dc' \operatorname{grad} c'\right) + \mathbf{v}'c' \operatorname{grad} \bar{c} + D(\operatorname{grad} c')^2 - \\ - c' \operatorname{div}(\overline{\mathbf{v}'c'}) = 0. \quad (6.1.5)$$

Averaging of this equation gives

$$\frac{\partial}{\partial t}\overline{\left(\frac{c'^2}{2}\right)} + \operatorname{div}\left(\frac{1}{2}\overline{\mathbf{v}c'^2} - D\overline{c' \operatorname{grad} c'}\right) + \\ + \overline{\mathbf{v}'c'} \operatorname{grad} \bar{c} + D\overline{(\operatorname{grad} c')^2} = 0. \quad (6.1.6)$$

If equation (6.1.6) is integrated over volume V, and we assume that the integral of the divergence can be transformed into a surface integral which is smaller than the volume integral, then on the basis of (6.1.1) we have

$$\frac{\partial P^*}{\partial t} + \int_V \left[\overline{v'_i c'} \frac{\partial \bar{c}}{\partial x_i} + D\overline{\left(\frac{\partial c'}{\partial x_i}\right)^2}\right] dV = 0. \quad (6.1.7)$$

Equation (6.1.7) characterizes the variation in the measure of homogeneity P^* with time. Since quantity $\overline{v'_i c'}$ is the density of the turbulent flux, the variation in P^* is due to two processes: increasing inhomogeneity due to turbulent mixing of the substance and decreasing inhomogeneity due to molecular diffusion. In the steady case $\frac{\partial P^*}{\partial t} = 0$, and both processes balance each other:

$$\int_V \overline{v'_i c'} \frac{\partial \bar{c}}{\partial x_i} dV = -\int_V D\overline{\left(\frac{\partial c'}{\partial x_i}\right)^2} dV. \quad (6.1.8)$$

Since volume V was selected arbitrarily, it can be assumed that the assumption of steadiness is satisfied also for individual parts, in which case

$$-\overline{v'_i c'} \frac{\partial \bar{c}}{\partial x_i} = D\overline{(\operatorname{grad} c')^2}. \quad (6.1.9)$$

In the approximation of the semiempirical theory the turbulence flux of substance c can be expressed in the form

$$\overline{v_i'c'} = -K_c \frac{\partial \bar{c}}{\partial x_i}, \tag{6.1.10}$$

where K_c is the coefficient of eddy diffusion of impurity c. Then

$$K_c(\operatorname{grad}\bar{c})^2 = D\overline{(\operatorname{grad} c')^2}. \tag{6.1.11}$$

Here quantity $K_c(\operatorname{grad}\bar{c})^2$ represents the measure of inhomogeneity arising per unit time due to turbulence, and quantity $N = D\overline{(\operatorname{grad} c')^2}$ the measure of inhomogeneity vanishing per unit time due to molecular diffusion.

Quantity N is similar to the rato of dissipation of eddy energy ε. This analogy underlies the analysis of micropulsations of the impurity concentration in the flow, since the velocity fluctuation in turbulent flows has been investigated more thoroughly, both theoretically and experimentally.

Similar considerations can also be employed in examining the pulsations of meteorological variables in clouds, on the assumption that these pulsations are also due to turbulence of the medium and that the turbulence characteristics are to a certain extent identical.

Experimental data /3/ show that the inhomogeneities in clouds are usually of the order of 10^4 cm. Experimental data on temperature and velocity fluctuations, variability of the water content and cloud visibility verify the contention that these inhomogeneities are due to turbulence.

Until recently, the participation of turbulence in cloud processes was understood as purely mechanical mixing and transport, This role of turbulence is understood and quite natural. In fact, in the present-day study of the propagation of any impurity in the atmosphere or clouds nobody treats this process without allowance for eddy diffusion. On the other hand, as strange as this may seem, research into condensation processes was conducted using averaged characteristics although, without doubt, the supersaturation, which is directly related to the vertical velocity and temperature, should undergo fluctuations in a turbulent medium.

The relationship between the pulsational component of supersaturation and its ordinary component is determined by the relation between the average updraft speed and the rate of vertical pulsations. Neglect of turbulence in considering phase transitions resulted in the fact that inhomogeneity scales of the order of 10^{-1}–10^{4} cm have, in essence, been omitted from the theory of cloud formation.

Among the very few attempts at utilizing fluctuational processes for explaining the formation of cloud droplets, one should note in the first place the studies of Belyaev /1, 2/, who attributes widening of the droplet spectrum to the fluctuational nature of supersaturation and differences in the ages of particles. Unfortunately, the selection of fluctuation in supersaturation was to some extent arbitrary in these interesting and original studies. Although the above studies did not resolve the problem of the role of fluctuational processes in the formation of the spectrum, the idea itself of using fluctuations of certain parameters in examining the growth of cloud particles by condensation is promising. Later research of this type was carried out into growth by condensation and was termed stochastic /11, 2.22, 15/.

To construct a comprehensive theory of stochastic condensation, it is necessary to examine in detail the relationship between the turbulence and meteorological element fluctuations in a cloud, to establish the structure of these elements and the effect of this structure on phase transtions, and to develop a reasonably convenient mathematical tool for computation. The difficulty in solving these problems is due not only to complete absence of theoretical studies on these questions, but also to the extreme scarcity of experimental data on the measurement of meteorological element pulsations in clouds.

The theory of fluctuations in conservative passive impurities, developed for the pure atmosphere, will be used to investigate the structure of meteorological elements, or the fine cloud structure. Individual aspects of the applicability of this theory will be examined individually in the course of analyzing fluctuations in each one of the elements. We shall first deal with the question of the extent of the similarity of turbulent characteristics of the medium in the pure atmosphere and in the clouds, and correspondingly of the effect of the new phase (dropwise) on the structure of the turbulent flow, determined to some extent by the rate of dissipation of eddy energy.

The presence of particles in air results in the appearance of two additional mechanisms of eddy energy dissipation, one of which is due to the reconstruction of the flow velocity field about the particles, while the second is due to the motion of particles relative to the medium as a result of inertia. Energy dissipation arising from the first cause was in effect considered by Einstein in the problem of the effective viscosity of suspensions /4.13/. Assuming that the particles are small relative to the characteristic dimensions of the flow inhomogeneities, and that the total volume of the particles is small compared with the volume of the medium, the expression for the effective viscosity η_{ef} has the form

$$\eta_{ef}=\eta\left(1+\frac{5}{2}\frac{w}{\rho_2}\right), \tag{6.1.12}$$

where w is the impurity concentration or, when applied to clouds, the water content.

Suppose the water content of clouds does not exceed 10 g/m^3, $\frac{w}{\rho_2}\sim 10^{-5}$, and the correction for the effective viscosity is extremely small. In this case the additional mechanism of energy dissipation in clouds can be neglected. In the more general case, when w is not small, it is necessary to introduce a correction for the additional energy dissipation:

$$\frac{\varepsilon'}{\varepsilon}=\frac{5}{2}\frac{w}{\rho_2}, \tag{6.1.13}$$

where ε is the energy dissipation rate and ε' the rate of energy dissipation at particles.

In considering the second additional dissipation mechanism we shall assume that the particles move independently of one another and have dimensions which are small compared with the internal turbulence scale λ_0. Then, according to /14/, the velocity $\mathbf{u}$ of the particle relative to the medium can be expressed in the form

$$\mathbf{u}=\gamma\mathbf{v}(t\,|\,t_1,\,\mathbf{r})-\beta\gamma e^{-\beta t}\int_0^t \mathbf{v}(\xi\,|\,t_1,\,\mathbf{r})\,e^{\beta\xi}\,d\xi, \tag{6.1.14}$$

where $\mathbf{v}(\xi\,|\,t_1,\mathbf{r})$ is the Lagrangian velocity of the medium at time ξ subject to the condition that at time t_1 the given element was located at point $\mathbf{r}$; $\beta=\frac{9\eta_1}{2\rho_2R^2}$ is the reciprocal of the particle relaxation time; $\gamma=-\frac{1-\frac{\rho_1}{\rho_2}}{1+\frac{\rho_1}{\rho_2}}$ is some constant; ρ_2 is the particle density; ρ_1 is the density of the medium; R is the particle radius.

If $\frac{1}{\beta}<\tau_0=\left(\frac{\nu_1}{\varepsilon}\right)^{1/2}$ has the characteristic time scale of eddy fluctuations, it follows from (6.1.14) that in the first approximation

$$\mathbf{u}=\frac{\gamma}{\beta}\frac{d\mathbf{v}}{dt}. \qquad (6.1.15)$$

Energy dissipation ε_i'' per unit time due to the work of forces F_i resisting the motion of the ith particle is given by

$$\varepsilon_i''=\frac{\int\limits_0^T F_i\,d\mathbf{l}}{T}=6\pi\eta_1 R_i\frac{\int\limits_0^T \mathbf{u}^2\,dt}{T}=6\pi\eta_1 R_i\overline{(\mathbf{u})^2}. \qquad (6.1.16)$$

Here, the bar over a quantity denotes averaging over some time T sufficiently large compared with the turbulence time scale. With allowance for equation (6.1.15) we have

$$\varepsilon_i''=\frac{6\pi\eta_1 R_i\gamma^2}{\beta_i^2}\overline{\left(\frac{d\mathbf{v}}{dt}\right)^2}. \qquad (6.1.17)$$

On the assumption that dissipation at particles does not substantially change the flow structure, it can be assumed in line with Yaglom /19/ that

$$\overline{\left(\frac{d\mathbf{v}}{dt}\right)^2}=3\frac{\varepsilon^{3/2}}{\nu_1^{1/2}}.$$

Moreover, assuming $\gamma^2=1$ and passing on to the dissipation at particles per unit volume, we derive

$$\frac{\varepsilon''}{\varepsilon}=\frac{8\pi\varepsilon^{1/2}\rho_2^2}{9\nu_1^{3/2}\rho_1}\int\limits_0^\infty R^5 f(R)\,dR=\frac{8\pi\varepsilon^{1/2}\rho_2^2}{9\nu_1^{3/2}\rho_1}n\overline{R^5}, \qquad (6.1.18)$$

where n is the particle concentration and $f(R)$ the droplet size distribution function. Estimates show that, as far as clouds are concerned, $\frac{\varepsilon''}{\varepsilon}$ does not exceed 10^{-4}.

It can be concluded that cloud droplets cannot have a perceptible mechanical effect on the characteristics of turbulent flow. This makes it possible to establish in cloud processes laws derived for the turbulence structure in the free atmosphere. Apparently the presence of the dropwise phase manifests itself most perceptibly in considering temperature fluctuations, which can also have some effect on the dynamics of the turbulent flow.

2. FLUCTUATIONS IN ATMOSPHERIC VARIABLES AND THEIR STRUCTURE ACCORDING TO OBUKHOV AND TATARSKII

The previously noted analogy between the rate of smoothing out the measure of inhomogeneity P^* and the rate of eddy energy dissipation ε allows one to employ similarity theory and dimensional analysis and construct the structural and spectral functions of the conservative passive impurity field, similarly to the structural and spectral functions of the velocity field in turbulent flow. Without entering into the details of these studies, we limit ourselves to treating the general pattern of fluctuation inception.

Suppose that, due to the operation of a velocity field of scale l, there arises some concentration fluctuation c' of scale l. If the scale l is sufficiently large, then, due to small gradients, the resulting inhomogeneity cannot be smoothed out by molecular diffusion. (The corresponding estimates and relationships can be easily obtained from equation (6.1.7).) Consequently, the inhomogeneity will persist in a stable form until it is broken up by other, smaller eddies. This breakup process will continue until the inhomogeneity attains a scale for which molecular diffusion is effective.

The measure of the inhomogeneity generated by a large eddy is then transmitted to increasingly smaller eddies, up to scales at which molecular diffusion becomes effective. In the steady-state case the transmission rate of the measure of inhomogeneity is constant and equal to N. Since the formation time of a fluctuation in the homogeneity measure of scale l is $\frac{l}{v_l}$, then

$$N = \frac{\overline{(c_l')^2} v_l}{l},$$

whence, since $v_l \approx (\varepsilon l)^{1/3}$ (ε is the rate of eddy energy dissipation),

$$\overline{(c_l')^2} \sim \frac{N l^{2/3}}{\varepsilon^{1/3}}. \qquad (6.2.1)$$

The above pattern corresponds to the breakup and dissipation of eddies in turbulent flow, so enabling one to apply the theory of turbulence. Obukhov /13/ was the first to employ qualitative considerations in obtaining the structural function for the concentration of conservative passive impurities:

$$D_c(r)=\begin{cases} c_c^2 r^{2/3} & \text{for } L\gg r\gg l_0 \\ c_c^2 l_0^{2/3}\left(\frac{r}{l_0}\right)^2 & \text{for } r\ll l_0, \end{cases} \tag{6.2.2}$$

where

$$c_c^2=a^2\frac{N}{\varepsilon^{1/3}}, \quad l_0=\left(\frac{27a^6D^3}{\varepsilon}\right)^{1/4}, \tag{6.2.3}$$

a is a constant, D is the impurity diffusion coefficient, and l_0 characterizes the scale corresponding to the initial appearance of diffusion processes which aid in smoothing out concentration inhomogeneities transmitted by eddies of size differing from that of larger eddies.

The limitation on the external scale L is due to the fact that turbulence for large scales cannot be regarded as isotropic. Thus Obukhov's "two-thirds law" for conservative passive impurities, on the assumption of isotropicity, is valid only for certain scales. In particular, in the atmosphere, starting with certain scales the turbulence regime starts to be affected by buoyancy (Archimedes) forces. An estimate of the scale L_* at which these forces have a perceptible effect can be obtained from similarity and dimensional considerations, by adding to ε and N a parameter reflecting the role of buoyancy forces.

It was suggested by Kabanov /8/ that this parameter should be the quantity $\alpha\frac{g}{T}\left(\frac{dT}{dz}+\gamma_a\right)$, where α is the ratio of the eddy viscosity coefficient to the eddy thermal diffusivity coefficient, g is the acceleration of gravity, while γ_a is the adiabatic lapse rate. In this form the parameter reflects the nature of the buoyancy forces (deviations of the mean lapse rate from γ_a) as well as their intensity. The above three parameters can be used to construct a unique combination whose dimension is length and which determines the scale L_*:

$$L_*=\varepsilon^{1/2}\left[\alpha\frac{g}{\overline{T}}\left(\frac{d\overline{T}}{dz}+\gamma_a\right)\right]^{-3/4}. \tag{6.2.4}$$

In the next section this scale will be derived in analyzing temperature fluctuations. In order to write N in a more graphic form, we shall use an expression obtained in the preceding section:

$$N=D\overline{(\text{grad }c')^2}=K_c(\text{grad }\bar{c})^2.$$

Quantity ε, entering (6.2.3), can be expressed in terms of average values:

$$\varepsilon = \frac{1}{2} \nu_1 \overline{\left(\frac{\partial v_i}{\partial x_j} + \frac{\partial v_j}{\partial x_i} \right)^2},$$

or in the form

$$\varepsilon = K \left(\frac{\partial \overline{v_i}}{\partial x_j} \right)^2. \tag{6.2.5}$$

Expression (6.2.3) thus assumes the form

$$c_c^2 = a^2 \left[K \left(\frac{\partial \overline{v_i}}{\partial x_j} \right)^2 \right]^{-1/3} K_c (\operatorname{grad} \overline{c})^2. \tag{6.2.6}$$

Relationships (6.2.2), (6.2.3) and (6.2.6) are basic for characteristics of fluctuations in conservative passive impurity. It should be noted that these expressions were justified experimentally. Temperature fluctuations are the ones most thoroughly explored.

The two-thirds law has been confirmed by measuring fluctuations in absolute humidity /6/ and the spectra of fluctuations in the refractive index of the troposphere /20, 21/. Processing of these experimental data yields the constant a. According to Tatarskii /16/

$$a \approx 2.4. \tag{6.2.7}$$

There are no doubts at present that this theory describes satisfactorily the principal laws governing fluctuations in a conservative passive impurity. These important results, which provide the key to the study of fluctuations in an impurity in the atmosphere, are in line with the Eulerian approach to the problem and describe the spatial distribution of the impurity concentration at some time. An approach of this kind is very important in the study of wave propagation in a turbulent atmosphere and visibility fluctuations, and also when measuring some atmospheric properties from aircraft.

However, there exists an entire class of problems which requires not an instantaneous space section, but knowledge of the laws governing the behavior of some elementary volume. If this volume has some impurity concentration value corresponding to it, then the problem of the time variation of the concentration in this air element requires another approach. Consideration of the variation in the properties of some element of a medium is usually termed a Lagrangian analysis (it corresponds to an analysis of processes in a coordinate system moving together with the given element of the medium).

As in the case of the Eulerian approach, in the Lagrangian approach we should employ laws governing the variation in variables such as the temperature or velocity in a turbulent flow. In the theory of turbulence the Lagrangian characteristics of the medium have been investigated in reasonable detail. They are of particular importance in considering mutual diffusion in problems of the propagation of impurities from sources. When studying the fluctuations in certain meteorological elements we shall attempt to express the numerical characteristics of these parameters in terms of quantities $\mathbf{v}$ and T, which can be described by various theoretical methods and experimental results.

In problems pertaining to the study of various processes in the atmosphere, it is primarily necessary to know the Lagrangian characteristics, so imparting particular importance to the second method. In this approach it is possible to study fluctuations in quantities which are not conservative. Since the transition to variables $\mathbf{v}$ and T in each case requires separate consideration, the method will be illustrated by specific examples.

3. TEMPERATURE FLUCTUATIONS IN THE ATMOSPHERE

We shall consider the theory of fluctuations of conservative passive impurities in the atmosphere using temperature fluctuations as an illustration. Note first that the temperature in the atmosphere is not conservative, since it changes during the ascent of air due to its expansion. As a conservative quantity we can use the potential temperature

$$H = T + \gamma_a z. \tag{6.3.1}$$

Over reasonably wide limits of variation in T and z, quantity γ_a, the adiabatic lapse rate, can be regarded as constant:

$$\gamma_a = \frac{g}{c_p} = 0.98 \cdot 10^{-4} \text{ deg/cm}. \tag{6.3.2}$$

For scales smaller than L_* the temperature can be regarded as passive. Therefore the structural function for T has the form

$$D_T(r)=\begin{cases} c_T^2 r^{2/3}, & l_0 \ll r \ll L_* \\ c_T^2 l_0^{2/3}\left(\frac{r}{l_0}\right)^2, & r \ll l_0, \end{cases} \tag{6.3.3}$$

where

$$c_T^2=a^2\left[K\left(\frac{\partial \bar{v}_i}{\partial x_j}\right)^2\right]^{-1/3} K_T(\mathrm{grad}\,\overline{H})^2. \tag{6.3.4}$$

The difference between expression (6.3.4) and the corresponding expression (6.2.6) is that the structural function $D_T(r)$ refers to temperature fluctuations, while the expression for C_T^2 involves grad $\overline{H}$. The fact that the fluctuations in T are proportional not to the total gradient of T, but only to the gradient of $\overline{H}$, has the following physical meaning. At some level z_1 the temperature T, following equation (6.3.1), will be a function of $H(z)$ and z :

$$T=T(z_1,\ H(z_1)).$$

Suppose a given air element finds itself at level z_2 as a result of turbulent mixing. Since $H(z)$ does not change during the travel of the volume while z assumes a new value, the same volume at level z_2 will have the temperature

$$T=T(z_2,\ H(z_1)),$$

which will differ from the value of T at level z_2 by an amount

$$\Delta T=T(z_2,\ H(z_2))-T(z_2,\ H(z_1))=$$
$$=\frac{\partial T}{\partial H}\frac{dH}{dz}\Delta z=\frac{dH}{dz}\Delta z.$$

It also follows that fluctuations which arise are proportional to the gradient of $\overline{H}$.

It is now possible to estimate those scales at which the buoyancy forces have a marked effect on the turbulent flow structure. For example, if the temperature stratification is stable, these will be the scales at which the eddy energy expended in overcoming the buoyancy forces is commensurable with the rate of dissipation ε of eddy energy, i. e.,

$$A_l=\varepsilon,$$

where A_l is the average work done by eddies of scale l against buoyance forces per unit air mass per unit time. This quantity is equal to

$$A_l \approx \frac{g}{T} v_l \Delta T_l.$$

Since $v_l \approx (\varepsilon l)^{1/3}$ and $\Delta T_l \approx \frac{d\overline{H}}{dz} l$,

$$A_l \approx \frac{g}{\overline{T}} \varepsilon l^{4/3} \frac{d\overline{H}}{dz}.$$

It follows that, since $A_l = \varepsilon$, the scale

$$l \approx L_* \approx \varepsilon^{1/2} \left(\frac{g}{\overline{T}} \frac{d\overline{H}}{dz} \right)^{-3/4}$$

is in agreement with (6.2.4), obtained on the basis of dimensional analysis.

We finally note that l_0 is determined in accordance with (6.2.3), in which the diffusion coefficient should be replaced by the thermal diffusivity. The temperature fluctuations were determined in great detail in boundary layers for different atmospheric stratifications. The experimental data are much more sparse for the troposphere. Measurements at altitudes of the order of 500–700 m indicate that the value of C_T lies between 0 and 0.03 deg/cm$^{1/3}$.

The structure of the concentration of the conservative passive impurity was first considered for the case of the temperature field. Before developing an analytical approach for the case of clouds, we shall make some preliminary remarks and estimates. For convective clouds the effect of buoyancy can have a specific nature. However, according to experimental data /4/ the effect of these forces in cumulus is characteristic of scales greater than $L_* \sim \sim 10^4$ cm. At small scales there begin to appear additional effects associated with the discrete nature of the liquid phase, so a structural function constructed from similarity considerations cannot be employed in the viscous range.

For droplet concentrations of the order of 10^3 cm^{-3}, the average distance between particles $l \sim 10^{-1}$ cm can be taken as the minimum scale for which the theory presented in the preceding section is applicable. Since this quantity is of the order of the internal scale of turbulence, in essence we should restrict ourselves to the two-thirds law, i.e., to the inertial range of sizes.

Before passing on to consider the structure of temperature fluctuations in clouds, we shall make some estimates of the temperature effect of droplets. We shall deal with the effect of the specific heat of cloud droplets. In fact, when the air temperature changes, the cloud droplets also change their temperature. This process has a certain lag and affects the specific heat of the medium, since some of the heat is spent in changing the droplet temperature; here, this flux depends on the frequency characteristics of the fluctuations. If the air temperature differs from the droplet temperature by an amount ΔT, then as a result of temperature equalization between the droplets and the medium the air temperature changes by an amount ΔT_1, determined from the relationship

$$\frac{\Delta T_1}{\Delta T - \Delta T_1} = \frac{c_2 w}{c_p \rho_1}, \tag{6.3.5}$$

where c_2 is the specific heat of water and c_p the specific heat of air. Hence in the case of a cloud medium, one obtains the estimate

$$\frac{\Delta T_1}{\Delta T} \leqslant 4 \cdot 10^{-2}, \tag{6.3.6}$$

which shows that the effect of the specific heat of water can be neglected with a reasonable degree of accuracy.

Of much greater importance is the release of heat during condensation of vapor on droplets. The time τ to establish the quasi-steady condensation (evaporation) regime is

$$\tau = \frac{c_2 \rho_2 R^2}{3K_1}, \tag{6.3.7}$$

where R is the droplet radius. For cloud particles $\tau \approx 10^{-3}$ sec, and it can therefore be assumed that quasi-steady conditions are always attained in clouds.

To estimate the effect of phase transitions on the structure of the temperature field it is necessary to know the rate at which the supersaturation (undersaturation) of vapor arising as a result of temperature changes is smoothed out.

For the quasi-steady regime the vapor flux I_i to a droplet of radius R_i in the Maxwellian equation approximation is given by the expression

$$I_i = 4\pi K_3 R_i \delta_0. \tag{6.3.8}$$

The total vapor flux per unit volume is

$$I=4\pi K_3\delta_0\int_0^\infty Rf(R)\,dR=4\pi K_3\delta_0 n\bar{R}, \tag{6.3.9}$$

where n is the vapor concentration.

Suppose there exists a supersaturation δ_0 in the vapor–droplet system at time $t=0$. We shall consider the variation in δ_0 with time when this system is closed. Since the variation in vapor density in this case equals its flux I to the droplets, we have

$$\frac{d\delta_0}{dt}=-4\pi\frac{\rho_2}{\rho}K_3 n\bar{R}\delta_0, \tag{6.3.10}$$

from which it follows on the assumption of $4\pi\frac{\rho_2}{\rho}K_3\bar{R}n\approx$ const that

$$\delta_0(t)=\delta(0)\,e^{-\beta_1 t}, \tag{6.3.11}$$

where

$$\beta_1=4\pi\frac{\rho_2}{\rho}K_3 n\bar{R}. \tag{6.3.12}$$

Quantity β_1 characterizes the rate of smoothing out of the supersaturation in the vapor–droplet system. In the case of clouds

$$\beta_1\approx 1\ \mathrm{sec}^{-1},$$

which means that for processes with characteristic time $\tau\gg 1$ sec one must consider the heat released during phase transitions and assume that the transmission of vapor to the droplets occurs under quasi-steady conditions.

It is natural that the high-frequency temperature fluctuations with characteristic period $\tau\ll\beta_1^{-1}$ arising in clouds are unaffected by phase transitions. Outside the ranges of dissipation and of operation of buoyancy forces the time scales τ of pulsations correspond to space scales $l=\varepsilon^{1/2}\tau^{3/2}$. For sufficiently intense turbulence in clouds, the time scales β_1^{-1} will have the space scales $L_p=\beta_1^{-3/2}\varepsilon^{1/2}$ corresponding to them.

If $L_p\gg l_0=\nu_1^{3/4}\varepsilon^{-1/4}$ over the range $l_0\ll l\ll L_p$, the structural function of the temperature field will obey the Kolmogorov-Obukhov two-thirds law:

$$D_T(r)=aN\varepsilon^{-1/3}r^{2/3},\quad l_0\ll r\ll L_p, \tag{6.3.13}$$

where a is a constant; $N=\varkappa_1\overline{(\mathrm{grad}\,H')^2}$ is the rate of dissipation of temperature inhomogeneities by molecular thermal conductivity; $\varkappa_1$ is the coefficient of molecular thermal diffusivity; $H' = H - \bar{H}$ is the fluctuation in potential temperature.

Unlike turbulence under clear skies, in this case N cannot be expressed in terms of the average lapse rate. However, it can be expected on the whole that this range of sizes is either very small, or does not exist at all, and hence the principal effect on phase transitions is exerted by scales $l \gg L_p$, since τ given by equation (6.3.7) and β_1^{-1} from equation (6.3.12) are sufficiently small. If the temperature stratification in clouds deviates from wet adiabatic, temperature fluctuations on scales $l \gg L_p$ will in the main be determined by precisely this deviation $\frac{d\bar{T}}{dz} + \gamma_{\text{w.a}}$.

In this case we take as the conservative quantity with respect to temperature the pseudopotential temperature $H_{\text{w.a}}$ given by

$$H_{\text{w.a}} = T + \gamma_{\text{w.a}} z, \tag{6.3.14}$$

where z is the vertical coordinate while $\gamma_{\text{w.a}}$ is the wet-adiabatic lapse rate.

The value of $\gamma_{\text{w.a}}$ varies under real conditions from $5 \cdot 10^{-3}$ to $8 \cdot 10^{-3}$ deg/m, and for an individual cloud it can be assumed constant with reasonable accuracy. Further analysis can be conducted by analogy with the case of the free atmosphere, since $H_{\text{w.a}}$ in clouds was taken as the conservative passive impurity. Then, in the presence of a gradient $H_{\text{w.a}}$ there exist fluctuations in T with corresponding structural function

$$D_T(r) = C_T^2 r^{2/3}, \quad L_p \ll r \ll L_*, \tag{6.3.15}$$

where

$$C_T^2 = a^2 \left[K \left(\frac{\partial \bar{v}_i}{\partial x_j} \right)^2 \right]^{-1/3} K_T \left(\frac{d\bar{H}_{\text{w.a}}}{dz} \right)^2,$$

$$L_p = \beta_1^{-3/2} \varepsilon^{1/2}, \quad L_* = \varepsilon^{1/2} \left[\alpha \frac{g}{T} \left(\frac{d\bar{T}}{dz} + \gamma_{\text{w.a}} \right) \right]^{-3/4}.$$

The effect of phase transitions on turbulence in clouds was examined elsewhere /9/, where the concept was introduced of the phase turbulence scale L_p and expressions obtained for L_* and various other turbulence characteristics.

4. FLUCTUATIONS IN VAPOR DENSITY AND WATER CONTENT

To consider fluctuations in the water vapor density ρ in the absence of phase transitions (supersaturation $\delta_0 < 0$), we shall use as conservative quantity the specific humidity and potential temperature H.

Since $q = \frac{\rho}{\rho_1}$, where ρ_1 is the air density, ρ can be expressed in the form

$$\rho = q\rho_1 = q\frac{p_1}{R_{air}T} = \frac{qp_1}{R_{air}(H - \gamma_a z)}, \tag{6.4.1}$$

where p_1 is the air pressure while R_{air} is the gas constant for air. Similarly to temperature fluctuations, fluctuations in ρ are proportional to quantity θ, which is obtained by differentiating equation (6.4.1) with respect to z on the assumption that q and H are functions of z:

$$\theta = \left(\frac{\partial\rho}{\partial q}\frac{dq}{\partial z} + \frac{\partial\rho}{\partial H}\frac{dH}{dz}\right) = \frac{p_1}{R_{air}T}\left(\frac{dq}{dz} - \frac{q}{T}\frac{dH}{dz}\right). \tag{6.4.2}$$

The structural function has the form

$$D_\rho(r) = \begin{cases} c_\rho^2 r^{2/3} & \text{for } l_0 \ll r \ll L_* \\ c_\rho^2 l_0^{2/3}\left(\frac{r}{l_0}\right)^2 & \text{for } r \ll l_0, \end{cases}$$

where

$$c_\rho^2 = a^2\left[K\left(\frac{\partial\overline{v_i}}{\partial x_j}\right)^2\right]^{-1/3} K_\rho\bar{\theta}^2,$$

$$\bar{\theta} = \frac{p_1}{R_{air}T}\left(\frac{d\bar{q}}{dz} - \frac{q}{T}\frac{d\overline{H}}{dz}\right). \tag{6.4.3}$$

Relationship (6.4.2) shows that fluctuations in vapor density are due not only to the gradient of specific humidity, but also to the gradient of potential temperature. We shall consider fluctuations in ρ in the Lagrangian sense /11/:

$$\frac{d\rho}{dt} = \frac{d}{dt}\left(\frac{qp_1}{R_{air}T}\right) = \frac{q}{R_{air}T}\frac{dp_1}{dt} - \frac{qp_1}{R_{air}T^2}\frac{dT}{dt}$$

If we neglect processes associated with radiation and heat transfer then

$$\rho_1 c_p \frac{dT}{dt} = \frac{dp_1}{dt}, \tag{6.4.4}$$

whence

$$\frac{d\rho}{dt} = \rho\left(\frac{c_p}{R_{\text{air}}} - 1\right)\frac{1}{T}\frac{dT}{dt}. \tag{6.4.5}$$

It is easy to show that fluctuations in ρ are due only to temperature fluctuations and are not a function of q. In fact, integration of equation (6.4.5) yields

$$\ln\rho = \left(\frac{c_p}{R_{\text{air}}} - 1\right)\ln T + d.$$

Separation of the systematic and pulsational parts gives

$$\frac{\rho'}{\rho} = \left(\frac{c_p}{R_{\text{air}}} - 1\right)\frac{T'}{T}. \tag{6.4.6}$$

Since $\frac{c_p}{R_{\text{air}}} \approx 3.5$, the relative fluctuations in vapor density exceed by 150% the temperature fluctuations. It is of interest that in the Eulerian approach the amplitude of fluctuations is not found to increase. In fact, when $\frac{d\bar{q}}{dt} = 0$, $\frac{\overline{\theta}}{\rho} = \frac{1}{\rho}\frac{dH}{dz}$. This difference is quite clear, since during the motion of elementary volumes the variation in temperature as a result of expansion and compression of air is possible also when $\frac{d\overline{H}}{dz} = 0$, i.e., when there are no fluctuations in the Eulerian sense.

Consider the question of the water content in a cloud. As the conservative characteristic in this case one can take the quantity

$$\Pi = w - (\gamma_{\text{a}} - \gamma_{\text{w.a}})\frac{c_p}{L}z. \tag{6.4.7}$$

The variation in water content w during the ascent of an elementary volume over height Δz is given by the expression

$$\Delta w = \frac{\partial w}{\partial \Pi} \frac{d\Pi}{dz} \Delta z. \tag{6.4.8}$$

The structural function $D_w(r)$ of the water content is then given by

$$D_w(r) = C_w^2 r^{2/3}, \quad l_1 \ll r \ll L_*, \tag{6.4.9}$$

where

$$C_w^2 = a^2 \left[K \left(\frac{\partial \bar{v}_i}{\partial x_j} \right)^2 \right]^{-1/3} K_w \left(\frac{d\bar{\Pi}}{dz} \right)^2.$$

The value of l_1 is determined by the average distance between particles:

$$l_1 = n^{-1/3} \sim 0.1 \text{cm}.$$

In fact, one can refer to the water content spectrum only for reasonably large scales ($\gg l_1$), since the concept of "water content" is valid only for a sufficiently small volume containing a sufficiently small number of droplets. At small distances, where the discreteness of the droplet content becomes substantial, it becomes meaningless and the concept of the "water content spectrum" also loses its meaning.

The technique of considering the fluctuations of various quantities in turbulent flows is based on the assumption that this quantity is conservative and passive. While the question of passivity is solved rather simply and uniquely, the requirement of conservativeness imposes a substantial limitation on the theory. In essence, this was encountered from the very start in the study of temperature fluctuations. This problem was solved by converting to the temperature $H = T + \gamma_a z$ which is a conservative characteristic of the medium.

The path to the solution consists in formulating such combinations of variables that would satisfy the laws of conservation. On the basis of this method, for example, fluctuations in the refractive index were considered. On the whole, this approach consists in the following. The quantity under study should be expressed in terms of conservative quantities (which do not vary upon moving in space) and quantities whose value is determined uniquely by the coordinates. The resulting expressions yield, by differentiation with respect to conservative parameters, the principal equation defining the amplitude of fluctuations in the sought quantity.

A similar technique was used in this book while considering temperature fluctuations in a cloud, when the pseudopotential temperature $H_{w.a}$ replaced the potential temperature. It should, however, be immediately stipulated that conversion to $H_{w.a}$ is no longer so obvious and rigorous as in the case of a pure atmosphere. The fact that $\gamma_{w.a}$ is not constant does not excessively complicate the problem. The main feature of this transition is that in examining temperature fluctuations in clouds we ignore the effect of the time lag.

When a volume element moves in space its temperature does not immediately become equal to the pseudopotential temperature. The process occurs with some lag, allowance for which involves solving the corresponding differential equation. The effect of lag is not so obvious when temperature is used as an illustration. However, on considering the fluctuations in vapor density and the supersaturation this effect is more substantial. It is of importance, since if the lag is great for the case of temperature, the conservative quantity is H (potential temperature), while if it is small, then $H_{w.a}$ (the pseudopotential temperature) is the conservative quantity.

The question of fluctuations in dynamic quantities thus requires solving the corresponding time-dependent equation and does not always yield satisfactory results. Some aspects of this approach will be presented when investigating fluctuations in quantities ρ and δ_0. The Lagrangian approach in essence is not subject to limitations of this kind and is more promising in the study of fluctuations in dynamic quantities. The point is that then we are dealing immediately with time-dependent quantities and the effect of lag can be taken into account without much difficulty. However, it should be stipulated at once that reasonably simple expressions can be obtained only if certain simplifying assumptions are introduced.

One example of a nonconservative quantity in clouds is the water vapor density. The existence of phase transitions results in the fact that any variation in external variables involves transmitting some of the vapor to the droplets or the evaporation of water from the droplets and a corresponding variation in vapor density ρ. If it is assumed that the vapor in the cloud is in equilibrium with the droplet system, i. e., that the excess vapor arising during air updrafts is completely converted into droplets and the vapor density is maintained at a value equal to the density of saturated vapor, then the Eulerian approach can be used. In this case

$$\rho = \rho_0. \qquad (6.4.10)$$

According to the above estimates, the characteristic time of excess vapor dissipation is $\tau = \frac{1}{\beta_1} \approx 1$ sec. Therefore, this approximation is valid for processes with time scales much greater than 1 sec. It cannot be used for high-frequency processes. Quantity β_1 was estimated for a typical cloud; thus, for the initial stage of cloud development or for the region near the cloud boundaries, the values of τ can be substantially greater and the utility of (6.4.10) will be more limited. Since ρ_0 can be expressed in terms of conservative quantities, it is easy to obtain a structural function for ρ. Here

$$\frac{d\rho_0}{dH_{\text{w.a}}} = \frac{d\rho_0}{dT} = \frac{\rho_0}{T}\left(\frac{L}{R_v T} - 1\right). \tag{6.4.11}$$

Then $\overline{\theta}$ satisfies

$$\overline{\theta} = \frac{\rho_0}{T}\left(\frac{L}{R_v T} - 1\right)\frac{d\overline{H}_{\text{w.a}}}{dz}. \tag{6.4.12}$$

If it is remembered that temperature fluctuations in a cloud are defined by the quantity $\frac{d\overline{H}_{\text{w.a}}}{dz}$, it is easy to show that

$$\frac{\rho'}{\rho} = \left(\frac{L}{R_v T} - 1\right)\frac{T'}{T} \approx 18\,\frac{T'}{T}, \tag{6.4.13}$$

i.e., the amplitude of the relative fluctuations in vapor density exceeds 18-fold the amplitude of relative temperature fluctuations.

It is noteworthy that, since the relationship between T and ρ is general, relationship (6.4.13) is valid over a wider range of scales and is not based on turbulence theory. In particular, if the fluctuations do not obey the two-thirds law, the structural function for ρ' can be derived from experimental data on T'.

It appears to this author that the Lagrangian approach makes possible the study of fluctuations in ρ in more detail and the refinement of the characteristics of these fluctuations.

We consider the continuity equation for the medium:

$$\frac{\partial \rho_c}{\partial t} + \operatorname{div}(\rho_c \mathbf{v}_0) = -I, \tag{6.4.14}$$

where $\rho_c = \rho + \rho_1$, while I is the flux of vapor to the droplets. Then

$$\frac{d\rho_1}{dt} + \rho_1 \operatorname{div} \mathbf{v}_0 + \frac{d\rho}{dt} + \rho \operatorname{div} \mathbf{v}_0 = -I.$$

In the first approximation, if air diffusion is neglected

$$\frac{d\rho_1}{dt}+\rho_1 \operatorname{div} \mathbf{v}_0=0, \tag{6.4.15}$$

whence

$$\frac{d\rho}{dt}+\rho \operatorname{div} \mathbf{v}_0=-I. \tag{6.4.16}$$

If equation (6.4.15) is employed for eliminating div $\mathbf{v}_0$ in equation (6.4.16), we obtain

$$\frac{d\rho}{dt}-\frac{\rho}{\rho_1}\frac{d\rho_1}{dt}=-I, \tag{6.4.17}$$

or

$$\frac{d}{dt}\left(\frac{\rho}{\rho_1}\right)=-\frac{I}{\rho_1}. \tag{6.4.18}$$

It is known that I is defined by the expression

$$I=\int_0^\infty \frac{dm}{dt}\psi(m)\,dm, \tag{6.4.19}$$

where $\psi(m)$ is the droplet mass distribution function, while m is the mass of a droplet. Since

$$\frac{dm}{dt}=4\pi K_3\rho_2\left(1-\frac{\rho_0}{\rho}\right)r,$$

and in view of the fact that $\psi(m)\,dm=f(r)\,dr$, and designating by $F_1=\frac{4\pi\rho_2}{\rho}K_3Rn$ a quantity proportional to the first moment of the droplet size distribution function, we can write

$$I=(\rho-\rho_0)F_1. \tag{6.4.20}$$

Substitution of this value of I into equation (6.4.17) yields

$$\frac{d\rho}{dt}=-(\rho-\rho_0)F_1+\frac{\rho}{\rho_1}\frac{d\rho_1}{dt}. \tag{6.4.21}$$

Since

$$\frac{d\rho_1}{dt}=\frac{1}{R_{air}T}\frac{dp_1}{dt}-\frac{\rho_1}{T}\frac{dT}{dt}, \tag{6.4.22}$$

$$\rho_1 c_p\frac{dT}{dt}=\frac{dp_1}{dt}+LI=\frac{dp_1}{dt}+LF_1(\rho-\rho_0), \tag{6.4.23}$$

the expression for $\frac{d\rho_1}{dt}$ becomes

$$\frac{d\rho_1}{dt}=\frac{\rho_1}{T}\left(\frac{c_p}{R_{air}}-1\right)\frac{dT}{dt}-\frac{LF_1}{R_{air}T}(\rho-\rho_0). \tag{6.4.24}$$

Equation (6.4.21) can then be expressed in the form

$$\frac{d\rho}{dt}=\left(1+\frac{L\rho}{\rho_1 R_{air}T}\right)F_1(\rho_0-\rho)+\frac{\rho}{T}\left(\frac{c_p}{R_{air}}-1\right)\frac{dT}{dt}. \tag{6.4.25}$$

Since factor $(1+\frac{L\rho}{\rho_1 R_v T})$ is a slowly varying function, the solution to equation (6.4.25) is

$$\rho(t)=\rho(0)\left[\frac{T(0)}{T(t)}\right]^{\alpha}\exp\left(-\int_0^t\beta_1\,dt\right)+\beta_1\left[\frac{T(0)}{T(t)}\right]^{\alpha}\exp\left(-\int_0^t\beta_1\,dt\right)\times$$
$$\times\int_0^t\left[\rho_0(\tau)\left(\frac{T(\tau)}{T(0)}\right)^{\alpha}\exp\left(\int_0^{\tau}\beta_1\,d\tau\right)\right]d\tau, \tag{6.4.26}$$

where

$$\beta_1=\left(1+\frac{L\rho}{R_{air}T\rho_1}\right)F_1, \tag{6.4.27}$$

$$\alpha=\left(\frac{c_p}{R_{air}}-1\right). \tag{6.4.28}$$

If we consider reasonably large periods of time, the first term in equation (6.4.26) can be neglected, in which case

$$\rho(t)=\beta_1\exp\left(-\int_0^t\beta_1\,dt\right)\int_0^t\rho_0(\tau)\left(\frac{T(\tau)}{T(0)}\right)^{\alpha}\exp\left(\int_0^{\tau}\beta_1\,d\tau\right)d\tau. \tag{6.4.29}$$

The value of β_1 usually varies reasonably slowly, and hence equation (6.4.29) can be simplified:

$$\rho(t)=\beta_1 \exp(-\beta_1 t)\int_0^t \rho_0(\tau)\left(\frac{T(\tau)}{T(0)}\right)^{\alpha} \exp(\beta_1\tau)\,d\tau. \qquad (6.4.30)$$

If, in addition, $\frac{1}{\beta_1}$ is small compared with the characteristic time of variation in ρ_0 and T, the contribution to the integral is determined by factor $\exp(\beta_1\tau)$. Then

$$\rho(t)=\left[1+\left(\frac{c_p}{R_{air}}+\frac{L}{R_v T}-2\right)\left(t+\frac{1}{\beta_1}\right)\frac{1}{T}\frac{dT}{dt}\right]\rho_0. \qquad (6.4.31)$$

Over the range

$$\frac{1}{\beta_1} \ll t \ll \frac{T}{v_z \gamma_{w.a}}$$

equation (6.4.31) assumes the form

$$\rho(t)=\left(1+20\,\frac{\gamma_{w.a}\, v_z t}{T_0-\gamma_{w.a} v_z t}\right)\rho_0 \approx \rho_0\left(1+20\,\frac{\Delta T}{T}\right). \qquad (6.4.32)$$

Since $\frac{1}{\beta_1}\approx 1$ sec, and when $v_z \approx 30$ cm/sec, $\frac{T}{\gamma_{w.a} v_z}\approx 2\cdot 10^5$ sec, the range of variation in t can be quite large. If t is sufficiently small, one can take as the first approximation of $\rho(t)$

$$\rho=\rho_0. \qquad (6.4.33)$$

These simple mathematical manipulations were carried out in order to illustrate the limitations imposed on the process if it is assumed that equation (6.4.32) is satisfied.

Note that in (6.4.27) ρ can be replaced by ρ_0; here β_1 will not depend on the supersaturation:

$$\beta_1=\left(1+\frac{L\rho_0}{R_{air} T \rho_1}\right)F_1. \qquad (6.4.34)$$

The value of β_1 is close to 1 sec^{-1}. As noted above, for the initial stage of development and near the cloud boundaries it can be smaller than unity and ρ can change rapidly. In this case, equation (6.4.21) implies that approximation (6.4.32) becomes inapplicable.

5. FLUCTUATIONS IN SUPERSATURATION

In the absence of phase transitions ($\delta_0 < 0$), supersaturation in the atmosphere can be treated as a conservative impurity:

$$\delta_0 = \left(1 - \frac{\rho_0}{\rho}\right) = \left(1 - \frac{M}{qM_1}\frac{e_0}{p_1}\right), \tag{6.5.1}$$

where ρ_0 and e_0 are the saturated vapor density and pressure above a flat surface, M is the molecular weight of the vapor, and M_1 is the molecular weight of air. By analogy with the preceding, θ is given by

$$\theta = \frac{\partial \delta_0}{\partial q}\frac{dq}{dz} + \frac{\partial \delta_0}{\partial H}\frac{dH}{dz} = \frac{M}{M_1 q p_1}\left[\frac{e_0}{q}\frac{dq}{dz} - \frac{de_0}{dH}\frac{dH}{dz}\right].$$

According to the Clausius-Clapeyron relation

$$\frac{de_0}{dH} = \frac{d}{dT}e_0 \approx \frac{\rho_0 L}{T} = \frac{e_0 L}{R_v T^2}, \tag{6.5.2}$$

where L is the heat of condensation. Since $\dfrac{M}{qM_1}\dfrac{e_0}{p_1} = 1 - \delta_0$, we can write for $\bar{\theta}$

$$\bar{\theta} = (1 - \delta_0)\left(\frac{d \ln \bar{q}}{dz} - \frac{L}{R_v T^2}\frac{d\bar{H}}{dz}\right), \tag{6.5.3}$$

$$C_\delta^2 = a^2\left[K\left(\frac{\partial \bar{v}_i}{\partial x_j}\right)^2\right]^{-1/3} K_\theta \bar{\theta}_\delta^2. \tag{6.5.4}$$

It should be noted that phase transitions are not always absent for negative δ_0. The presence in the atmosphere of hygroscopic condensation nuclei can result in the conversion of some quantity of vapor into nuclei, and vice versa. However, in the majority of cases, with the possible exception of near-zero values of δ_0, these vapor fluxes can be neglected.

Consider the case when the specific humidity gradients are small. In general, the spatial inhomogeneity of the potential temperature is induced by a much larger number of factors than the inhomogeneity in q. This case is therefore the most probable. The structural function for the supersaturation can be expressed in the same form as the structural function for the temperature, but the expression for $\bar{\theta}$ will contain $(1 - \delta_0)\dfrac{L}{R_v T}$ as a multiplier.

Since both fluctuations are due to the same causes, it is possible to establish a direct relation between fluctuations in a given quantity and to obtain an expression for the ratio of the amplitudes of these fluctuations:

$$\frac{\delta_0'}{\frac{\Delta T}{T}} = -(1-\delta_0)\frac{L}{R_v T} \approx -19(1-\delta_0). \qquad (6.5.5)$$

This estimate shows that when $\delta_0 \ll 1$ (this condition is always valid in the atmosphere), the amplitude of fluctuations in δ_0 is almost 20-fold greater than the amplitude of the relative temperature fluctuations. This estimate enables one to employ experimental data on temperature fluctuations in the study of processes associated with variations in δ_0.

We shall now examine the variability in δ_0 using the Lagrangian approach. Neglecting diffusion and allowing for (6.5.1), we have

$$\frac{d\delta_0}{dt} = \frac{d}{dt}\left(1 - \frac{R_{\text{air}}T}{q}\frac{\rho_0}{p_1}\right) = -\frac{\rho_0 R_{\text{air}}}{qp_1}\frac{dT}{dt} + \frac{\rho_0 R_{\text{air}} T}{qp_1^2}\frac{dp_1}{dt} - \frac{R_{\text{air}}T}{qp_1}\frac{d\rho_0}{dT}\frac{dT}{dt}. \qquad (6.5.6)$$

In line with the Clausius-Clapeyron relation

$$\frac{d\rho_0}{dT} = \frac{\rho_0}{T}\left(\frac{L}{R_v T} - 1\right). \qquad (6.5.7)$$

Equation (6.5.6) then yields

$$\frac{d\delta_0}{dt} = \frac{\rho_0 R_{\text{air}} T}{qp_1^2}\frac{dp_1}{dt} - \frac{\rho_0 LM}{qM_1 p_1 T}\frac{dT}{dt}. \qquad (6.5.8)$$

With the aid of the equation $\rho_1 c_p \frac{dT}{dt} = \frac{dp_1}{dt}$, one can relate δ_0 either to pressure or to temperature fluctuations. Thus, expressing the right-hand side of equation (6.5.8) in terms of pressure variations, we obtain

$$\frac{d\delta_0}{dt} = (1-\delta_0)\left(1 - \frac{LM}{M_1 c_p T}\right)\frac{1}{p_1}\frac{dp_1}{dt}. \qquad (6.5.9)$$

Before analyzing the above expression, one important remark should be made. When using the Eulerian approach to study fluctuations in conservative impurities we assumed that, when volume elements of the medium are interchanged between any two levels, the pressure of the corresponding level is established in these elementary volumes. This meant that we disregarded pressure fluctuations. This assumption is unjustified and requires additional study, since the presence of disturbances in the atmosphere definitely results in pressure fluctuations which, in turn, should affect fluctuations in the conservative passive impurity. These estimates, in our opinion, can be derived from the Lagrangian approach to the problem.

The total derivative of p_1 is given by

$$\frac{dp_1}{dt}=\frac{\partial p_1}{\partial t}+v_i\frac{\partial p_1}{\partial x_i}\approx\frac{\partial p_1}{\partial t}+v_z\frac{\partial p_1}{\partial z}=\frac{\partial p_1}{\partial t}-g\rho_1 v_z, \quad (6.5.10)$$

since the horizontal components can be neglected compared with the vertical component. The pressure variation in time can be induced by a large variety of processes, which have their own time scales. Rapidly varying processes are not usually regular, but are random. The order of magnitude of $\frac{\partial p_1}{\partial t}$ can be assessed on the basis of experimental measurements of microfluctuations in atmospheric pressure, presented by Golitsyn /5/. The spectra of pressure fluctuations over a large time range are presented elsewhere /10/.

The order of magnitude of $\frac{\partial p_1}{\partial t}$ is estimated on the assumption that

$$\frac{\partial p_1}{\partial t}\sim\left[\overline{\left(\frac{\partial p_1}{\partial t}\right)^2}\right]^{1/2}=\int\limits_0^\infty \omega^2 F(\omega)\,d\omega, \quad (6.5.11)$$

where $F(\omega)$ is the spectral density of pressure fluctuations.

Figure 25 shows the graph of function $\omega^2 F(\omega)$, constructed from Golitsyn's results /5/. The integral of this function is approximately $0.2\sigma_p$, where

$$\sigma_p=(75\pm 1.4)\ \text{dynes/cm}^2. \quad (6.5.12)$$

It follows that

$$\frac{\partial p_1}{\partial t}\sim(1.5\pm 0.3)\ \text{dynes/cm}^2\cdot\text{sec}. \quad (6.5.13)$$

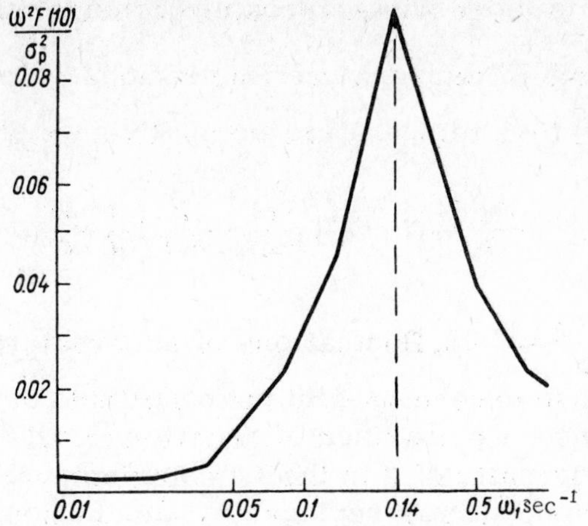

FIGURE 25. Graph of function $\omega^2 F(\omega)$.

$F(\omega)$ is the spectral density of pressure fluctuations.

Here, the bulk pertains to the range with characteristic time below 30 sec and an average value of the order of 10 sec. Bearing in mind that $g\rho_1 \approx 1$ g/cm$^2 \cdot$ sec and that v_z in the atmosphere is of the order of several tens of centimeters per second ($v_z \approx 30-40$ cm/sec, where v_z is treated both as an average and as the pulsational component of the vertical velocity), we can conclude that the contribution of $\frac{\partial p_1}{\partial t}$ to equation (6.5.10) does not exceed 7–10%.

If it is remembered that the experimental data were obtained at wind speeds of 10 m/sec in the surface layer, where the turbulence intensity is higher, it can be assumed that the real values of $\frac{\partial p_1}{\partial t}$ will be even smaller. It should be noted that the final conclusion on the smallness of the role of $\frac{\partial p_1}{\partial t}$ in Lagrangian pressure fluctuations can be made only when experimental data on pulsations in p_1 in the free atmosphere are available. However, it is possible even now to neglect, with sufficient justification, the effect of time fluctuations in pressure and to express $\frac{d\delta_0}{dt}$ in the form

$$\frac{d\delta_0}{dt} = -(1-\delta_0)\left(1 - \frac{LM}{c_p T M_1}\right)\frac{g v_z}{R_{\text{air}} T}. \qquad (6.5.14)$$

However, it is more advantageous to consider the time variation in δ_0 on the basis of temperature fluctuations. Replacing $\frac{dp_1}{dt}$ in equation (6.5.8) by a temperature derivative, we obtain

$$\frac{d\delta_0}{dt} = (1-\delta_0)\left(\frac{c_p}{R_{\text{air}}} - \frac{L}{R_v T}\right)\frac{1}{T}\frac{dT}{dt}. \qquad (6.5.15)$$

Since $\frac{L}{R_v T} - \frac{c_p}{R_v} \approx 15.5$, fluctuations of supersaturation in the Lagrangian sense exceed 15-fold the amplitude of relative temperature fluctuations. Comparison of equation (6.5.15) and (6.5.3) shows that the inhomogeneity of q in the Lagrangian approach disappeared from the equation, but was replaced by an additional effect, associated with the pressure variation (the additional term $\frac{c_p}{R_v}$ in (6.5.15)). Integration of equation (6.5.15) yields

$$\ln(1-\delta_0) = \ln d - \left(\frac{L}{R_v T} - \frac{c_p}{R_{\text{air}}}\right)\ln T. \qquad (6.5.16)$$

Separating the systematic and fluctuational parts and assuming that $T' \ll \overline{T} \approx T$, we derive

$$\delta_0' = -(1-\delta_0)\left(\frac{L}{R_v T} - \frac{c_p}{R_{\text{air}}}\right)\frac{T'}{T}. \qquad (6.5.17)$$

It is seen by comparing expressions (6.5.5) and (6.5.17) that the different approach yielded similar results with somewhat different numerical coefficients. The meaning of these differences is clear, since in the Eulerian approach one compares δ' at one altitude, while in the Lagrangian it is compared at different altitudes. On the whole, the difference in coefficients (19 and 15) is not substantial, and the data which can be obtained experimentally in the Eulerian approximation can be taken into consideration when dealing with Lagrangian characteristics of fluctuations.

In addition, the possibility of representing the fluctuations in ρ and δ_0 in terms of temperature fluctuations is, in principle, important, since it enables one to utilize more reliable and complete experiments and a more developed theory.

As with the vapor density, the supersaturation is also not conservative. To investigate its fluctuations it is necessary to relate it to some other characteristic of the medium, the variation of which is known. Such a relationship can be obtained in the form

$$\delta_0 = Av_z + \frac{F_1}{F_2}, \tag{6.5.18}$$

where

$$A = \frac{c_p(\gamma_a - \gamma_{w.a})\rho_1}{LK_3F_1\rho},$$

$$F_1 = 4\pi\frac{\rho_2}{\rho}\int_0^\infty \frac{r^2}{r+\xi} f(r)\,dr,$$

$$F_2 = 4\pi\frac{\rho_2}{\rho_1}\int_0^\infty \frac{r}{r+\xi}[B - \Phi(c)]\,f(r)\,dr. \tag{6.5.19}$$

Formula (6.5.18) as such is not new or original, but has been imparted meaning and so carries new content and information. Quantity v_z denotes the total (rather than the average) vertical velocity, which varies randomly. The equality is taken in the stochastic sense and characterizes the equality of the distribution functions of the left-and right-hand sides. Equation (6.5.18) makes it possible to find the distribution of the random variable δ_0 if the distribution of v_z is known. The necessary treatment will be carried out somewhat later.

Consider now the question of fluctuations in δ_0 in more detail. We start with equation (6.4.17), according to which

$$\frac{d\rho}{dt} = -I + \frac{\rho}{\rho_1}\frac{d\rho_1}{dt}. \tag{6.5.20}$$

In accordance with the results of section 10 of Chapter 2 we express I in the form

$$I = \int_0^\infty \frac{dm}{dt} f(r)\,dr = 4\pi\rho_2K_3\int_0^\infty \left[\frac{r^2}{r+\xi}\delta_0 - \frac{B - r\Phi(c)}{r+\xi}\right] f(r)\,dr. \tag{6.5.21}$$

In terms of the notation

$$F_1 = \frac{4\pi\rho_2}{\rho}K_3\int_0^\infty \frac{r^2}{r+\xi} f(r)\,dr,$$

$$F_2 = \frac{4\pi\rho_2}{\rho}K_3\int_0^\infty \frac{r}{r+\xi}[B - r\Phi(c)]\,f(r)\,dr,$$

we have

$$I=(F_1\delta_0-F_2)\,\rho. \tag{6.5.22}$$

It follows from the equation of state that

$$\frac{d\rho_1}{dt}=\frac{1}{R_{\text{air}}T}\,\frac{dp_1}{dt}-\frac{\rho_1}{T}\,\frac{dT}{dt}. \tag{6.5.23}$$

However, $\rho=\dfrac{\rho_0}{1-\delta_0}$, and in accordance with the Clausius-Clapeyron relation $\dfrac{d\rho_0}{dt}=\dfrac{\rho_0}{T}\left(\dfrac{L}{R_{\text{v}}T}-1\right)\dfrac{dT}{dt}$. Thus equation (6.5.20) assumes the form

$$\frac{d\delta_0}{dt}=\frac{\rho_0}{\rho}\left[-\frac{L}{R_{\text{v}}T}\,\frac{d\ln T}{dt}+\frac{d\ln p_1}{dt}-\frac{I}{\rho}\right]. \tag{6.5.24}$$

Derivatives $\dfrac{dT}{dt}$ and $\dfrac{dp_1}{dt}$ can be related using the energy balance equation. In particular, on the assumption that heat is lost only in phase transitions we can set

$$\rho_c c_p\frac{dT}{dt}=\frac{dp_c}{dt}+LI. \tag{6.5.25}$$

It will be assumed that the vapor content of the air is small ($\rho\ll\rho_1$). This always applies, provided the temperature in the cloud is small. Then $\rho_c\approx\rho_1$, $p_c\approx p_1$ and equation (6.5.25) becomes

$$\rho_1 c_p\frac{dT}{dt}=\frac{dp_1}{dt}+LI. \tag{6.5.26}$$

Employing equation (6.5.26) and (6.5.22), the equation for δ_0 has the form

$$\frac{1}{1-\delta_0}\,\frac{d\delta_0}{dt}=\left[-\frac{L}{R_{\text{v}}T^2}\,\frac{dT}{dt}+\frac{1}{p_1}\,\frac{dp_1}{dt}-F_1\delta_0+F_2\right], \tag{6.5.27a}$$

$$\frac{1}{1-\delta_0}\,\frac{d\delta_0}{dt}=\left[\left(\frac{c_p}{R_{\text{air}}}-\frac{L}{R_{\text{v}}T}\right)\frac{1}{T}\,\frac{dT}{dt}-\right.$$
$$\left.-\left(1+\frac{L}{R_{\text{air}}T}\right)F_1\delta_0+\left(1+\frac{L}{R_{\text{air}}T}\right)F_2\right], \tag{6.5.27b}$$

$$\frac{1}{1-\delta_0}\frac{d\delta_0}{dt}=\left[\left(1-\frac{LM}{c_pM_1}\right)\frac{1}{p_1}\frac{dp_1}{dt}-\right.$$
$$\left.-\left(1+\frac{L^2}{R_vc_pT}\frac{\rho}{\rho_1}\right)F_1\delta_0+\left(1+\frac{L^2\rho}{R_vc_pT\rho_1}\right)F_2\right]. \qquad (6.5.27c)$$

These equations describe the variation of the supersaturation in the system and are relaxation-type equations. The characteristic time for establishing equilibrium can be estimated from the formula

$$\tau=\frac{1}{F_1}\approx\frac{1}{4\pi D_v\bar{R}n}, \qquad (6.5.28)$$

and was found to be quite small. For processes with characteristic times much greater than τ we can use the quasi-steady approximation, according to which

$$\delta_0=\frac{1}{F_1}\left(\frac{1}{p_1}\frac{dp_1}{dt}-\frac{L}{R_vT^2}\frac{dT}{dt}\right)+\frac{F_2}{F_1}, \qquad (6.5.29a)$$

$$\delta_0=\frac{1}{F_1}\frac{\left(\frac{c_p}{R_{air}}-\frac{L}{R_vT}\right)}{\left(1+\frac{L}{R_{air}T}\right)}\frac{1}{T}\frac{dT}{dt}+$$
$$+\frac{F_2}{F_1}\approx\frac{1}{F_1}\frac{\left(\frac{L}{R_vT}-\frac{c_p}{R_{air}}\right)}{\left(1+\frac{L}{R_{air}T}\right)}\gamma_{w.a}v_z+\frac{F_2}{F_1} \qquad (6.5.29b)$$
$$\left(\text{here } \frac{dT}{dt}\approx-\gamma_{w.a}v_z\right),$$

$$\delta_0=\frac{1}{F_1}\frac{\left(1-\frac{LM}{c_pM_1}\right)}{\left(1+\frac{L^2\rho}{R_vc_pT\rho_1}\right)}\frac{1}{p_1}\frac{dp_1}{dt}+\frac{F_2}{F_1}\approx$$
$$\approx\frac{\left(\frac{LM}{c_pM_1}-1\right)}{F_1\left(1+\frac{L^2\rho}{R_vc_pT\rho_1}\right)}\frac{gv_z}{R_{air}T}+\frac{F_2}{F_1}, \qquad (6.5.29c)$$

where

$$\frac{dp_1}{dt}\approx-v_zg\rho_1=-\gamma_av_z\rho_1c_p.$$

Finally, δ_0 can also be represented in the form

$$\delta_0=\frac{c_p(\gamma_a-\gamma_{w.a})\rho_1v_z}{F_1L\rho}+\frac{F_2}{F_1}. \qquad (6.5.30)$$

Since ratio $\frac{F_2}{F_1}$ can be regarded as depending little on time over a range of conditions, we introduce the transformation $\delta = \delta_0 - \frac{F_2}{F_1}$ and consider the variability in δ, using equation (6.5.27c) in the form

$$\frac{d\delta}{dt} = Bv_z - \beta_1 \delta, \tag{6.5.31}$$

where

$$B = \left(\frac{LM}{c_p M_1} - 1 \right) \frac{g}{R_{\text{air}} T},$$

$$\beta_1 = \left(1 + \frac{L^2}{R_v c_p T} \frac{\rho}{\rho_1} \right) F_1.$$

If B and β_1 are regarded as constant, we consider the variation in δ with v_z. The latter is represented as the Fourier integral

$$v_z = \int_0^\infty (\alpha \cos \omega t + \sigma \sin \omega t)\, d\omega.$$

Further regarding B and β_1 as constant we express δ in the form

$$\delta = \int_0^\infty (\gamma \cos \omega t + \lambda \sin \omega t)\, d\omega.$$

This yields the relation between γ, λ and α, σ:

$$\gamma = B \frac{\beta_1 \alpha - \omega \sigma}{\omega^2 + \beta_1^2}, \tag{6.5.32}$$

$$\lambda = B \frac{\omega \alpha - \beta_1 \sigma}{\omega^2 + \beta_1^2}. \tag{6.5.33}$$

Upon introducing the Lagrangian spectral function for vertical fluctuations $F_\delta(\omega)$, we derive

$$F_v(\omega) = \frac{\alpha^2(\omega) + \sigma^2(\omega)}{T_1},$$

where a reasonably wide time interval was selected as T_1.

If the spectral function of supersaturation is denoted by $F_\delta(\omega)$, then

$$F_\delta(\omega) = \frac{\gamma^2(\omega) + \lambda^2(\omega)}{T_1},$$

in which case, using equations (6.5.15) and (6.5.16),

$$\frac{F_\delta(\omega)}{F_v(\omega)} = \frac{\gamma^2 + \lambda^2}{\alpha^2 + \sigma^2} = B^2 \frac{1}{\omega^2 + \beta_1^2}. \tag{6.5.34}$$

By introducing a spectral function of supersaturation, which would be applicable in the presence of quasi-equilibrium between the supersaturation and velocity $\Phi_\delta(\omega)$, i. e., in the absence of inertia $(\delta_0 = \frac{B}{\beta_1} v_z)$, we obtain

$$\Phi_\delta(\omega) = \frac{B^2(\alpha^2 + \sigma^2)}{\beta_1^2 T_1}. \tag{6.5.35}$$

It follows that

$$\varkappa(\omega) = \frac{F_\delta(\omega)}{\Phi_\delta(\omega)} = \frac{\beta_1^2}{\omega^2 + \beta_1^2}. \tag{6.5.36}$$

The graph of this function for different values of β_1 is plotted in Figure 26.

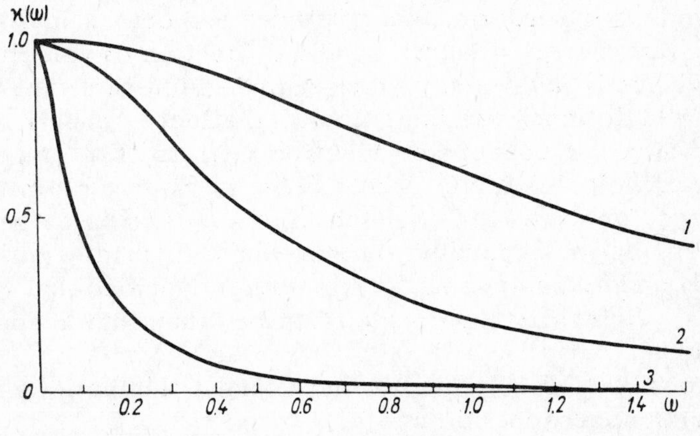

FIGURE 26. Plot of conversion function $\varkappa(\omega)$ characterizing the distortion of the spectral function of supersaturation

Finally, we assume that the Lagrangian correlation function for vertical fluctuations in air has the form

$$R_L(t)=\exp\left(-\frac{t}{\tau}\right), \tag{6.5.37}$$

where τ is the correlation time. Then the expression for $F_\delta(\omega)$ can be obtained directly:

$$F_\delta(\omega)=\frac{2}{\pi}\overline{(v_z')^2}\frac{\tau}{1+\omega^2\tau^2}, \tag{6.5.38}$$

and, with allowance for (6.5.34) and (6.5.38), it assumes the form

$$F_\delta(\omega)=\frac{2}{\pi}\overline{(v_z')^2}B^2\frac{\tau}{(\omega^2+\beta_1^2)(1+\omega^2\tau^2)}. \tag{6.5.39}$$

In accordance with /7/, τ can be expressed in the form

$$\tau=c\frac{\overline{(v_z')^2}}{\varepsilon}, \tag{6.5.40}$$

where c is some constant of the order of unity and ε is the rate of eddy energy dissipation. If it is assumed that $\varepsilon=10$ cm^2/sec^3 and $\overline{(v_z')^2}=2,500$ cm^2/sec^3, then $\tau\approx 4$ min. It is thus demonstrated that fluctuations in supersaturation do not always follow velocity fluctuations and smoothing occurs in the high-frequency region.. Formula (6.5.34) makes it possible to construct the spectral function of supersaturation from a known spectral function of velocity fluctuation

However, it is noteworthy that estimates indicate that for all real values of β_1 allowance for the smoothing effect of equation (6.5.18), i.e., allowance for conversion function $\varkappa(\omega)$, is of no importance, since the principal contribution to $F_\delta(\omega)$ is made by lower frequencies, for which the correction is small ($\varkappa$ is close to unity).

The assumption regarding the existence of quasi-equilibrium between v_z and δ_0 thus seems to this author justified and verified by estimates. Naturally, function $\varkappa$ must be taken into account in individual cases.

Relationship (6.5.18) enables one to treat fluctuations in δ_0 also in the Eulerian approach. Since

$$D_v(r)=\frac{4}{3}c\varepsilon^{2/3}r^{2/3},\ l_0\ll r\ll L, \tag{6.5.41}$$

we have

$$D_\delta(r)=\frac{4}{3}cA^2\varepsilon^{2/3}r^{2/3},\ L_p\ll r\ll L. \tag{6.5.42}$$

According to experimental data /22/,

$$c \approx 1.4. \tag{6.5.43}$$

The relation between fluctuations in supersaturation and fluctuations in temperature and in updrafts is considered in a somewhat different form by Mazin /12/, but his results are in agreement.

Chapter 7

THEORY OF STOCHASTIC CONDENSATION

1. STOCHASTIC EQUATION OF DROPLET GROWTH

Growth of particles in a cloud by condensation is usually treated on the basis of the following classical model. It is assumed that the droplet grows in some temperature, velocity and supersaturation fields which vary regularly and that their variations can be determined from the averaged heat and moisture balance equations. The difference in particle sizes is due to differences in the lifetimes and in the sizes of the condensation nuclei from which they formed. This approach does not explain the formation of naturally observed droplet distributions.

If the principal assumptions made in these calculations are examined, the first thing to doubt is the feasibility of using averaged values of external parameters. It has already been shown earlier in this book that the external parameters due to turbulence (in the presence of gradients of average quantities) undergo fluctuations, the characteristics of which can often be obtained from similarity and dimensional considerations. These fluctuations must affect the rate of phase transitions. If, however, they have scales exceeding $l\approx(\pi R)^{-3/2}n^{-1/2}$ and τ, then they can be taken into account within the framework of the balance equations presented in Chapter 5, but used there in a somewhat different sense. The theory dealing with allowance for higher frequency and smaller scale fluctuations has not yet been developed.

The general scheme of considering the effect of fluctuations consists in the fact that the right-hand side of the droplet growth equation is ascribed a stochastic meaning, since the supersaturation δ_0 varies according to some random law. An idea of this kind was put forward by Belyaev /6.1, 6.2/ who, however, implemented it formally, since it was assumed that δ_0 has a normal distribution with some arbitrarily specified amplitude.

The desirability of employing a statistical description of the growth of an individual droplet is quite evident. Just as it is unthinkable to examine the propagation of a weightless impurity without allowance for turbulence, it is also inexpedient when considering phase transitions to make allowance only for the averaged cooling of the air mass. The principal difficulty does not consist in establishing the expedience of this method, but in establishing the fundamental regularities governing the fluctuations of the supersaturation in turbulent flow.

The analysis conducted in the preceding chapter enables a stochastic model of droplet growth by condensation to be constructed. Research into the fine structure of clouds has shown that δ_0 and the vertical velocity v_z are functionally related, and that this relation persists for both averaged and pulsational values /6.7/. The effect of this relation can be easily followed by examining the following model problem.

Following the results of the preceding chapter we assume that the equation

$$\delta_0=\frac{c_p(\gamma_a-\gamma_{w.a})\rho_1}{LK_3F_1\rho}v_z \tag{7.1.1}$$

has a stochastic meaning, since v_z is a random variable. The equation of droplet growth should then also be taken in the stochastic sense:

$$\frac{dR^2}{dt}=\frac{2c_p(\gamma_a-\gamma_{w.a})\rho_1}{LF_1\rho}v_z \tag{7.1.2}$$

(here, for simplicity, the growth equation is taken in the simplest form). The solution to the problem is

$$R^2(t)-R_0^2=\frac{2c_p(\gamma_a-\gamma_{w.a})\rho_1}{L\rho}\int_0^t\frac{v_z}{F_1}dt. \tag{7.1.3}$$

For simplicity, we shall assume that F_1 depends little on time, i. e., $F_1\approx n\overline{R}\approx t^{1/3}$, and that this dependence can be negleeted. In this case

$$R^2(t)=R_0^2+B\left[\overline{v}_zt+z'\right], \tag{7.1.4}$$

where

$$B=\frac{2c_p(\gamma_a-\gamma_{w.a})\rho_1}{LF_1\rho},$$

while z' is the variation in the vertical droplet coordinate due to fluctuations in the vertical wind speed, i. e., the vertical motion of the droplet due to turbulence.

It follows that the particle size is determined not so much by the average updraft velocity (in the more general case this is the average cooling rate of the air mass), but also by its turbulent motion. However, it should be remembered that the functional relationship between the particle size, time and coordinates is to some extent arbitrary, since we assumed that adiabatic conditions prevail (singling out of the average velocity and expressing the integral in the form of equation (7.1.4) makes no allowance for the distortion of the spectrum, and the assumption concerning the constancy of B) and that the actual velocity of the particle fall is neglected. Therefore, in a more rigorous examination there should be no direct relationship between particle coordinates and size. This should be remembered when extending the results to real systems.

In order to examine whether equation (7.1.4) is satisfied we shall solve the following problem. Suppose an air layer (sufficiently thick, so that boundary conditions can be neglected), containing monodisperse droplets at some time, cools uniformly (the cooling rate is determined by the updraft velocity $\bar{v}_z$). We shall determine the distortion of the droplet size distribution function.

The form of the distribution function can be established when the initial coordinates of all the particles arriving at a given volume element are known at time t /5/. If this element is chosen to be layer dz at level z, then the distribution of particles arriving from different levels to this layer (on the assumption that the vertical motion due to turbulence has a normal distribution) can be expressed in the form

$$\Psi(z') = \frac{1}{(4\pi K_z t)^{1/2}} \exp\left(-\frac{z'^2}{4K_z t}\right). \tag{7.1.5}$$

Further, since

$$z' = \frac{1}{B}\left[R^2(t) - R_0^2\right] - \bar{v}_z t, \tag{7.1.6}$$

and having reference to the fact that the equation is stochastic, the particle size distribution function can be written as

$$f(R, t) = \frac{R}{(\pi B^2 K_z t)^{1/2}} \exp\left\{-\frac{\left[\bar{v}_z t - \frac{1}{B}(R^2 - R_0^2)\right]^2}{4K_z t}\right\}. \tag{7.1.7}$$

Bearing in mind the approximations underlying this approach, and remembering that, in addition to the previously mentioned assumptions equation (7.1.7) disregards the disappearance and appearance of particles and their departure from the cloud, it is noteworthy that the operation of turbulence results in broadening of the distribution function, formation of the fraction of large droplets (which grow more rapidly than on the average), and the retention of some quantity of small droplets. The variation in the distribution function is determined by the eddy diffusion coefficient K_z (the magnitude of this variation can be estimated) and a number of other variables which lend themselves to measurement. The distribution function is plotted in Figure 27.

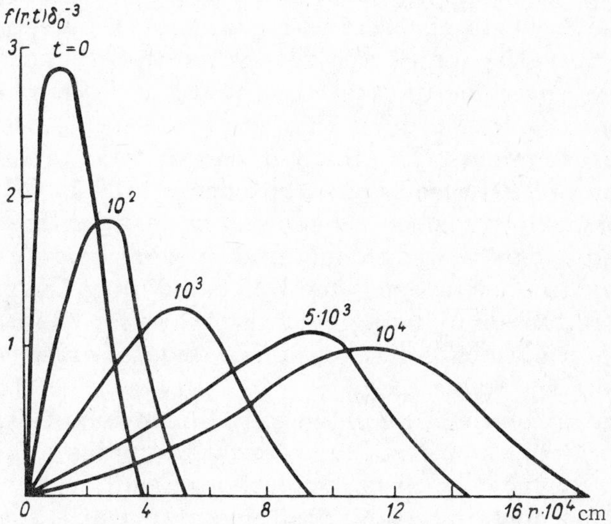

FIGURE 27. Graph of droplet size distribution function for different times ($K_z = 10^5$ cm/sec, $v_z = 5$ cm/sec, $R_0 = 0.5 \cdot 10^{-4}$ cm, $B = 2 \cdot 10^{11}$ cm)

It is clear that the variance in the droplet distribution function increases with time, while the distribution maximum shifts to the right. The droplets grow much more rapidly than according to classical concepts. Distribution (7.1.7) is not convenient and does not at all reflect the kinetics of the spectrum formation at the condensation stage. It does not incorporate spatial inhomogeneity or the initial function and was obtained on the assumption that z' follows a normal distribution.

As in the case of Brownian diffusion, when the stochastic Langevin equation is inconvenient for the study of impurity admixtures /5/, here, too, the stochastic condensation equation is inconvenient for the study of spectrum formation kinetics. Here, apparently, it is also unnecessary to construct equations (such as Kolmogorov's equation) which make it possible to examine the problem by means of ordinary differential equations in the space of the droplet coordinates and dimensions.

From the standpoint of a more correct consideration of this equation it is most probably necessary to return to equations (7.4.2) [sic], which are valid over a much wider range of conditions, are very important and substantially simplify the problem. On their basis the droplet growth problem can be reduced to that of the diffusion of particles in turbulent flow, i. e., to finding the distribution function of z. This problem was extensively investigated and at present several schemes are available for calculations of this type. Their use allows one to obtain the curve of $f(R)$ in one form or another.

The development of the theory is most promising on the basis of the semiempirical theory of turbulence, which is valid subject to a number of limitations for reasonably wide time intervals. The Sutton theory can be mentioned among other models /7/. Droplet growth can also be investigated by considering Lagrangian stochastic characteristics, or by using certain empirical equations. A direct analysis of the stochastic equation of droplet growth is presented, for example, by Mazin /2.22/.

Consideration must be given to the question of droplet mixing in a cloud. During stochastic growth there arises a doubt whether the droplets will grow in large populations together, i. e., whether some local volume contains droplets of one size, while another volume contains droplets of another size, while on the average these will yield a size distribution valid for large scales. Had this been so, particle coalescence would become very difficult, since the velocity at which almost identical particles approach each other is close to zero.

The validity of this assumption is now assessed. For a concentration of $n \approx 10^3$ cm^{-3} the average interdroplet distance is $l \approx 10^{-1}$ cm. Consider the inter diffusion of two droplets located at such a distance from one another. Since l is approximately on the boundary of the inertia interval, it is possible to employ the Lagrangian structural function in this interval. The rms interparticle distance depends on time /6.7/:

$$\sigma^2 = c\varepsilon t^3, \qquad (7.1.8)$$

where ε is the rate of eddy energy dissipation and c is a constant of the order of unity.

Assuming that $\sqrt{\sigma^2} = 10^4$ cm, we obtain $t_1 = 3.5$ min when $\varepsilon = 10$ cm^2/sec^3. Thus, during 3.5 min the particle can travel a distance of the order of 100 m. Since spectrum formation requires more time, the particles are fully mixed.

On the other hand, mixing should be such that, on a scale l during a characteristic time τ of diffusion relaxation, the relative particle motions are not so great, so it would be possible to make allowance for the effect of collective factors on the basis of diffusion equations without convective terms. If it is assumed that l is sufficiently small and corresponds to the viscous interval of turbulent fluctuations, then the characteristic time τ_0 during which particles markedly change position (it is assumed that the characteristic relaxation time is smaller than τ_0 and that the particle is carried away by the flow) is

$$\tau_0 = \frac{\overline{v_l^2}}{l} = \sqrt{\frac{1}{15}\frac{\varepsilon}{\nu_1}}\,, \tag{7.1.9}$$

where ν_1 is the kinematic viscosity of air.

Hence

$$\frac{\tau}{\tau_0} = \frac{\sqrt{15}\, l^2 \nu_1^{1/2}}{4\pi D_v \varepsilon^{1/2}} \approx \frac{\nu_1^{1/2}}{\pi D_v \varepsilon^{1/2} \overline{R}n}. \tag{7.1.10}$$

If $\dfrac{\tau}{\tau_0} < 1$, then neglect of convective vapor transport is entirely valid. In the opposite case, the validity of using the ordinary balance equation should be treated separately.

2. TRANSPORT OF NONCONSERVATIVE QUANTITIES IN TURBULENT FLOW

The current theory in the study of atmospheric diffusion of impurities is usually based on assumptions that the impurity is passive and conservative. If at least one of these assumptions is not satisfied, special studies are needed. The previously considered equation governing the growth of an individual droplet is insufficient for the study of the evolution of the distribution function and hence it is necessary to derive an equation describing the behavior of $f(r, t)$. Since the rate of droplet growth due to turbulent fluctuations is determined by the pulsation of the vertical wind speed component, there appears an actual possibility of writing the semiempirical equation for the variation in $f(r, t)$ by analogy with the semiempirical equation of eddy diffusion. Here, it is also necessary to make the above assumptions concerning the conservative and passive properties.

Recall that an impurity is regarded as passive if it does not alter the dynamic characteristics of the flow. This assumption can only be made conditionally with respect to droplets since condensation release of heat generally alters the flow dynamics. If it is assumed that in clouds $\delta_0 \ll 1$ and that the vapor content of air can be determined with reasonable accuracy from equilibrium conditions in accordance with the Clausius-Clapeyron relation, then the release of heat can be referred not to droplets, but regarded as a property of the medium, the temperature of which varies during ascents in line with the wet-adiabatic lapse rate $\gamma_{w.a.}$

The term conservative is applied to an impurity whose characteristics do not change when a volume element containing this impurity moves in space. The droplet size distribution function is not conservative, since the rate of growth by condensation is a function of the updraft velocity. As a result, any vertical motion imparted to the droplet by the flow alters the droplet size and accordingly results in the nonconservativeness of $f(R, \mathbf{r}, t)$. In order to obtain a clearer idea about the transport mechanism of a nonconservative quantity, we shall consider the following auxiliary problem.

Suppose some substance c is transported through some elementary volume dV due to the motion $\mathbf{v}$ of the medium and due to some diffusion mechanism described by diffusion coefficient D. If we restrict ourselves for simplicity to the one-dimensional case, then for a conservative substance

$$j(x) = vc + D\frac{dc}{dx}. \tag{7.2.1}$$

We now assume that substance c is not conservative, i.e., its properties, specified by some quantity s, change on moving in space. Then the flux will no longer satisfy equation (7.2.1). Since quantity s is a function of x, then upon interchanging volumes with coordinates x and $x+dx$ one no longer compares $c(s, x)$ and $c(s, x+dx)$, but functions $c(s, x)$ and $c(s+A\,dx, x+dx)$, where $A = \dfrac{ds}{dx}$.

In fact, a substance with parameter s at point x, moving through distance dx, also changes parameter s by an amount $A\,dx$. Hence

$c(s, x)$ can be compared precisely with $c(s+A\,dx,\ x+dx)$, since when quantity s moves through distance dx it becomes $s+A\,dx$, while $c(s, x)\to c(s+A\,dx,\ x+dx)$. Therefore, during diffusion exchange of elementary volumes the diffusion flux is not determined by the expression $D\frac{\partial c}{\partial x}$, but by the operator

$$D\left(\frac{\partial}{\partial x}+A\frac{\partial}{\partial s}\right). \tag{7.2.2}$$

The flux then assumes the form

$$j_x=v_x c+D\left(\frac{\partial}{\partial x}+A\frac{\partial}{\partial s}\right)c(s,\ x). \tag{7.2.3}$$

Consider further the variation in the amount of substance in some volume. We again take into account the variation in s due to movement of the substance in space. In this connection, the variation in layer dx is due not to the difference between fluxes $j(s, x)$ and $j(s, x+dx)$, but, with consideration of the change in s, to the difference

$$j(s,\ x)-j(s+A\,dx,\ x+dx).$$

In view of the above, the balance equation is

$$\frac{\partial c}{\partial t}+\left(\frac{\partial}{\partial x}+A\frac{\partial}{\partial s}\right)\left[v_x c-D\left(\frac{\partial}{\partial x}+A\frac{\partial}{\partial s}\right)c\right]=0. \tag{7.2.4}$$

It follows that

$$\frac{\partial c}{\partial t}+\frac{\partial}{\partial x}(v_x c)+A\frac{\partial}{\partial s}(v_x c)-D\left(\frac{\partial}{\partial x}+A\frac{\partial}{\partial s}\right)^2 c=0. \tag{7.2.5}$$

Allowance for nonconservativeness in the diffusion problem was thus reduced to replacing the operator

$$D\frac{\partial}{\partial x}\ \text{ by }\ D\left(\frac{\partial}{\partial x}+A\frac{\partial}{\partial s}\right)^2,$$

where $A=\frac{\partial s}{\partial x}$.

If s is a known function of x, then by writing this expression in explicit form it is possible to omit the second parameter and not worry about the conservativeness of the substance. However, the relationship between s and x is usually of a local nature and can be firmly established for small variations in x. At large scales, and when allowance is made for other mechanisms causing a variation in c separately as a function of x and as a function of s, these local relationships break down and c cannot be treated as a function of one independent variable.

In this case it is necessary to introduce this second quantity s and, as a result of the nonconservativeness, make allowance for local relationships in the form of an operator of the above type. This kind of breakdown in relationships between s and x occurs, for example, when considering the kinetics of cloud processes, when sedimentation and coalescence, resulting in the appearance of new droplets, lead to a breakdown in the relation between the droplet coordinates and its size.

Since operator $D\left(\frac{\partial}{\partial x}+A\frac{\partial}{\partial s}\right)^2$ makes allowance for nonconservativeness of the impurity in the most general form, we shall extend the results to the case of eddy diffusion. Distribution function $f(s, \mathbf{r}, t)$ in the kinetic equation is not conservative, since

$$\frac{ds}{dz}=\frac{ds}{dt}\frac{dt}{dz}=\frac{1}{v_z}\frac{ds}{dt}\neq 0. \qquad (7.2.6)$$

Therefore, we shall assume that this results in a relationship between $\overline{f'v'_i}$ and the average characteristics of the medium. In the approximation of the semiempirical turbulence theory the relationship usually is

$$\overline{f'v'_i}=-K_{ij}\frac{\partial\bar{f}}{\partial x_j} \qquad (7.2.7)$$

and cannot be formally extended to the case of a nonconservative substance.

In line with the above deliberations, we assume

$$\overline{f'v'_i}=-K_{ij}\left(\frac{\partial}{\partial x_j}+A_j\frac{\partial}{\partial s}\right)\bar{f}, \qquad (7.2.8)$$

where

$$A_j=A\delta_{iz}; \qquad (7.2.9)$$

K_{ij} is the tensor of eddy diffusion coefficients.

Equation (7.2.8) can be employed in the kinetic equation to consider only average quantities. It should be specified that the use of the semiempirical theory of eddy transport is not always a sufficiently acceptable method of investigating the process. When allowance for turbulence is made by some other technique, the effect of nonconservativeness can also be taken into account similarly to the above.

3. KINETIC EQUATION DEFINING THE EVOLUTION OF THE CLOUD DROPLET DISTRIBUTION FUNCTION IN THE APPROXIMATION OF THE SEMIEMPIRICAL THEORY OF TURBULENCE

The direct use of a stochastic equation, such as equation (7.1.2), for investigating the evolution of cloud droplets is not too convenient, since it does not allow the inhomogeneity of the medium and the boundary conditions to be taken into consideration with sufficient accuracy. A more effective method is that of the kinetic equation describing the behavior of the distribution function. For instantaneous values of the velocity of the medium, the balance equation governing the number of particles yields

$$\frac{\partial f}{\partial t}+(v_i-v_s\delta_{iz})\frac{\partial f}{\partial x_i}+\frac{\partial}{\partial r}\left(\frac{\partial r}{\partial t}f\right)=\Phi. \qquad (7.3.1)$$

Here, Φ is a function characterizing the appearance or disappearance of droplets in the volume, $\mathbf{v}$ is the flow velocity, v_s is the gravitational droplet fall velocity, and $\delta_{iz}=\begin{cases}1 \text{ when } i=z\\ 0 \text{ when } i\neq z.\end{cases}$

Before averaging equation (7.3.1) we shall assume that, from the viewpoint of fluctuations, the processes are adiabatic, while heat transport by radiation and mixing can be neglected when considering fluctuations in f by treating them as processes with reasonably large characteristic times which should affect the averaged velocities. Thus in averaging we shall formally apply the first theorem of thermodynamics, although then we shall keep the resulting equations only for pulsational quantities, assuming that the variation in the average values of T and p_1 with time occurs in a more complex manner. If the rate of droplet growth is expressed in the quite general form

$$\frac{dr}{dt}=\frac{1}{4\pi(1-\delta_0)}\frac{\rho_0}{\rho_2}[\omega_1(r)\delta_0+\omega_2(r)], \tag{7.3.2}$$

where $\omega_1(r)$ and $\omega_2(r)$ are functions which (in accordance with the results obtained in section 10 of Chapter 2) can be specified by

$$\omega_1(r)=4\pi\frac{\rho_2}{\rho}\frac{K_3}{r+\xi},$$

$$\omega_2(r)=4\pi\frac{\rho_2}{\rho}\frac{K_3}{r+\xi}\left[\Phi(c)-\frac{B}{r}\right], \tag{7.3.3}$$

then the vapor balance equation (6.5.27) becomes

$$\frac{1}{1-\delta_0}\frac{d\delta_0}{dt}+\frac{L}{R_vT}\frac{d\ln T}{dt}-\frac{d\ln p_1}{dt}=-\delta_0F_1-F_2, \tag{7.3.4}$$

where, in line with (6.5.21),

$$F_1(t)=\int_0^\infty r^2\omega_1(r)f(r,t)\,dr,$$

$$F_2(t)=\int_0^\infty r^2\omega_2(r)f(r,t)\,dr.$$

In the quasi-steady approximation, the satisfaction of which was discussed above (6.5.29) /2.22, 2/,

$$\delta_0F_1=\frac{d\ln p_1}{dt}-\frac{L}{R_vT}\frac{d\ln T}{dt}-F_2. \tag{7.3.5}$$

If we apply the first law of thermodynamics under the same limitations as were noted before, then

$$\rho_1c_p\frac{dT}{dt}=\frac{dp_1}{dt}+L\rho(F_1\delta_0-F_2), \tag{7.3.6}$$

and one can eliminate from equation (7.3.5) the pressure and temperature derivatives

$$\delta_0F_1=\alpha\frac{d\ln p_1}{dt}-F_2, \tag{7.3.7}$$

where

$$\alpha = \frac{\left(1 - \frac{LM}{c_p M_1}\right)}{\left(1 + \frac{L^2}{c_p R_{\text{air}} T} \frac{\rho_0}{\rho_1}\right)}.$$

Averaging of equation (7.3.7), in the first approximation, yields

$$\bar{\delta}_0 \int_0^\infty r\omega_1(r) \bar{f}(r, t)\, dr = \bar{\alpha} \frac{d \ln \bar{p}_1}{dt} - \int_0^\infty r\omega_2(r) \bar{f}(r, t)\, dr - \\ - \int_0^\infty r\omega_1(r) \overline{\delta_0' f'(r, t)}\, dr, \tag{7.3.8}$$

$$\delta_0' \int_0^\infty r\omega_1(r) \bar{f}(r, t)\, dr = \bar{\alpha} \frac{1}{\bar{p}_1} \frac{dp_1'}{dt} - \int_0^\infty r\omega_2(r) f'(r, t)\, dr - \\ - \bar{\delta}_0 \int_0^\infty r\omega_1(r) f'(r, t)\, dr. \tag{7.3.9}$$

The fluctuations in $f(r, t)$ can be induced by fluctuations in p_1 and T as well as fluctuations in droplet concentration. Since the principal contribution to pulsational components is made by $\frac{dp_1'}{dt}$ and $\frac{dT}{dt}$, compared with p_1 and T, then, omitting the averaging sign, we have

$$\delta_0' = \frac{\alpha}{F_1 p_1} \frac{dp_1'}{dt} + \frac{F_1'}{F_1}. \tag{7.3.10}$$

However $\frac{dp_1}{dt} \approx \frac{\partial p_1}{\partial t} - g\rho_1 v_z$, and the principal contribution to $\frac{dp_1'}{dt}$ is made by fluctuations in v_z /6.12/. Thus

$$\delta_0' = -\frac{\alpha g}{R_{\text{air}} T} \frac{v_z'}{F_1} + \frac{F_1'}{F_1}. \tag{7.3.11}$$

Equation (7.3.2) with allowance for (7.3.5) and (7.3.11) yields

$$\frac{dr}{dt} = \frac{1}{4\pi(1-\delta_0)} \frac{\rho_0}{\rho_2} \left[\frac{\omega_1}{F_1} \frac{d \ln p_1}{dt} - \frac{\omega_1 L}{F_1 R_v T} \frac{d \ln T}{dt} - \frac{\omega_1 F_2}{F_1} + \right. \\ \left. + \omega_2 + \frac{F_1'}{F_1} - \frac{\alpha g}{R_{\text{air}} T} \frac{\omega_1}{F_1} v_z' \right]. \tag{7.3.12}$$

Substitution of equation (7.3.12) into (7.3.1) and subsequent averaging should result in equations describing the behavior of $f(r, t)$ in turbulent flow. Subsequently, we shall restrict ourselves to considering the effect of fluctuations v'_z. The presentation will follow the treatment in /6/.

Substituting (7.3.7) into equation (7.3.1) gives

$$\frac{\partial f}{\partial t}+(v_i-v_s\delta_{iz})\frac{\partial f}{\partial x_i}+v_z\frac{\partial}{\partial r}(\beta_1 f)+\frac{\partial}{\partial r}(\beta_2 f)=\Phi, \qquad (7.3.13)$$

where

$$\beta_1(r)=\frac{\rho_0 a g\omega_1(r)}{4\pi\rho_2 F_1 R_{\text{air}} T}, \quad \beta_2(r)=\frac{\rho_0}{4\pi\rho_2}\left[\omega_2(r)-\omega_1(r)\frac{F_1}{F_2}\right].$$

Allowance for nonconservativeness, carried out in the preceding section, resulted in the appearance of new terms in the expression for the turbulent flux f. Here, this effect is due to the third term in equation (7.3.13) and results in the appearance of a local relationship between variables r and z.

We introduce the transformation $f(r,\ t)\,dr=f_1(s)\,ds$, corresponding to the law of conservation of the number of particles. Variable s is selected as follows:

$$f_1(s,\ t)=f(r,\ t)\frac{dr}{ds}=\beta_1 f(r,\ t).$$

Then

$$\frac{\partial f_1}{\partial t}+v_i\frac{\partial f_1}{\partial x_i}+v_s\frac{\partial f_1}{\partial s}-v_s\frac{\partial f_1}{\partial z}+\frac{\partial}{\partial s}\left(\frac{\beta_2}{\beta_1}f_1\right)=\beta_1\Phi,$$
$$s=\int\beta_1^{-1}\,dr. \qquad (7.3.14)$$

Upon substituting variables $\zeta=\dfrac{(z+s)}{2}$, $\eta=\dfrac{(z-s)}{2}$, we get

$$\frac{\partial f_1}{\partial t}+\left(\mathbf{v}\hat{\nabla}\right)f_1-\frac{1}{2}v_s\left(\frac{\partial}{\partial\zeta}-\frac{\partial}{\partial\eta}\right)f_1+$$
$$+\frac{1}{2}\left(\frac{\partial}{\partial\zeta}-\frac{\partial}{\partial\eta}\right)\left(\frac{\beta_2}{\beta_1}f_1\right)=\beta_1\Phi, \qquad (7.3.15)$$

where

$$\left(\mathbf{v}\hat{\nabla}\right)=v_x\frac{\partial}{\partial x}+v_y\frac{\partial}{\partial y}+v_z\frac{\partial}{\partial\zeta}.$$

In terms of variables x, y and ζ, function f is conservative, since any shift of these variables in space does not alter the particle radius. As is usual in the approximation of semiempirical turbulence theory, operator $(\mathbf{v}\hat{\nabla})$, written for instantaneous values of f_1 and $\mathbf{v}$, is replaced by an operator written for the averaged quantity:

$$\left(\mathbf{v}\hat{\nabla}\right)\to\frac{\partial}{\partial x_i}K_{ij}\frac{\partial}{\partial x_j}. \qquad (7.3.16)$$

Using this approximation and assuming that tensor K_{ij} is diagonal, we derive (omitting the averaging sign)

$$\frac{\partial f_1}{\partial t}+(\mathbf{v}\hat{\nabla})f_1+\frac{1}{2}\left(\frac{\partial}{\partial\zeta}+\frac{\partial}{\partial\eta}\right)\left(\frac{\beta_2}{\beta_1}f_1-v_s f_1\right)=\beta_1\Phi+$$
$$+K\left(\frac{\partial^2}{\partial x^2}+\frac{\partial^2}{\partial y^2}\right)f_1+\frac{\partial}{\partial\zeta}K_z\frac{\partial}{\partial\zeta}f_1. \qquad (7.3.17)$$

Conversion to variables x, y, z, s, t yields

$$\frac{\partial f_1}{\partial t}+(v_i-v_s\delta_{iz})\frac{\partial f_1}{\partial x_i}+v_z\frac{\partial f_1}{\partial s}+\frac{\partial}{\partial s}\left(\frac{\beta_2}{\beta_1}f_1\right)=$$
$$=K\left(\frac{\partial^2}{\partial x^2}+\frac{\partial^2}{\partial y^2}\right)f_1+\left(\frac{\partial}{\partial z}+\frac{\partial}{\partial s}\right)K_z\left(\frac{\partial}{\partial z}+\frac{\partial}{\partial s}\right)f_1+\beta_1\Phi. \qquad (7.3.18)$$

Finally, reverting to function $f=\frac{f_1}{\beta_1}$ and variable τ we obtain

$$\frac{\partial f}{\partial t}+(v_i-v_s\delta_{iz})\frac{\partial f}{\partial x_i}+v_z\frac{\partial}{\partial r}(\beta_1 f)+$$
$$\frac{\partial}{\partial r}(\beta_2 f)=K\left(\frac{\partial^2}{\partial x^2}+\frac{\partial^2}{\partial y^2}\right)f+$$
$$+\frac{1}{\beta_1}\left(\frac{\partial}{\partial z}+\beta_1\frac{\partial}{\partial r}\right)K_z\left(\frac{\partial}{\partial z}+\beta_1\frac{\partial}{\partial r}\right)\beta_1 f+\Phi. \qquad (7.3.19)$$

If it is remembered that the first law of thermodynamics is valid for short times and that for averaged quantities it is necessary to make more rigorous allowance for heat and mass transfer, we can write

$$\frac{df}{dt}+v_s\frac{\partial f}{\partial z}+\frac{\rho_0}{4\pi\rho_2 F_1}\left\{\left[\frac{d\ln p_1}{dt}-\frac{L}{R_v T}\frac{d\ln T}{dt}\right]-F_2\right\}\times$$
$$\times\frac{\partial}{\partial r}(\omega_1 f)+\frac{\rho_0}{4\pi\rho_2}\frac{\partial}{\partial r}(\omega_2 f)=K\left(\frac{\partial^2}{\partial x^2}+\frac{\partial^2}{\partial y^2}\right)f+$$
$$+\frac{1}{\beta_1}\left(\frac{\partial}{\partial z}+\beta_1\frac{\partial}{\partial r}\right)K_z\left(\frac{\partial}{\partial z}+\beta_1\frac{\partial}{\partial r}\right)\beta_1 f+\Phi. \qquad (7.3.20)$$

Equation (7.3.20) contains, in addition to f, the unknown functions p_1, T, ρ and $\mathbf{v}$, which are to be determined from the corresponding equations of motion, continuity, heat balance and state.

4. LIMITS OF APPLICABILITY OF THE KINETIC EQUATION OF CONDENSATION

In spite of its quite complex form, equation (7.3.20) was derived on the basis of a number of important assumptions concerning the processes which occur. In the first place it is constructed on the basis of the fact that fluctuations in δ_0 are due to vertical velocity v_z. It was shown in deriving (7.3.11) that in addition to fluctuations v'_z, there exist also fluctuations in other quantities, especially in F_1. The latter quantity, which is an integral characteristic of the distribution function, undergoes fluctuations either due to fluctuations in the droplet concentration, or due to fluctuations in the first moment of the distribution function.

The averaging technique presented in the preceding section makes correct allowance for nonconservativeness of function f, but cannot take into account fluctuations in F_1. The question of the effect of fluctuations in F_1 on the formation of f was examined elsewhere /1, 8/, where the feasibility of taking this effect into account was shown and certain estimates of its role were made. However, it appears that a reliable technique for taking into account concentration fluctuations has not yet been developed and these results will not be presented.

It was assumed in deriving the equation that the impurity is passive, i. e., the presence of droplets does not hydrodynamically affect the turbulent flow structure. This condition is generally satisfied, although when the cloud possesses high water content the condition of passivity may not be satisfied; this should result in the appearance of a functional relationship between K and f. It was assumed in examining the transport that the droplets are carried away by turbulent fluctuations. This assumption is invalid for large droplets; however, since condensation growth is insignificant for such droplets, the introduction of corrections is not of great importance.

Equation (7.3.20) was based on the semiempirical theory of turbulence, so all limitations pertaining to this theory must also apply to equation (7.3.20). This equation is inapplicable for examining the evolution of the spectrum for small space and time scales. To solve problems of this type it is necessary to revert to a consideration of the stochastic equation of droplet growth, such as (7.3.12).

In this author's opinion, one of the most important limitations is that equation (7.3.20), as any other parabolic-type equation, assumes an infinite rate of perturbation propagation. This condition should be analyzed in detail when examining condensation, since an infinite rate results in the instantaneous appearance of large droplets in the system. Since the appearance of a small number of large droplets, in amounts by several orders of magnitude smaller than their total concentration, suffices for coalescence to set in, such particles can appear as a result of solving equation (7.3.20) fictitiously, by virtue of the approximate nature of the equation, thus giving rise to the development of coalescence. For this reason equation (7.3.20) should be replaced by a hyperbolic equation. This problem was examined in its application to turbulent transport /4/.

By analogy, the kinetic equation can assume the form

$$\frac{\partial^2 f}{\partial t^2}+2a\frac{df}{dt}-v_s\frac{\partial f}{\partial z}+\frac{\partial}{\partial r}\left(\frac{dr}{dt}f\right)=W^2\left(\frac{\partial^2}{\partial x^2}+\frac{\partial^2}{\partial y^2}\right)f+ \\ +\frac{W}{\beta_1}\left(\frac{\partial}{\partial z}+\beta_1\frac{\partial}{\partial r}\right)W\left(\frac{\partial}{\partial z}+\beta_1\frac{\partial}{\partial r}\right)\beta_1 f+\Phi, \qquad (7.4.1)$$

where W is the mean absolute value of the rate of fluctuations, and a is the rate of variation in fluctuations; for sufficiently long times $\frac{W^2}{a}\rightarrow K$.

The use of an expression such as (7.4.1) substantially complicates the study of condensation processes; in a number of cases it is quite in order to employ equation (7.3.20), assuming here that the limits of its applicability are determined by the rate of propagation of the wave front, i. e., the maximum possible rate of droplet growth.

This limitation (remembering that β_1 and β_2 are not functions of r) can be expressed by the inequality

$$r\leqslant r_m=r_0+\beta_1 Wt+(\beta_1\bar{v}_z+\beta_2)\,t. \qquad (7.4.2)$$

The above solution to equation (7.3.20) can be used when $0<r<r_m$; for $r>r_m$ function f can be regarded as equal to zero. Quantity W in (7.4.2) can be estimated from additional considerations or on the basis of experimental data. The physical meaning of the limitation expressed by (7.4.2) can be presented more clearly by examining the following auxiliary problem.

We shall assume that a particle moves along the x axis in such a manner that over each time interval Δt it moves over segment l in either the positive or negative direction with equal probability. For a sufficiently long time $t\gg\Delta t$ the process can be described by the diffusion equation, and the probability of travel over large distances from the coordinate origin then has a normal distribution.

Nevertheless, for a finite time the particle cannot move from the coordinate origin over a distance greater than $\left(\frac{t}{\Delta t}\right) l = tW$, where $W = \frac{l}{\Delta t}$, i.e., over a distance it will pass through by moving during time t without changing direction. Velocity W in this case is the velocity of the front. If the particle moves nonuniformly and during time Δt_i moves over distance l_i, then the average wave front velocity is $W = \frac{\sum |l_i|}{\sum \Delta t_i}$.

Finally, consider the case of droplet growth. By analogy, we arrive at the average absolute velocity of vertical fluctuations. It should be remembered that the motion of the wave front is a linear function of time. If we treat the simplest case, then the distribution function $f(r, t)$ as the solution of a simplified equation such as (7.3.20) satisfies the normal distribution

$$f(r,\ t) = (4\pi K_z \beta_1^2 t)^{-1/2} \exp\left\{-\frac{[r - r_0 - (\beta_1 v_z + \beta_2)\, t]^2}{4\beta_1^2 K_z t}\right\}, \quad (7.4.3)$$

according to which the average value of r varies with time as $\bar{r} = r_0 + (\beta_1 v_z + \beta_2)\, t$, while the variance $\sigma = 2\beta_1 \sqrt{K_t t}$ of the distribution increases as $t^{1/2}$.

Since $r_m - \bar{r} = \beta_1 W t$, i.e., the wave front moves relative to $\bar{r}$ at constant velocity while broadening of the spectrum is proportional to $\sqrt{t}$, the fraction of fictitious particles in distribution (7.4.3) decreases with time (the contribution of that part of the distribution function which is truncated by the front decreases with increase in t). The value of $f(r, t)$ at which the spectrum should be truncated can be estimated by substituting into equation (7.4.3) the value of r_m:

$$f(r_m) = (4\pi K_z \beta_1^2 t)^{-1/2} \exp\left(-\frac{W^2 t}{4K_z}\right) = (4\pi K_z \beta_1^2 t)^{-1/2} \exp\left(-\frac{Qt}{4}\right). \quad (7.4.4)$$

The ratio of $f(r_m)$ to $f(\bar{r})$ yields the required estimate:

$$\frac{f(r_m)}{f(\bar{r})} = \exp\left(-\frac{W^2 t}{4K_z}\right). \quad (7.4.5)$$

The above estimate can be employed to check the applicability of the computational results to equation (7.3.20). It is noteworthy that both equation (7.4.1) and the estimates were obtained on the basis of a number of simplifications and assumptions and yield only an approximate picture of the features of cloud spectrum evolution.

For a more exact solution to the problem it is first necessary to make rigorous allowance for the finite nature of the transport velocity for turbulent flow when deriving equations such as (7.4.1).

5. SOLUTION TO SOME MODEL PROBLEMS. A SEMIANALYTIC METHOD OF SOLVING THE KINETIC EQUATION

Equation (7.3.20), in spite of its approximate nature from the standpoint of describing the process, is still too complicated for an analytic study. It is therefore of some interest to consider some simple model cases of its solution which, to some extent, characterize the behavior of the droplet distribution function.

a) Infinite homogeneous cloud with $v_z = \text{const}$. The droplet growth equation is taken in the form

$$\frac{dr^2}{dt} = Av_z, \tag{7.5.1}$$

where $A = \frac{\alpha}{R_v T} \frac{K_3}{F_1}$ is regarded as constant.

The kinetic equation for function $\varphi(s)$, where $s = r^2$, is

$$\frac{\partial\varphi}{\partial t} + Av_z \frac{\partial\varphi}{\partial s} = A^2 K_z \frac{\partial^2\varphi}{\partial s^2}. \tag{7.5.2}$$

Its solution, with variable s extended formally to the region of negative values, is the following:

$$\varphi(s, t) = \frac{1}{(4\pi A^2 K_z t)^{1/2}} \int_{-\infty}^{\infty} \varphi(\eta, 0) \exp\left[-\frac{(s-\eta-Av_z t)^2}{4A^2 K_z t}\right] d\eta. \tag{7.5.3}$$

If the initial distribution is specified by a delta function,

$$\varphi(\eta, 0) = Q\delta(\eta - s_0),$$

in which case

$$\varphi(s, t) = \frac{Q}{(4\pi A^2 K_z t)^{1/2}} \exp\left[-\frac{(s - s_0 - Av_z t)^2}{4A^2 K_z t}\right]. \tag{7.5.4}$$

Conversion to $f(r, t)$ is elementary: $f(r, t) = 2r\varphi(r^2, t)$. It follows that the maximum of the function is shifted to the region of small sizes approximately in proportion to $\sqrt{v_z t}$, the variance increases approximately in proportion to $\sqrt{K_z t}$, while the average radius is defined to be

$$\bar{r}=\frac{\int_0^\infty r f(r,\,t)\,dr}{\int_0^\infty f(r,\,t)\,dr} \tag{7.5.5}$$

and assumes the form

$$\bar{r}=(2A^2K_z t)^{1/2}\Gamma\left(\frac{3}{2}\right)\frac{D_{-3/2}(-z)}{D_{-1}(-z)}, \tag{7.5.6}$$

where $z=\dfrac{r_0^2+Av_z t}{A\sqrt{2K_z t}}$, D_ν is the parabolic cylinder function, and

$$\sigma^2=\overline{r^2}-\bar{r}^2=(2A^2K_z t)^{1/2}\left[\frac{D_{-2}(-z)}{D_{-1}(-z)}-\frac{\pi}{4}\left(\frac{D_{-3/2}(-z)}{D_{-1}(-z)}\right)^2\right]. \tag{7.5.7}$$

Allowance for the boundary effect at $s=0$ should alter the above expressions; here, the role of these changes is more important, the smaller the initial droplet radii.

On the assumption that particles are absorbed at $s=s_{\lim}$, while $\varphi(\eta)=Q\delta(\eta-s_0)$ at $t=0$, we can write

$$\varphi(s,\,t)=\frac{Q}{(4\pi A^2K_z t)^{1/2}}\left\{\exp\left[-\frac{(s-s_0)^2}{4A^2K_z t}\right]-\right.$$
$$\left.-\exp\left[-\frac{(s-2s_{\lim}+s_0)^2}{4A^2K_z t}\right]\right\}\exp\left[\frac{(s-s_0)\,v_z}{4AK_z}-\frac{v_z^2 t}{4K_z}\right]. \tag{7.5.8}$$

Finally, the condition of reflection from the boundary $s=s_{\lim}$ yields the solution

$$\varphi(s,\,t)=\frac{Q}{(4\pi A^2K_z t)^{1/2}}\left\{\exp\left[-\frac{(s-s_0)^2}{4A^2K_z t}\right]+\right.$$
$$\left.+\exp\left[-\frac{(s-2s_{\lim}+s_0)^2}{4A^2K_z t}\right]\right\}\times\exp\left[\frac{(s-s_0)\,v_z}{2AK_z}-\frac{v_z^2 t}{4K_z}\right]-$$
$$-\frac{Qv_z}{\sqrt{\pi}AK_z}\exp\left(\frac{v_z s}{AK_z}\right)\int_y^\infty \exp(-x^2)\,dx, \tag{7.5.9}$$

where

$$y=\frac{s-2s_{\lim}+s_0-Av_z t}{(4A^2K_z t)^{1/2}}.$$

The above solutions correspond to the simplest type of initial distribution. In the more general case, using Green's function it is possible to employ a standard method to derive a solution satisfying different initial distributions and boundary conditions.

b) Infinite cloud. The initial droplet distribution is a function of z; $v_z =$ const, $A =$const, $K_z =$ const. The kinetic equation assumes the form

$$\frac{\partial\varphi}{\partial t}+v_z\left(\frac{\partial}{\partial z}+A\frac{\partial}{\partial s}\right)\varphi=K_z\left(\frac{\partial}{\partial z}+A\frac{\partial}{\partial s}\right)^2\varphi. \tag{7.5.10}$$

This equation suggests the natural transformation

$$(t,\ s,\ z)\to(t,\ \xi,\ z),$$

where $\xi=z-\frac{s}{A}$. An equation in these variables is reduced to the form

$$\frac{\partial\varphi}{\partial t}+v_z\frac{\partial\varphi}{\partial z}=K_z\frac{\partial^2\varphi}{\partial z^2}, \tag{7.5.11}$$

and its Green's function can be expressed as follows:

$$\varphi(z,\ t)=\frac{Q(z_0)}{\sqrt{4\pi K_z t}}\exp\left[-\frac{(z-z_0-v_z t)^2}{4K_z t}\right]. \tag{7.5.12}$$

In addition, since ξ is not contained explicitly in the equation, we have

$$z-\frac{s}{A}=z_0-\frac{s_0(z_0)}{A}. \tag{7.5.13}$$

When the initial distribution is monodisperse and only the droplet concentration changes with altitude,

$$\varphi(z,\ s,\ t)=\frac{Q\left(z-\frac{1}{A}(s-s_0)\right)}{\sqrt{4\pi K_z t}}\exp\left\{-\frac{\left[\frac{1}{A}(s-s_0)-v_z t\right]^2}{4K_z t}\right\}. \tag{7.5.14}$$

If the initial radius is also a function of z_0, then if we set

$$z_0=\chi(z,\ s)$$

in (7.5.13) we obtain

$$\varphi(z,\ s,\ t)=\frac{Q\,[\chi(z,\ s)]}{\sqrt{4\pi K_z t}}\exp\left\{-\frac{[z-\chi(z,\ s)-v_z t]^2}{4K_z t}\right\}. \qquad (7.5.15)$$

In the more general case, when the initial droplet distribution is not monodisperse,

$$\varphi(z,\ s,\ t)=\int_0^\infty \frac{Q\left(z-\frac{1}{A}(s-s_0),\ S_0\right)}{\sqrt{4\pi K_z t}}\times$$

$$\times\exp\left\{-\frac{\left[\frac{1}{A}(s-s_0)-v_z t\right]^2}{4K_z t}\right\}ds_0. \qquad (7.5.16)$$

c) Cloud bounded from below. The initial distribution is not a function of altitude and can be expressed as a delta function. When $s=0$ particles are absorbed. At $z=0$ (cloud base) we shall assume that, due to the appearance of new droplets, the distribution function is equal to the initial distribution function. Equation (7.5.10) is most easily solved by introducing the variables

$$x=z-\frac{s}{A},$$

$$y=z+\frac{s}{A},$$

$$n=\varphi e^{\lambda t+\mu y}, \qquad (7.5.17)$$

where

$$\lambda=\frac{v_z^2}{4K_z},\quad \mu=\frac{v_z}{4K_z}.$$

Application of the coordinate transformation illustrated in Figure 28 yields

$$\frac{\partial n}{\partial t}=4K_z\frac{\partial^2 n}{\partial y^2}. \qquad (7.5.18)$$

This transformation resulted in the fact that the dependence on x manifests itself in terms of the boundary and initial conditions. It can be shown that the solution to the problem breaks up into a solution in two subdomains: for $x>0$ into a solution for initial conditions $\varphi(s,\ t,\ 0)=Q\delta(s-s_0)$ and absorption at $x=y$; for $x<0$ into a solution for zero initial conditions, absorption at $s=0$ and allowance for the source at the boundary.

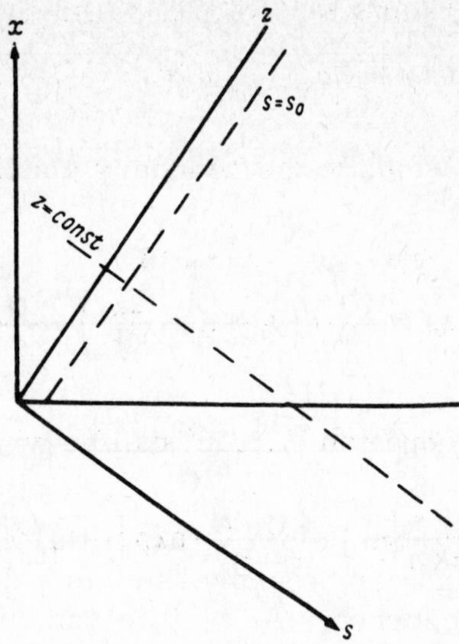

FIGURE 28. Transformation of coordinates

The solution to the problem with allowance for absorption at $y=y_{\lim}$ is

$$n(y, t)=\frac{1}{(16\pi K_z t)^{1/2}}\int_0^\infty n(y_{\lim}+\eta, 0)\left\{\exp\left[-\frac{(\eta-y)^2}{16K_z t}\right]-\right.$$
$$\left.-\exp\left[-\frac{(2y_{\lim}-\eta-y)^2}{16K_z t}\right]\right\}d\eta. \qquad (7.5.19)$$

The initial condition has the form

$$n(x, y, 0)=\varphi(s, z, 0)\,e^{\mu y}=Q\delta\left(\frac{A}{2}(y-x)-s_0\right)\exp\left(\frac{v_z y}{4K_z}\right). \qquad (7.5.20)$$

Thus, with allowance for the fact that $y_{\lim}=x$, integration of equation (7.5.19) and conversion to φ and variables s, z, t finally yields

$$\varphi(s, z, t)=\frac{Q}{2A(\pi K_z t)^{1/2}}\left\{\exp\left[-\frac{(s-s_0)^2}{4AK_z t}\right]-\right.$$
$$\left.-\exp\left[-\frac{(s+s_0)^2}{4AK_z t}\right]\right\}\exp\left[-\frac{(s-s_0)\,v_z}{2AK_z}-\frac{v_z^2 t}{4K_z}\right]. \qquad (7.5.21)$$

This solution is valid for $x > 0$, whence follows the condition

$$(s - s_0) < Az_0. \tag{7.5.22}$$

For the region $x < 0$ we have the boundary condition

$$y_0 = -x \qquad (z = 0),$$

$$\varphi(y,\ 0,\ t) = Q\delta(s - s_0) = \frac{2Q}{A}\,\delta\left(y_0 - x - \frac{2s_0}{A}\right) = \frac{Q}{A}\,\delta\left(x + \frac{s}{A}\right). \tag{7.5.23}$$

Then the solution to equation (7.5.18) can be written as follows:

$$n(y,\ t) = \frac{(y - y_0)}{4(\pi K_z)^{1/2}} \int\limits_0^t \frac{\psi(y_0,\ t)}{(t - \tau)^{3/2}} \exp\left[-\frac{(y - y_0)^2}{16K_z(t - \tau)}\right] d\tau, \tag{7.5.24}$$

where

$$\psi(y_0,\ t) = \frac{Q}{A} \exp\left[-\frac{v_z x}{4K_z} + \frac{v_z^2 t}{4K_z}\right] \delta\left(x + \frac{s}{A}\right).$$

By integrating with respect to t and converting to the starting variables we derive the expression

$$\varphi(s,\ z,\ t) = \frac{Q}{\sqrt{\pi}A} \exp\left(-\frac{v_z z}{2K_z}\right) \Gamma\left(\frac{1}{2},\ \frac{z^2}{4K_z t}\right) \delta\left(z - \frac{s}{A} + \frac{s_0}{A}\right), \tag{7.5.25}$$

which is valid when

$$(s - s_0) > Az.$$

The fact that the solution broke up into two parts, expressed by equations (7.5.21) and (7.5.25), is a consequence of the fact that the boundary and initial conditions manifest themselves differently and should be taken into account separately.

d) One of the assumptions, most important from the viewpoint of the mathematical simplification made in examining preceding examples (the assumption of constant A), immediately reduced the integrodifferential equation to a differential equation. If this assumption is dropped, the kinetic equation should be expressed in the form /9/

$$F^2 \frac{d\varphi}{\partial t} + aF \frac{\partial\varphi}{\partial s} = b \frac{\partial^2\varphi}{ds^2}, \tag{7.5.26}$$

where φ is the normalized distribution function of the square of the radius,

$$F(t)=\int_0^\infty s^{1/2}\varphi(s,\ t)\,ds,$$

$$a=\frac{\rho_0 v_z}{2\pi\rho_2 n}\frac{d}{dt}\left(\ln p_1-\frac{L}{R_v T}\ln T\right),$$

$$b=\left[\frac{\rho_0 g}{2\pi\rho_2 R_v T n}\frac{\left(1-\frac{M_1}{M}\frac{L}{c_p T}\right)}{\left(1-\frac{\rho_0 L^2}{\rho c_p T^2 R_{\text{air}}}\right)}\right]^2 K_z.$$

We shall assume that F is some known function of time. Then, introducing the variables $\tau=\int_0^t\frac{1}{F(t)}dt$ and $\psi(s,\ t)=s-s_0-a\int_0^t\frac{1}{F(t)}dt$, and in accordance with the transformations

$$\frac{\partial}{\partial t}\to\frac{\partial\tau}{\partial t}\frac{\partial}{\partial\tau},$$

$$\left(\frac{\partial}{\partial\tau}\right)_s\to\left(\frac{\partial}{\partial\tau}\right)_\psi-aF(t(\tau))\left(\frac{\partial}{\partial\psi}\right)_s,$$

$$\left(\frac{\partial}{\partial s}\right)_\tau\to\left(\frac{\partial}{\partial\psi}\right)_\tau, \tag{7.5.27}$$

we derive the equation

$$\frac{\partial\varphi}{\partial\tau}=b\,\frac{\partial^2\varphi}{\partial\psi^2}. \tag{7.5.28}$$

Here, the initial condition is expressed similarly, while the boundary conditions are satisfied after obtaining the fundamental solution to equation (7.5.28) and reverting to the old variables. This solution has the following form:

$$G(s,\ s_0,\ t)=\frac{1}{\left(4\pi b\int_0^t F^{-2}\,dt\right)^{1/2}}\exp\left[-\frac{\left(s-s_0-a\int_0^t\frac{1}{F}\,dt\right)^2}{4b\int_0^t\frac{1}{F^2}dt}\right]. \tag{7.5.29}$$

The solution satisfying the initial and boundary conditions can then be expressed as

$$\varphi(s, t) = \int_{-\infty}^{\infty} G(s, s_0, t)\,\varphi(s_0)\,ds_0. \tag{7.5.30}$$

Here, the initial conditions have been extended to the region of negative s, in order to satisfy the boundary conditions. For the simplest types of boundary conditions the technique of this extension is simple and is presented in the relevant mathematics courses. To find $F(t)$ we multiply both sides by $s^{1/2}$ and integrate with respect to s from $-\infty$ to $+\infty$:

$$F(t) = \int_{0}^{\infty}\int_{-\infty}^{\infty} s^{1/2} G(s, s_0, t)\,\varphi(s_0)\,ds_0\,ds. \tag{7.5.31}$$

In many cases this equation can be solved more easily than equation (7.5.26). After obtaining the solution, substitution into (7.5.30) yields the final result.

As an illustration, consider the case when the initial distribution is $\varphi(s_0) = \delta(s_0 - s_m)$. This is a not too important limitation for a diffusion-type process, if one considers the time at which the variance of the distribution is much greater than the initial one. Boundary conditions at $s = 0$ will not be specified, and instead the solution will be extended formally over the entire s axis and the solution to the Cauchy problem used. Such an approach is permissible if the boundary has little effect on the process (if s is sufficiently large), and in many cases is justified due to the presence of the second term in the left-hand side of equation (7.5.26), which shifts the distribution to the right along the s axis.

Since the question of specifying exact boundary conditions has not yet been clarified from the physical point of view, and since the introduction of any boundary conditions does not introduce special difficulties into the calculations, although it does complicate them, we shall restrict ourselves to a consideration of this case. Then, $G(s, t)$ is written in the same manner as equation (7.5.29), except that s_0 is replaced by s and, as is evident, has a normal distribution, while $F(t)$ assumes the form

$$F(t) = \frac{1}{2\sqrt{2}}\left(2b\int_0^t \frac{1}{F^2}\,dt\right)^{1/4} \exp\left[-\frac{\left(s_m + a\int_0^t \frac{1}{F}\,dt\right)^2}{2b\int_0^t \frac{1}{F^2}\,dt}\right] \times$$

$$\times D_{-3/2}\left(-\frac{s_{\mathrm{m}}+a\int\limits_0^t \frac{1}{F}\,dt}{\sqrt{2b\int\limits_0^t \frac{1}{F^2}\,dt}}\right). \tag{7.5.32}$$

For short times equation (7.5.32) has the asymptotic form

$$F(t)=\left(s_{\mathrm{m}}+a\int\limits_0^t \frac{1}{F}\,dt\right)^{1/2}, \tag{7.5.33}$$

in which case

$$F(t)=\left(s_{\mathrm{m}}^{3/2}+\frac{3}{2}\,at\right)^{1/3}. \tag{7.5.34}$$

The average value $\bar{s}$ is given by

$$\bar{s}=\left(s_{\mathrm{m}}^{3/2}+\frac{3}{2}\,at\right)^{2/3} \tag{7.5.35}$$

and the distribution variance by

$$\sigma^2=\frac{8b}{9a}\left[\left(s_{\mathrm{m}}^{3/2}+\frac{3}{2}\,at\right)^{1/3}-s_{\mathrm{m}}^{1/2}\right]. \tag{7.5.35'}$$

The above expressions are valid when $t\ll\min\left\{\frac{s_{\mathrm{m}}^{3}}{2b},\ \frac{2s_{\mathrm{m}}^{3/2}}{3a}\right\}$.

Similar relationships are obtained when $t\to\infty$:

$$t\gg\max\left\{\frac{8b}{3a^2},\ \frac{2s_{\mathrm{m}}^{3/2}}{3a}\right\},\quad F(t)\to\left(\frac{3}{2}\,dt\right)^{1/3},\quad \bar{s}\to\left(\frac{3}{2}\,dt\right)^{2/3},$$
$$\sigma^2\to\frac{4b}{a}\left(\frac{3}{2}\,dt\right)^{1/3}. \tag{7.5.36}$$

Analysis shows that quantity $z=\dfrac{s_0+a\int\limits_0^t \frac{1}{F(t)}\,dt}{\sqrt{2b\int\limits_0^t \frac{1}{F^2}\,dt}}$ has at least one minimum. If a and b are such that $z_{\min}\ll 1$, then

$$F(t) \approx \left[\frac{3b}{2^9}\left(\frac{\Gamma\left(\frac{1}{2}\right)}{\Gamma\left(\frac{5}{4}\right)}\right)^4\right]^{1/6} t^{1/6},$$

$$\bar{s} \approx \frac{2^{10}a}{5b}\left(\frac{\Gamma\left(\frac{5}{4}\right)}{\Gamma\left(\frac{1}{2}\right)}\right)^4\left[\frac{3b}{2^9}\left(\frac{\Gamma\left(\frac{1}{2}\right)}{\Gamma\left(\frac{5}{4}\right)}\right)^4\right]^{5/6} t^{5/6},$$

$$\sigma^2 \approx 2^3 3^{2/3}\left(\frac{\Gamma\left(\frac{5}{4}\right)}{\Gamma\left(\frac{1}{2}\right)}\right)^{4/3} b^{2/3} t^{2/3}. \qquad (7.5.37)$$

It is estimated that, if $t \ll \frac{2K_z}{v_z^2}$, one can use this asymptotic equation up to quite long times.

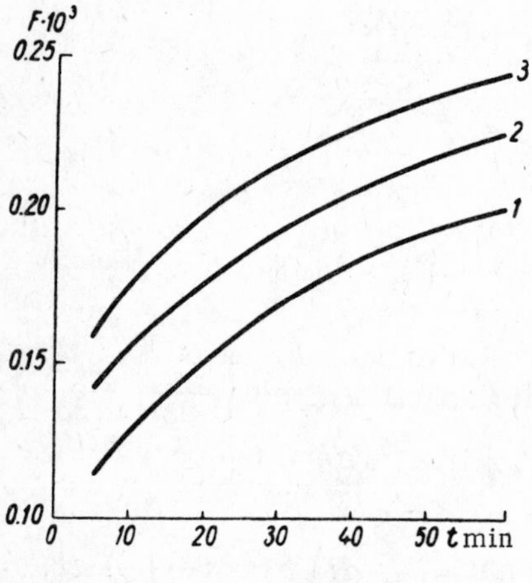

FIGURE 29. Graphs of $F(t)$ when: 1) $a = 0.2\cdot 10^{-14}$, $b = 0.4\cdot 10^{-25}$; 2) $a = 10^{-15}$, $b = 10^{-25}$; 3) $a = 0.2\cdot 10^{-14}$, $b = 0.4\cdot 10^{-24}$.

Computed curves of $F(t)$ for different a and b are presented in Figure 29. The calculations show that the solution to equation (7.5.26) has the same form as the solution to an equation with constant coefficients. The nonlinearity of the equation manifests itself by the different time dependences of $\bar{s}$ and σ^2. The nature of this dependence can be taken into account by employing the above technique.

6. ROLE OF STOCHASTIC CONDENSATION IN THE FORMATION OF CLOUD SPECTRUM DROPLETS

The stochastic condensation theory is presently in its early stages of development and it is still premature to talk about actual calculations of the condensation stage of cloud spectrum formation. One can only discuss theoretical results which this theory should yield, its limits of applicability, and its shortcomings as of now. A distinction should be made between the assumptions underlying the theory and which in essence limit its applicability, and limitations and assumptions made in order to simplify the treatment and obtain numerical results.

We shall examine the principal assumptions underlying the theory of stochastic condensation. First, the droplet growth occurs in variable vapor density, temperature and pressure fields. These fields undergo random variations in space and time due to atmospheric turbulence. Second, droplet growth can be approached on the basis of the ordinary equation governing growth by condensation with allowance for the variability in supersaturation resulting from variability in ρ, T and p_1. Third, fluctuations in supersaturation, which in the main govern the variability in the droplet growth rate, can be treated on the basis of the first law of thermodynamics in the adiabatic approximation; the principal contribution to fluctuations in δ_0 is made by air updrafts, for which $\delta_0' \sim v_z'$. Fourth, the kinetic equation describing the distortion of the distribution function in the approximation of the semiempirical theory of turbulence can be obtained by formal averaging of the equation written for instantaneous values, with allowance for the fact that $\delta_0' \sim v_z'$ and that the distribution function is expressed in variables such that it satisfies the conservativeness requirement.

The validity of the first two assumptions is obvious, but they do not determine the method of calculation of the process. The third assumption is based on the use of the equation of state, the validity of the quasi-steady assumption (which eliminates rapid processes), the slowness and relative homogeneity of the processes associated with radiative transport of energy, possibility of neglecting mixing during local shifts of volumes induced by turbulent motions. The conclusion that $\delta_0' \sim v_z'$ is realized on the assumption that the characteristic times of fluctuations in updraft velocities are much greater than the characteristic time of vapor removal from the system. Here, high-frequency fluctuations are not taken into account correctly. In addition, no allowance is made for the effect of surface tension and the presence of hygroscopic substances in the droplet.

The fourth assumption has the same limitations as the semi-empirical theory of turbulence. Since the distribution function forms over a time of the order of an hour, this approach is valid. The attempt to satisfy the conservativeness requirements, which is the reason for replacing variables in the kinetic equation, is quite natural and enabled the dependence of the droplet growth rate on the eddy diffusion coefficient to be established.

We shall now consider the effect of various factors on the droplet distribution function. The random nature of droplet growth in the medium results in the fact that some fraction of droplets grows more quickly than the average and can quite rapidly attain dimensions at which coalescence is possible. However, as a result of the linear relationship between δ_0' and v_z', on attaining the same altitude level due to turbulence the particles should have the same size (the result of adiabaticity).

This conclusion is incorrect and premature, since the coefficient relating δ_0 to v_z is a function of altitude and time, and hence particles moving at different speeds will intersect some altitudes having different values. In addition to the dependence of the correlating coefficient on z, we also have the effect of the sedimentation rate, which results in smoothing out of the distribution. Effects associated with the vertical inhomogeneity between variables governing the conditions of droplet growth are of importance.

In fact, the most important factor is the nonadiabaticity of cloud processes, which must be taken into account in calculating averaged quantities. As a result, the mixing of air masses at different temperature and humidity as well as the radiation effect induce marked changes in the vertical distribution of parameters. The unsteadiness of processes also leads to an increased variance. In the presence of these effects allowance for stochastic condensation has the meaning that particles, even upon leaving one elementary volume, have individual paths and grow at different rates.

The inhomogeneity induced by macroprocesses results in a different rate of droplet growth in each space element. The random nature of their motion results in the fact that different particles spend different times in a given space element and thus change their mass in a different manner.

Therefore, if we consider the droplet distribution at some level, its variance must be determined by the inhomogeneity of external variables, the nonadiabaticity and unsteadiness of the processes, and the boundary conditions. The primary effect should arise from phenomena having scales of the order of the characteristic size of the cloud. The formation and evaporation of droplets inside the cloud play a certain role in the growth of the variance.

From this point of view some of the simplest solutions to the kinetic equation should be interpreted with care, and should not be imparted a meaning which does not underlie the starting assumptions made during simplifications /3/. The results derived from the solution should be interpreted as estimates of the feasibility of converting a monodisperse distribution which is initially vertically homogeneous into a distribution with quite a large variance and the presence of a large particle fraction.

A special stipulation is needed during attempts at closely examining the microphysical content of stochastic condensation with respect to making allowance for the effect of fluctuations in droplet concentration on particle growth rate /1, 8/. Although such an effect can definitely occur, the method for its incorporation is far from the point when it is possible to consider actual estimates. The further development of the theory should definitely show the extent to which this phenomenon is to be taken into consideration. As to incorporating the effect of the averaged inhomogeneity of the concentration, this can be done within the framework of the previously discussed kinetic equation in terms of the dependence on coordinates and time of the first moment of the distribution function, contained in the coefficients.

BIBLIOGRAPHY

Chapter 1

1. D'yachenko, P.V. Experience in Applying Methods of Mathematical Statistics to the Study of Fog and Cloud Microstructure. — Trudy GGO, No.101. 1959.
2. Levin, L.M. Study of the Physics of Large-Grained Aerosols. — Moscow, Izdatel'stvo AN SSSR. 1961.
3. Litvinov, I.V. Distribution Functions of Raindrops. — Izvestiya AN SSSR, Seriya Geofizicheskaya, No.2. 1956.
4. Mason, B.J. The Physics of Clouds. Oxford, Clarendon Press. 1957.
5. Borovikov, A.M., I.P. Mazin, and A.N. Nevzorov. Distribution of Large Particles in Clouds of Different Forms. — Izvestiya AN SSSR, Fizika Atmosfery i Okeana 1, No.3. 1965.
6. Khrgian, A.Kh. The Physics of Clouds. Leningrad, Gidrometeoizdat. 1969.
7. Khrgian, A, Kh, and I.P. Mazin. Analysis of Methods for Describing Cloud Droplet Distribution Spectra. — Trudy TsAO, No.17. 1956.
8. Khrgian, A.Kh. and I.P. Mazin. Size Distribution of Cloud Droplets. — Trudy TsAO, No.7. 1952.
9. Shinyaev, B.M. Effect of Certain Substances on the Coefficient of Condensation of Water. — Problemy Fiziki Atmosfery, No.2. Leningradskii Gosudarstvennyi Universitet. 1967.
10. Best, A.C. Drop Size Distribution in Cloud and Fog. — Q.J.Roy.Meteorol.Soc. 77, No.333. 1951.
11. Deloncle, M. Etude photoélectrique des aérosols volatils. — Rev. d'opt. théor. et instrum. 42, No.4. 1963.
12. Hammeke, K. and E. Kappler. Eine neue Methode zur Bestimmung der Oberflächentemperatur des Wassers bei Verdampfungsversuchen. — Z. Geophys., Sonderland. 1953.
13. Jer Ru Maa. Evaporation Coefficient of Liquids. — Ind. Eng. Chem. Fundamentals 6, No.4. 1967.
14. Mache, H. Der Verdampfungskoeffizient des Wassers und zwei Verfahren zu seiner Bestimmung. — Z. Physik 107, No.5—6. 1937.
15. Mache, H. Weitere Versuche über den Verdampfungskoeffizienten des Wassers. — Z. Physik 110, No.3—4. 1938.
16. Prüger, W. Die Verdampfungsgeschwindigkeit der Flüssigkeiten. — Z. Physik 115, No.3—4. 1940.
17. Warner, J. The Microstructure of Cumulus Cloud. Part I: General Features of the Droplet Spectrum. — J. Atmos. Sci. 26, No.5. 1969.
18. Warner, J. The Microstructure of Cumulus Cloud. Part II: The Effect on Droplet Size Distribution of the Cloud Nucleus Spectrum and Updraft Velocity. — J. Atmos. Sci. 26, No.6. 1969.

Chapter 2

1. Aksel'rud, G.L. Diffusion from the Surface of a Sphere. — Zhurnal Fizicheskoi Khimii 27, No.10. 1953.
2. Aleksandrov, E.L. The Pressure of Water Vapor above Solutions. — Trudy IPG, No.9. 1967.
3. Aleksandrov, E.L., L.M.Levin, and Yu.S.Sedunov. Concerning the Growth by Condensation of Droplets on Hygroscopic Nuclei. — Trudy IPG, No.9. 1967.
4. Aleksandrov, E.L., L.M.Sedunov, and Yu.S.Sedunov. Growth by Condensation of a Droplet of a Solution. — Izvestiya AN SSSR, Fizika Atmosfery i Okeana 3, No.8. 1967.
5. Aleksandrov, E.L., L.M.Levin, and Yu.S.Sedunov. Growth by Condensation of Droplets on Hygroscopic Nuclei. — Trudy IEM, No.6. 1969.
6. Buikov, M.V. Diffusion and Thermal Relaxation of an Evaporating Droplet. — Inzhenerno-Fizicheskii Zhurnal 5, No.4. 1962.
7. Buikov, M.V. Kinetics of Heterogeneous Condensation during Adiabatic Cooling. — Kolloidnyi Zhurnal 28, No.2, 5. 1966.
8. Buikov, M.V. Unsteady Growth of a Droplet of a Solution. Concentration Relaxation. — Kolloidnyi Zhurnal 24, No.5. 1962.
9. Buikov, M.V. Unsteady Growth of a Droplet of a Solution. Thermal Relaxation. — Kolloidnyi Zhurnal 25, No.1. 1963.
10. Buikov, M.V. and S.S.Dukhin. Diffusion and Thermal Relaxation of an Evaporating Droplet. — Inzhenerno-Fizicheskii Zhurnal 5, No.3. 1962.
11. Van Dyke, M. Perturbation Methods in Fluid Mechanics. New York, Academic Press. 1964.
12. Volkov, F.G. and A.M.Golovin. Thermal and Diffusion Relaxation of an Evaporating Droplet with Internal Heat Generation. — Zhurnal Prikladnoi Matematiki i Tekhnicheskoi Fiziki, No.1. 1970.
13. Volkovitskii, O.A. and Yu.S.Sedunov. Some Refinements of the Theory of the Initial Condensation Stage in Clouds. — Trudy IEM, No.9. 1970.
14. Germogenova, T.A. The Extrapolated Length and Density near the Interface in Milne's Spherical Problem. — In: Sbornik "Nekotorye matematicheskie zadachi neitronnoi fiziki." MGU. 1960.
15. Gormatyuk, Yu.K. and Yu.S.Sedunov. Growth by Condensation of Droplets in the Presence of an as yet Undissolved Hygroscopic Nucleus. — Trudy IEM, No.10. 1970.
16. Davison, B. and J.B.Sykes. Neutron Transport Theory. Oxford, Clarendon Press. 1957.
17. Ermoshina, L.I. and S.L.Lebedev. Growth by Condensation of a Droplet on a Hygroscopic Particle. — Trudy IPG, No.7. 1967.
18. Carslaw, H.S. and J.C.Jaeger. Conduction of Heat in Solids. 2nd ed., Oxford University Press. 1959.
19. Kiryukhin, B.V. Water Vapor Pressure above Liquid and Freezing Solution Droplets. — Trudy GGO, No.24. 1950.
20. Levin, L.M. and Yu.S.Sedunov. Effect of Inertia on Aerosol Particle Deposition from Flow at Subcritical Stokes Numbers. — DAN SSSR 162, No.2. 1965.
21. Levich, V.G. Physicochemical Hydrodynamics. Moscow, Fizmatgiz. 1959.
22. Mazin, I.P. Theory of Particle Size Spectrum Formation in Clouds and Precipitation. — Trudy TsAO, No.64. 1965.
23. Marchuk, G.I. Nuclear Reactor Design Techniques. Moscow, Gosatomizdat. 1961.
24. Sedunov, Yu.S. Some Questions of Brownian Diffusion of Stokes Particles in a Spatially Inhomogeneous External Field. — Izvestiya AN SSSR, Seriya Geofizicheskaya, No.7. 1964.
25. Smirnov, V.I. Rates of Coalescence and Growth by Condensation of Aerosol Particles. — Trudy TsAO, No.92. 1969.

26. Smirnov, V.I. Rate of Growth by Condensation (or Evaporation) of a Spherical Droplet. — Trudy TsAO, No.55. 1964.
27. Solov'ev, N.D. Absorption of Moisture by Hygroscopic Particles in a Cloud. — Trudy TsNMS 5. 1963.
28. Spiro, N.S. Concentrations and Pressures Ratios in Saturated Aqueous Salt Solutions. — Zhurnal Fizicheskoi Khimii, No.10. 1962.
29. Timofeev, M.P. and M.V.Shvets. Evaporation of Fine Water Droplets. — Meteorologiya i Gidrologiya, No.2. 1948.
30. Fuchs, N.A. Evaporation and Droplet Growth in Gaseous Media. Moscow, Izdatel'stvo AN SSSR. 1958.
31. Fuchs, N.A. The Mechanics of Aerosols. Oxford, Pergamon Press. 1964.
32. Fuchs, N.A. On the Rate of Fine Droplet Evaporation in a Gaseous Atmosphere. — Zhurnal Eksperimental'noi i Tekhnicheskoi Fiziki 4, No.7. 1934.
33. Fuchs, N.A. Advances in Aerosol Mechanics. Moscow, Izdatel'stvo AN SSSR. 1961.
34. Chapman, S. and T.G.Cowling. The Mathematical Theory of Non-Uniform Gases. 2nd ed., Cambridge University Press. 1952.
35. Junge, C. Air Chemistry and Radioactivity. New York, Academic Press. 1963.
36. Acrivos, A.,and T.D.Taylor. Heat and Mass Transfer from Single Spheres in Stokes Flow. — Phys. Fluids 5. 1962.
37. Davison, B. Influence of a Black Sphere and of a Black Cylinder upon the Neutron Density in an Infinite No-Capturing Medium. — Proc. Phys. Soc., A 64. 1951.
38. Howell, W.E. The Growth of Cloud Drops in Uniformly Cooled Air. — J. Meteorol. 6, No.2. 1949.
39. Keith, C.H. and A.B.Arons. The Growth of Sea-Salt Particles by Condensation of Atmospheric Water Vapor. — J. Meteorol. 11, No.3. 1954.
40. Marshak, R.E. Note on the Spherical Harmonic Method as Applied to the Milne Problem for the Sphere. — Phys. Rev. 71. 1947.
41. Maxwell, J.C. Collected Scientific Papers 2. Cambridge. 1890.
42. Mordy, W.A. Computations of the Growth by Condensation of a Population of Cloud Droplets. — Tellus 11, No.1. 1959.
43. Neiburger, M. and P.W.Chien. Computations of the Growth of Cloud Drops by Condensation Using an Electronic Digital Computer. — Geophys. Monog., No.5. 1960.
44. Ogiwara, S. and T.Kobayasi. On the Growth of Water Droplets around Hygroscopic Particles on Convective Clouds and Its Application to Artificial Precipitation. — Committee for Rainmaking in Japan, Rep.1. 1954.
45. Sahni, B.C. The Effect of a Black Sphere on the Flux Distribution on an Infinite Moderator.— J. Nucl. Energy 20, No.11/12. 1966.
46. Seidel, W. and R.E.Marshak. Upper and Lower Bounds for the Asymptotic Neutron Density in the Milne Problem for the Sphere. — Canad.J.Phys. 29, No.1. 1951.
47. Taylor, T.D. Heat Transfer from Single Spheres in a Low Reynolds Number Slip Flow. — Phys. Fluids 6, No.7. 1963.
48. Wright, P.G. The Effect of the Transport of Heat on the Rate of Evaporation of Small Droplets. I. Evaporation into a Large Excess of a Gas. — Proc. Roy. Soc. Edinburgh. Sec. A, 66. 1961—62.

Chapter 3

1. Ivanov, V.N. and R.L.Stratonovich. Lagrangian Turbulence Characteristics. — Izvestiya AN SSSR, Seriya Geofizicheskaya, No.10. 1963.

2. Cadle, R.D. Particles in the Atmosphere and Space. New York, Van Nostrand–Reinhold. 1966.
3. Laktionov, A.G. Determination of the Concentration of Cloud Condensation Nuclei. — DAN SSSR 165, No.6. 1965.
4. Laktionov, A.G. On the Relationship between the Condensation Activity of Cloud Nuclei and their Size. — Izvestiya AN SSSR, Fizika Atmosfery i Okeana 3, No.1. 1967.
5. Laktionov, A.G. Vertical Distribution of Cloud Condensation Nuclei in the Free Atmosphere. — DAN SSSR **176**, No.2. 1967.
6. Laktionov, A.G. and L.I.Ermoshina. Comparison of the Concentration of Cloud Condensation Nuclei and Aitken Nuclei in the Free Atmosphere. — Trudy IEM, No.20. 1971.
7. Levin, L.M. and Yu.S.Sedunov. Some Problems of the Theory of Atmospheric Condensation Nuclei. — Trudy IPG, No.9. 1967.
8. Levin, L.M. and Yu.S.Sedunov. Some Problems of the Theory of Condensation Nuclei.— DAN SSSR **170**, No.1. 1966.
9. Obukhov, A.M. Description of Turbulence in Terms of Lagrangian Variables. — Advances in Geophysics, N.Y., Vol.6. 1959.
10. Rozenberg, G.O. Properties of Atmospheric Aerosols from Optical Data. — Izvestiya AN SSSR, Fizika Atmosfery i Okeana 3, No.9. 1967.
11. Selezneva, E.S. Atmospheric Aerosols. Leningrad, Gidrometeoizdat. 1966.
12. Chandrasekhar, S. Stochastic Problems in Physics and Astronomy. — Rev. Mod. Phys. 15 (1):1–89. 1943.
13. Junge, C. Air Chemistry and Radioactivity. New York, Academic Press. 1963.
14. Yaglom, A.M. Acceleration Field in Turbulent Flow. — DAN SSSR **167**, No.5. 1949.
15. Allee, P.A. Annual Variation of Aitken Nuclei Concentration of Washington, D.C. — Mon. Wea. Rev. 95, No.12. 1967.
16. Auer, A.H. A Cumulus Cloud Design for Continental Airmass Regimes. – J. Rech. Atmos. 3, No.3. 1967.
17. Bónis, K. On the Kinetics of Condensation of Atmospheric Water Vapour on Soluble Nuclei. — Időjárás 73, No.2. 1969.
18. Brown, M.J., R.K.Krauss, and R.M.Smith. Dust Deposition and Weather. — Weatherwise 21, No.2. 1968.
19. Cadle, R.D. and E.R.Frank. Particles in the Fume from 1967 Kilauea Eruption. — J.Geophys. Res. 73, No.14. 1968.
20. Cadle, R.D., A.L.Lazrus, and J.P.Shedlovsky. Comparison of Particles in the Fume from Eruption of Kilauea, Mayon and Arenal Volcanoes. — J. Geophys. Res. **74**, No.13. 1969.
21. Carnuth, W. Zur Abhängigkeit des Aerosolpartikelspektrums von meteorologischen Vorgängen und Zuständen. — Arch. Met. Geoph. Biokl. A16, No.4. 1967.
22. Carnuth, W. and R.Reiter. Simultaneous Measurements of the Aerosol Particle Size Spectra at 700, 1,800 and 3,000 m above Sea Level. — J. Rech. Atmos. 2, No.2–3. 1966.
23. Clark, W.E. and K.T.Whitby. Concentration and Size Distribution Measurements of Atmospheric Aerosols and a Test of the Theory of Self-Preserving Size Distributions. — J. Atmos. Sci. 24, No.6. 1967.
24. Day, G.J. Some Airborne Observations of Condensation Nucleus Concentration. — Geofis. Pura e Appl. 31, No.2. 1955.
25. Durbin, W.G. Some Aircraft Observations of the Vertical and Horizontal Distributions of Chloride Particles. — Geofis. Pura e Appl. **42**, No.1. 1959.
26. Dyer, A.J. and B.B. Hicks. Global Spread of Volcanic Dust from the Bali Eruption of 1963. — Q. J. Roy. Meteorol. Soc. **94**, No.402. 1968.

27. El Nadi, A.F. and S.W.Banoub. Condensation Nuclei and Meteorological Factors at Gisa, Egypt. — Geofis. Pura e Appl. 49, No.2. 1961.

28. Feldstein, M. Air Pollution: Bay Area. — Clinical Toxicology 2, No.3. 1969.

29. Fletcher, N.H. Size Effect in Heterogeneous Nucleation. — J. Chem. Phys. 29, No.3. 1958.

30. Friedlander, S.K. and G.M.Hidy. New Concepts in Aerosol Size Spectrum Theory. — Proc. 7th Intern. Conf. Condensation and Ice Nuclei. Prague. 1969.

31. Hobbs, P.V., L.F.Radke, and S.E.Shumway. Cloud Condensation Nuclei from Industrial Sources and their Apparent Influence on Precipitation in Washington State. — J. Atmos. Sci. 27, No.1. 1970.

32. Hogan, A.W. Experiments with Aitken Counters in Maritime Atmosphere. — J. Rech. Atmos. 3, No.1—2. 1968.

33. Hoidale, G.B. and A.J.Blanco. An Infrared Spectrascopic View of the Nature of Giant and Large Particle Atmospheric Dust. — J. Rech. Atmos. 3, No.4. 1968.

34. Howell, W.E. Growth of Cloud Drops in Uniformly Cooled Air. — J. Meteorol 6, No.2. 1949.

35. Jaenicke, R. and C.Junge. Studien zur oberen Grengröbe des natürlichen Aerosoles. — Beitr. Phys. Atmosph. 40, No.1—2. 1967.

36. Jiusto, J.E. Aerosol and Cloud Microphysics Measurements in Hawaii. — Tellus 19, No.3. 1967.

37. Jiusto, J.E. Maritime Concentrations of Condensation Nuclei. — J.Rech.Atmos 2, No.2—3. 1966.

38. Jiusto, J.E. and W.C.Kocmond. Note on Cloud Nucleus Measurements in Lannemezan, France. — J. Rech. Atmos. 3, No.1—2. 1968.

39. Junge, C. Comment on "Concentration and Size Distribution Measurements of Atmospheric Aerosols and a Test of the Theory of Self-Preserving Size Distributions." — J. Atmos. Sci. 26, No.3. 1969.

40. Junge, C., E.Robinson, and F.L.Ludwig. A Study of Aerosols in Pacific Air Masses. — J. Appl. Meteorol. 8, No.3. 1969.

41. Köhler, H. On the Problem of Condensation in the Atmosphere. — Nova Acta Reg. Soc. Sci. Upsaliensis, Ser.4, Vol.14, No.9. 1950.

42. Krastanov, L. Vrhu nykoi os novnyi vproszi v mikrofizikata na oblacity. — Trudove Centr. Meteorol. Inst.1, Sofia. 1941.

43. Laktionov, A.G. Photoelectric Measurements of Condensation Cloud Nuclei. — J. Rech. Atmos. 3, No.1—2. 1968.

44. Law, J. The Vertical Distribution of Condensation Nuclei near the Ground. — Geofis. Pura e Appl. 50, No.3. 1961.

45. Lee, R.E. and R.K.Patterson. Size Determination of Atmospheric Phosphate, Nitrate, Chloride and Ammonium Particulate in Several Urban Areas. — Atmospheric Environment 3, No.3. 1969.

46. Levin, L.M. and Y.S.Sedunov. The Theoretical Model of Condensation Nuclei. The Mechanism of Drop Formation in Clouds. — J. Rech. Atmos. 2, No.2—3. 1966.

47. Marwitz, J.D. and A.H.Auer. Cloud Nuclei Spectra and Updrafts beneath Convective Cloud Bases in the High Plains. — J. Appl. Meteorol. 7, No.3. 1968.

48. McCaldin, R.O., N.T.Stephens, and L.W.Johnson. Atmospheric Aerosols. — Science 166, No.3903. 1969.

49. McClaine, L.A., R.V.Allen, and R.K.McConnel. Volcanic Smoke Clouds. — J. Geophys. Res. 73, No.16. 1968.

50. Mészáros, E. On the Distribution of Water Soluble Particles in the Atmosphere. — Tellus 20, No.3. 1968.

51. Mészáros, E. On the Thermodynamics of the Condensation on Water Soluble and Mixed Nuclei. — Időjárás 73, No.1. 1969.

52. Mészáros, E. Répartition verticale de la concentration des particules de chlorures dans les basses couches de l'atmosphère. – J. Rech. Atmos. 1, No.1. 1964.

53. Mészáros, E. The Size Distribution of Nitrate and Soluble Calcium Particles. – Ann. Meteorol., No.4. 1969.

54. Mészáros, E. and A. Mészáros. Konzentration und Grössenverteilung von Aerosolpartikeln mikroskopischer Grösse mit Rücksicht auf ihre Aktivität im Kondensationsprozess. – Meteorologie. Ergebnisse Konf. Meteorol. Liblice Prag 1964, Prague. 1966.

55. Nady, A. Vertical Profile of the Concentration of Large and Giant Atmospheric Particles. – Idöjárás 73, No.1. 1969.

56. O'Connor, T.C. Condensation Nuclei in Maritime Air. – J. Rech. Atmos. 2, No.2–3. 1966.

57. O'Connor, T.C. and V.P.V. Flanagan. The Measurement of Size Distribution in Aitken Nuclei. – Geofis. Pura e Appl. 50, No.3. 1961.

58. O'Connor, T.C., W.P. Sharkey, and V.P.V. Flanagan. Observations on the Aitken Nuclei in Atlantic Air. – Q. J. Roy. Meteorol. Soc. 87, No.371. 1961.

59. Podzimek, J. Relation between Concentration of Giant Chloride Nuclei and Exchange in the Atmosphere. – Geofis. Pura e Appl. 42, No.1. 1959.

60. Podzimek, J. and I. Černoch. Höhenverteilung der Konzentrationen von Riesenkernen aus Chloriden und Sulphaten. – Geofis. Pura e Appl. 50, No.3. 1961.

61. Pollak, L.W. and T. Murphy. Sampling of Condensation Nuclei by Means of a Mobile Photoelectric Counter. – Arch. Meteorol. Geophys. Biokl. A 5, No.1. 1952.

62. Prospero, J.M. and E. Bonatti. Continental Dust in the Atmosphere of the Eastern Equatorial Pacific. – J. Geophys. Res. 74, No.13. 1969.

63. Ramana Murty, Bh.V., A.K. Roy, and R.K. Kapoor. Sources of Origin and Meteorological Importance of Hygroscopic and Ice-Forming Nuclei. – Tellus 19, No.1. 1967.

64. Rau, W. Gröbe und Häufigkeit der Chloridteilchen in kontinentalen Aerosol und ihre Beziehung zum Gefrierkerngehalt. – Meteorol. Rundschau 8, No.9/10. 1955.

65. Sekhon, R.S. and Bh.V. Ramana Murty. Some Characteristic Features of Hygroscopic and Nonhygroscopic Aerosols at Delhi. – J. Atmos. Sci. 23, No.6. 1966.

66. Squires, P. and S. Twomey. A Comparison of Cloud Nucleus Measurements over Central North America and the Caribbean Sea. – J. Atmos. Sci. 23, No.4. 1966.

67. Squires, P. and S. Twomey. The Relation between Cloud Drop Numbers and the Spectrum of Cloud Nuclei. Physics of Precipitation. – Geophys. Monograph., No.5, Baltimore. 1960.

68. Tester, J. Condensation Nuclei Counts on the Slopes of Little Whiteface Mountain in New York State. – Pure and Appl. Geoph. 57, No.1. 1964.

69. Twomey, S. Measurements of Natural Cloud Nuclei. – J. Rech. Atmos. 1, No.3. 1963.

70. Twomey, S. On the Composition of Cloud Nuclei in the Northeastern United States. – J. Rech. Atmos. 3, No.4. 1968.

71. Twomey, S. The Nuclei of Natural Cloud Formation. Part II. The Supersaturation in Natural Cloud and the Variation of Cloud Droplet Concentration. – Geofis. Pura e Appl. 43, No.2. 1959.

72. Twomey, S. and G. T. Severynse. On the Relation between Sizes of Particles and their Ability to Nucleate Condensation of Natural Clouds. – J. Rech. Atmos. 1, No.2. 1964.

73. Twomey, S. and J. Warner. Comparison of Measurements of Cloud Droplets and Cloud Nuclei. – J. Atmos. Sci. 24, No.6. 1967.

74. Twomey, S. and T.A. Wojciechowski. Observations of the Geographical Variation of Cloud Nuclei. – J. Atmos. Sci. 26, No.4. 1969.

75. Vonnegut, B., and R.L. Neubauer. Counting Sodium Containing Particles in the Atmosphere by their Spectral Emission in a Hydrogen Flame. – Bull. Amer. Meteorol. Soc. 34, No.4. 1953.

76. Whioby, K.T. and B.T.H.Lin. Atmospheric Aerosol Size Distribution. – Proc. 7th Intern. Conf. Condensation and Ice Nuclei, Prague. 1969.

Chapter 4

1. Akul'shina, L.G. et al. Photoelectric Instrument for Measuring the Spectrum and Concentration of Liquid Aerosol Particles. – Trudy IPG, No.7. 1967.
2. Aleksandrov, E.L. and Yu.S.Sedunov. Method of Estimating the Supersaturation Arising during the Formation of Droplets in Clouds. – DAN SSSR 188, No.5. 1969.
3. Buikov, M.V. Heterogenous Condensation Kinetics during Adiabatic Cooling. – Kolloidnyi Zhurnal 28, No.2. 1966.
4. Volkovitskii, O.A. Modeling of the Initial Condensation Stage of the Formation of the Cloud Spectrum in a Chamber. – In Sbornik: "Simpozium po fizike oblakov, Sofiya 1967." Sofia. 1969.
5. Volkovitskii, O.A. and A.G.Laktionov. Investigation of the Initial Cloud Genesis Stage in a Chamber. – Izvestiya AN SSSR, Fizika Atmosfery i Okeana 5, No.3. 1969.
6. Volkovitskii, O.A. and A.G.Laktionov. Variation in the Size and Spectrum of Fog Droplets in a Cloud Chamber during Growth by Condensation. – Izvestiya AN SSSR, Fizika Atmosfery i Okeana 6, No.3. 1970.
7. Volkovitskii, O.A., A.G.Laktionov, and Yu.S.Sedunov. Investigation of the Initial Stage of Cloud Spectrum Formation. – In: Sbornik "VIII Vsesoyuznaya konferentsiya po fizike oblakov i aktivnym vozdeistviyam, Tbilisi, 1969." Leningrad, Gidrometeoizdat. 1970.
8. Volkovitskii, O.A. and Yu.S.Sedunov. Calculation of the Concentration of Droplets and Maximum Supersaturation at the Initial Cloud Genesis Stage. – Meteorologiya i Gidrologiya, No.1. 1970.
9. Kachurin, L.G. and V.G.Morachevskii. Kinetics of Phase Transitions of Water in the Atmosphere. – Leningrad, Leningradskii Gosudarstvennyi Universitet. 1965.
10. Laktionov, A.G. and Yu.S.Sedunov. Dependence of Maximum Supersaturation and Concentration of Droplets Formed in Air Updrafts on the Spectrum of Cloud Nuclei. – Trudy IEM, No.6. 1969.
11. Landau, L.D. and E.M.Lifshits. Mechanics of Continuous Media. Moscow, Gostekhizdat. 1954.
12. Moiseenko, Yu.I. and G.G.Shchelchkov. Automatic Multipoint System for Measuring Microphysical Properties of Fogs in Experimental Devices. – Trudy IEM, No.1. 1969.
13. Sedunov, Yu.S. Kinetics of the Initial Condensation Stage on Clouds. – Izvestiya AN SSSR, Fizika Atmosfery i Okeana 3, No.1. 1967.
14. Sedunov, Yu.S. Nume.ical Experiments on the Modification of the Kinetics of Cloud Spectrum Formation by Adding Condensation Nuclei. – Trudy IEM, No.6. 1969.
15. Smirnov, V.I. Generalized Kinetic Boltzmann Equation and Some Equations of the Kinetics of Polydisperse Systems. – Trudy TsAO, No.47. 1963.
16. Twomey, S.A. Cloud Condensation Nuclei. Atmospheric Aerosols and Radioactive Air Pollution. – Proc. 4th Intern. Conf. on Condensation Nuclei. Leningrad, Gidrometeoizdat. 1964.
17. Auer, A.H. A Cumulus Cloud Design for Continental Airmass Regimes. – J. Rech. Atmos. 3, No.3. 1967.
18. Deloncle, M. Etude photoélectrique des aérosols volatils. – Rev. d'opt. théor. et instrum. 42, No.4. 1963.

19. Howell, W.E. Growth of Cloud Drops in Uniformly Cooled Air. — J. Meteorol. 6, No.2. 1949.
20. Jiusto, J.E. and W.C. Kocmond. Note on Cloud Nucleus Measurements in Lannemezan, France. — J. Rech. Atmos. 3, No.1—2. 1968.
21. Kornfeld, P. Numerical Solution for Condensation of Atmospheric Vapor on Soluble and Insoluble Nuclei. — J. Atmos. Sci. 27, No.2. 1970.
22. Laktionov, A.G. and O.A. Volkovitsky. Investigation of the Initial Condensation Stage of Cloud Formation in the Chamber. — Pure and Appl. Geophys. 77, No.6. 1969.
23. Marwitz, J.D. and A.H. Auer. Cloud Nuclei Spectra and Updrafts beneath Convective Cloud Bases in the High Plains. — J. Appl. Meteorol. 7, No.3. 1968.
24. Squires, P. and S. Twomey. A Comparison of Cloud Nucleus Measurements over Central North America and the Caribbean Sea. — J. Atmos. Sci. 23, No.4. 1966.
25. Warner, J. The Microstructure of Cumulus Cloud. Part I: General Features of the Droplet Spectrum. — J. Atmos. Sci. 26, No.5. 1969.
26. Warner, J. The Microstructure of Cumulus Cloud. Part II: The Effect on Droplet Size Distribution of the Cloud Nucleus Spectrum and Updraft Velocity. — J. Atmos. Sci. 26, No.6. 1969.

Chapter 5

1. Buevich, Yu.A. Kinetics of Mass Transfer between a System of Polydisperse Particles and the Surroundings. — Zhurnal Prikladnoi Matematiki i Tekhnicheskoi Fiziki, No.1. 1966.
2. Buikov, M.V. Evaporation of a Polydisperse Fog. — Kolloidnyi Zhurnal 24, No.4. 1962.
3. Kachurin, L.G. Supersaturation of Vapor and Growth of Droplets by Condensation in Water Clouds. — Meteorologiya i Gidrologiya, No.8. 1953.
4. Kachurin, L.G., L.E. Alant'eva, and Hsia Yung Jen. Vapor Concentration and Rate of Droplet Growth in Water Aerosols. — Izvestiya AN SSSR, Seriya Geofizicheskaya, No.9. 1961.
5. Kachurin, L.G. and V.G. Morachevskii. Kinetics of Phase Transition of Water in the Atmosphere. Leningrad, Leningradskii Gosudarstvennyi Universitet. 1965.
6. Stepanov, A.S. Kinetic Equation for Diffusion Growth of Particles. — Zhurnal Tekhnicheskoi i Matematicheskoi Fiziki. 1971.

Chapter 6

1. Belyaev, V.I. Lagrange Method in the Kinetics of Cloud Processes. Leningrad, Gidrometeoizdat. 1964.
2. Belyaev, V.I. Size Distribution of Droplets in a Cloud Undergoing Condensation Development. — Izvestiya AN SSSR, Seriya Geofizicheskaya, No.8. 1961.
3. Vul'fson, N.I. Investigation of Convective Motions in the Free Atmosphere. Moscow, Izdatel'stvo AN SSSR. 1961.
4. Vul'fson, N.I. and V.N. Ivanov. Temperature Field Structure in Cumulus. — DAN SSSR 159, No.4. 1964.
5. Golitsyn, G.S. Time-Dependent Spectrum of Microfluctuations in Atmospheric Pressure. — Izvestiya AN SSSR, Seriya Geofizicheskaya, No.8. 1964.
6. Elagina, L.G. Variation in Frequency Spectra of Fluctuations in Absolute Humidity in the Boundary Layer of the Atmosphere. — Izvestiya AN SSSR, Seriya Geofizicheskaya, No.12. 1963.

7. Ivanov, V.N. and R.L.Stratonovich. Lagrangian Characteristics of Turbulence. — Izvestiya AN SSSR, Seriya Geofizicheskaya, No.10. 1963.
8. Kabanov, A.S. Turbulence Spectrum in the Free Atmosphere with Allowance for Buoyancy Forces. — Trudy TsAO, No.98. 1970.
9. Kabanov, A.S. and I.P.Mazin. Effect of Phase Transitions on Turbulence in Clouds. — Trudy TsAO, No.98. 1970.
10. Kolesnikova, V.N. and A.S.Monin. Spectrum of Variations in Meteorological Fields. — Izvestiya AN SSSR, Fizika Atmosfery i Okeana 1, No.7. 1965.
11. Levin, L.M. and Yu.S.Sedunov. Fluctuations in Vapor Concentration and Supersaturation in the Atmosphere. — Trudy IPG, No.9. 1967.
12. Mazin, I.P. Relation between Fluctuations in Supersaturation in Clouds and Fluctuations in Temperature and Updrafts. — Trudy TsAO, No.79. 1967.
13. Obukhov, A.M. Temperature Field Structure in Turbulent Flow. — Izvestiya AN SSSR, Seriya Geofizicheskaya i Geograficheskaya 13, No.1. 1949.
14. Sedunov, Yu.S. Mutual Motion of Stokes Particles in Turbulent Flow. — Izvestiya AN SSSR, Seriya Geofizicheskaya, No.5. 1963.
15. Sedunov, Yu.S. Fine Structure of Clouds and its Role in the Formation of the Cloud Particle Spectrum. — Izvestiya AN SSSR, Fizika Atmosfery i Okeana 1, No.7. 1965.
16. Tatarskii, V.I. Theory of Fluctuational Phenomena during the Propagation of Waves in a Turbulent Atmosphere. Moscow, Izdatel'stvo AN SSSR. 1969.
17. Tsvang, L.R. Certain Characteristics of the Spectra of Temperature Flcutuations in the Boundary Layer of the Atmosphere. — Izvestiya AN SSSR, Seriya Geofizicheskaya, No.10. 1963.
18. Yaglom, A.M. Local Structure of the Temperature Field in Turbulent Flow. — DAN SSSR 69, No.6. 1949.
19. Yaglom, A.M. Acceleration Field in Turbulent Flow. — DAN SSSR 167, No.5. 1949.
20. Bolgiano, R. The Role of Turbulent Mixing in Scatter Propagation. — Proc. IRE, AP-5, No.2. 1968.
21. Grain, C.M. Survey of Airborne Microwave Refractometer Measurements. — Proc. IRE 43 (1405). 1955.
22. Pousend, A.A. Experimental Evidence for the Theory of Local Isotropy. — Proc. Cam. Phil. Soc. 41, No.4. 1948.

Chapter 7

1. Kabanov, A.S., I.P.Mazin, and V.I.Smirnov. Effect of Spatial Inhomogeneity of the Concentration of Nascent Droplets on their Size Spectrum in a Cloud. — Izvestiya AN SSSR, Fizika Atmosfery i Okeana 6, No.3. 1970.
2. Mazin, I.P. Temperature and Humidity Stratification in Clouds. — Trudy TsAO, No.71. 1966.
3. Mazin, I.P. and V.I.Smirnov. Theory of the Formation of the Size Spectrum of Cloud Droplets during Stochastic Condensation. — Trudy TsAO, No.89. 1969.
4. Monin, A.S. and A.M.Yaglom. Statistical Hydromechanics, Part 1. Moscow, Nauka. 1965.
5. Sedunov, Yu.S. Some Problems of Brownian Difffusion of Particles in a Spatially Inhomogeneous External Field. — Izvestiya AN SSSR, Seriya Geofizicheskaya, No.7. 1964.

6. Sedunov, Yu.S. Some Problems of the Kinetics of Condensation Processes in Clouds. — Izvestiya AN SSSR, Fizika Atmosfery i Okeana 5, No.1. 1969.
7. Sutton, O.G. Micrometeorology. New York, McGraw-Hill. 1953.
8. Smirnov, V.I. and A.S.Kabanov. Effect of Horizontal Inhomogeneity of Air Updraft Velocities on the Spectrum of Cloud Droplet Sizes. — Izvestiya AN SSSR, Fizika Atmosfery i Okeana 6, No.12. 1970.
9. Vasiljeva, K.I. and Y.S.Sedunov. The Condensation Stage of the Cloud Spectrum Development and Semianalytical Method of its Investigation. — Proc. 7th Intern. Conf. Condensation and Ice Nuclei, Prague and Vienna. 1969.

SUBJECT INDEX